SYMMETRIES AND REFLECTIONS

Scientific Essays of Eugene P. Wigner

Ulli Steltzer

SYMMETRIES AND REFLECTIONS

Scientific Essays of Eugene P. Wigner

Indiana University Press · Bloomington & London · 1967

EDITORIAL NOTE

Professor Wigner is not only a great scientist but a scientist with an unusual gift for conveying the results of scientific research to the non-specialist, and an unusual concern for the problems that humanity faces in applying science. In selecting the writings in this volume we have endeavored to bring together many of these intellectually accessible but widely scattered writings. We hope they will be as stimulating to the reader as they were to the editors.

WALTER J. MOORE
Professor of Chemistry,
Indiana University

MICHAEL SCRIVEN
Professor of the History and
Philosophy of Science,
Indiana University

I wish to join the Editors of this volume in the expression of appreciation to Drs. F. Seitz and Alvin M. Weinberg for their permission to reproduce articles in the volume which we have written jointly. Even more do I wish to thank them, and many others of my past students, for all the technical facts and all the insights with which they enriched my thinking.

E. P. W.

CONTENTS

I

SYMMETRY AND OTHER PHYSICAL PROBLEMS

II

NUCLEAR ENERGY

III

EPISTEMOLOGY AND QUANTUM MECHANICS

IV

REFLECTIONS

I

SYMMETRY AND OTHER PHYSICAL PROBLEMS

1

Invariance in Physical Theory

Initial Conditions, Laws of Nature, Invariance

The world is very complicated and it is clearly impossible for the human mind to understand it completely. Man has therefore devised an artifice which permits the complicated nature of the world to be blamed on something which is called accidental and thus permits him to abstract a domain in which simple laws can be found. The complications are called initial conditions; the domain of regularities, laws of nature. Unnatural as such a division of the world's structure may appear from a very detached point of view, and probable though it is that the possibility of such a division has its own limits,[1] the underlying abstraction is probably one of the most fruitful ones the human mind has made. It has made the natural sciences possible.

The possibility of abstracting laws of motion from the chaotic set of events that surround us is based on two circumstances. First, in many cases a set of initial conditions can be isolated which is not too large a

Address presented at the celebration honoring Professor Albert Einstein on March 19, 1949, in Princeton. Reprinted by permission from the *Proceedings of the American Philosophical Society,* Vol. 93, No. 7 (December, 1949).

[1] The artificial nature of the division of information into "initial conditions" and "laws of nature" is perhaps most evident in the realm of cosmology. Equations of motion which purport to be able to predict the future of a universe from an arbitrary present state clearly cannot have an empirical basis. It is, in fact, impossible to adduce reasons against the assumption that the laws of nature would be different even in small domains if the universe had a radically different structure. One cannot help agreeing to a certain degree with E. A. Milne, who reminds us (*Kinematic Relativity,* Oxford Univ. Press, 1948, page 4) that, according to Mach, the laws of nature are a consequence of the contents of the universe. The remarkable fact is that this point of view could be so successfully disregarded and that the distinction between initial conditions and laws of nature has proved so fruitful.

set and, in spite of this, contains all the relevant conditions for the events on which one focuses one's attention. In the classic example of the falling body, one can disregard almost everything except the initial position and velocity of the falling body; its behavior will be the same and independent of the degree of illumination, the neighborhood of other objects, their temperature, etc. The isolation of the set of conditions which do influence the experiment is by no means a trivial problem. On the contrary, it is a large fraction of the art of the experimenter and on our occasional trips through laboratories all of us theoreticians have been periodically impressed by the difficulties of this art.

However, the possibility of isolating the relevant initial conditions would not in itself make possible the discovery of laws of nature. It is, rather, also essential that, given the same essential initial conditions, the result will be the same no matter where and when we realize these. This principle can be formulated, in the language of initial conditions, as the statement that the absolute position and the absolute time are never essential initial conditions. The statement that absolute time and position are never essential initial conditions is the first and perhaps the most important theorem of invariance in physics. If it were not for it, it might have been impossible for us to discover laws of nature.

The above invariance is called in modern mathematical parlance invariance with respect to displacement in time and space. Again, it may be well to remember that this invariance may have limitations. If the universe should turn out to be grossly inhomogeneous, the laws of nature on the fringes of the universe may be quite different from those which we are studying; and it is not impossible that an experimenter inside a closed room is in principle able to ascertain whether he is in the midst, or near the fringes, of the universe, whether he lives in an early epoch of the expansion of the universe, or at an advanced stage of this process. The postulate of the invariance with respect to displacement in space and time disregards this possibility, and its application on the cosmological scale virtually presupposes a homogeneous and stationary universe. Present evidence clearly points to the approximate nature of the latter assumption.

Invariance

What are the other laws of invariance? One can distinguish between two types of laws of invariance: the older ones which found their perfect, and perhaps final, formulation in the special theory of relativity, and the new one, yet incompletely understood, which the general theory of relativity brought us.

The older theories of invariance postulate, in addition to the irrelevance of the absolute position and time of an event, the irrelevance of its orientation and finally, the irrelevance of its state of motion, as long as this remains uniform, free of rotation, and on a straight line. The former theorems are geometrical in nature and appear to be so self-evident that they were not formulated clearly and directly until about the turn of the last century. The last one, the irrelevance of the state of motion, is far from self-evident, as all of us know who have tried to explain it to a layman. There would be no such principle of invariance if Newton's second law of motion read "All bodies persist in their state of rest unless acted upon by an external force"; on the contrary, the scope of this invariance could be extended considerably if the bodies maintained their state of acceleration rather than their velocity in the absence of an external force. It is fitting that this principle was first enunciated, in full clarity, by Newton in his *Principia*.

The fact that the older principles of invariance are the products of experience rather than *a priori* truths can also be illustrated by our gradual abandonment of a very plausible principle, the principle of similitude. This principle, formulated perhaps most clearly by Fourier, demands that physical experiments can be scaled; that the absolute magnitude of objects be irrelevant from the point of view of their behavior on the proper scale. The existence of atoms, of an elementary charge, and of a limiting velocity spelled the doom of this principle.

The formulae describing what I am calling the older principles of invariance were first given completely by Poincaré, who derived them from the equations of electrodynamics. He also recognized the group property of the older principles of invariance and named the underlying group after Lorentz. The significance and general validity of these principles were recognized, however, only by Einstein. His papers on special relativity also mark the reversal of a trend: until then, the principles of invariance were derived from the laws of motion. Einstein's work established the older principles of invariance so firmly that we have to be reminded that they are based only on experience. It is now natural for us to try to derive the laws of nature and to test their validity by means of the laws of invariance, rather than to derive the laws of invariance from what we believe to be the laws of nature.

The general theory of relativity is the next milestone in the history of invariance. The fact that it is the first attempt to derive a law of nature by selecting the simplest invariant equation would in itself justify the epithet. More important, in my opinion, is that the general theory of relativity attempts to give the range of the validity of the older theorems of invariance and to replace them with a single, more general theorem. The limitation of the older theorems of invariance is given by the structure of space which manifests itself in a variable curvature. Since the curvature is, in principle, observable, a displacement from a region of low curvature to one with a high curvature does not leave the laws of nature invariant. It is true that the old fashioned physicist can always blame the differences in the laws of nature, as they are valid for different points of the universe, on the absence or proximity of masses. This, however, restores the general validity of the older invariances only by making them meaningless. Clearly, if two points in space-time are equivalent only if they are surrounded by the same distribution of masses, their equivalence will be the exception rather than the rule.

The new principle of invariance which the general theory of relativity substitutes for the older ones is that all actions are transmitted by fields which transmit the perturbations from point to point. Expressed more phenomenologically: the events in one part of space depend only on the fields, i.e., on the measurable quantities, in the neighborhood of that part of space—the effect of events outside moves in only with a finite velocity.* This postulate of invariance is much bolder, and has much less artificiality than the older postulate of invariance with respect to the inhomogeneous Lorentz group. The above formulation is a little more phenomenological than the customary one. The customary requirement of invariance with respect to all differentiable coordinate transformations is, however, included in it. Both postulates express the fact that the laws of physics and of geometry involve only local measurements such as can be expressed by differential equations. In particular, the definition of a preferred Galilean coordinate system, by reference to other, distant Galilean coordinate systems, is barred by the postulate that all the information which is necessary to describe the immediate

---

* It will be noted that the principle postulated is not invariance with respect to general coordinate transformations but the less abstract principle of the absence of action at a distance. This principle, as here formulated, shares most properties of invariance postulates. (Note added with the proofs of this book.)

future of the region in question can be obtained by local measurements. Hence information relating to distant points cannot add anything relevant to the knowledge of local conditions, as would be the case if they would enable one to define preferred coordinate systems.

Invariance in Quantum Mechanics

When the great paradoxes of atomic physics first became apparent about thirty years ago, it was easy to despair to such a degree of our ability to understand the laws of physics as to propose throwing into the winds all laws of physics, excepting the conservation laws for energy and momenta. It was, in fact, Einstein who recommended such a procedure.[2]

The efforts of the past thirty years culminated in having accomplished just that: we now believe that we have a consistent theory of atomic processes, consistent with the older concepts of space and time, and of invariance. This theory is based on an analysis of the measuring process, carried out principally by Heisenberg and Bohr, which emphasizes the effect of the measurement on the measured object. It is thus contradictory to the simple concept of mapping out the field, the concept which underlies the customary formulation of general relativity. In particular, the measurement of the curvature of space caused by a single particle could hardly be carried out without creating new fields which are many billion times greater than the field under investigation.[3]

Very little effort has been made so far to modify the concepts of the general theory of relativity with an appreciation of the effect of the act of measurement on the object of the measurement. However, the older principles of invariance are in harmony with quantum mechanics and this harmony is more complete, the interdependence of quantum equations and the theory of their invariance is more intimate, than it was in pre-quantum theory.

Let me first stress the points of similarity between the role of invariance in classical and quantum theories. The principles of invariance have a dual function in both theories. On the one hand, they give a

---

[2] H. Poincaré, "Dynamics of Electrons," *Compt. Rend.*, 140, 1504 (1905); "Sur la dynamique de l'électron," *Circolo Mat. Palermo Rend.*, 21, 129 (1906).

[3] An interesting problem in this connection was broached recently by M. F. M. Osborne, "Quantum Theory Restrictions on the General Theory of Relativity," *Bull. Am. Phys. Soc.*, 24, 2 (Berkeley Meeting), Paper A-3 (1949).

necessary condition which all fundamental equations must satisfy: the irrelevant initial conditions must not enter in a relevant fashion into the results of the theory. Second, once the fundamental equations are given, the principles of invariance furnish, in the form of conservation laws and otherwise, powerful assistance toward their solution. The conservation laws for linear momentum and energy, for angular momentum and the motion of the center of mass, can be derived both in classical theory and in quantum mechanics from the invariance of the equations with respect to infinitesimal displacements and rotations in space-time.[4]

However, with these points of analogy, the similarity between the roles of invariance in classical and in quantum physics is pretty much at an end. The reason is, fundamentally, that the variety of states is much greater in quantum theory than in classical physics and that there is, on the other hand, the principle of superposition to provide a structure for the greatly increased manifold of quantum mechanical states. The principle of superposition renders possible the definition of states the transformation properties of which are particularly simple. It can in fact be shown that every state of any quantum mechanical system, no matter what type of interactions are present, can be considered as a superposition of states of elementary systems. The elementary systems correspond mathematically to irreducible representations of the Lorentz group and as such can be enumerated. Since the equations of motion of the states of elementary systems are completely determined by their invariance properties, every state is a linear combination of states the history of which is completely known. However, in the description by irreducible states, the form of almost all physically important operators remains unknown and, in fact, depends on the system, the types of interactions, etc. This leads to a rather strange dilemma: in the customary description the form of the physically important operators is known but the time dependence of the states is unpredictable or difficult to calculate. In the description just mentioned, the situation is opposite: the time dependence of the states follows from the invariance properties, but the form of the physically

---

[4] In classical theory, this observation is due to F. Klein's school. Cf. also F. Engel, "Uber die zehn allgemeinen Integrale der klassischen Mechanik," *Nachr. Kgl. Ges. Wiss. Göttingen*, p. 270 (1916); also G. Hamel, "Die Lagrange-Eulerschen Gleichungen der Mechanik," *Z. Math. Phys.*, 50, 1 (1904), and E. Bessel-Hagen, "Uber die Erhaltungssätze der Elektrodynamik," *Math. Ann.*, 84, 258 (1921).

important operators is hard to establish. There is one exception to this; the states of elementary particles are formed by the superposition of the states of a single invariant set. As a result, the possible equations of elementary particles can easily be enumerated and some progress has been made recently also toward the invariant theoretic determination of the operators for the most important physical quantities. The property which makes a particle elementary in the sense of the above statement is that it shall have no internal coordinate which would permit an invariant division of its states into two or more groups. It is certainly no accident that all elementary particles, including the light quantum, obey irreducible equations and hence form elementary systems in the above sense. Since the rigid body is what may be considered classical mechanics' closest analogue to an elementary particle, the group theoretical description of the motion of a rigid body must be considered the closest analogue to the above result.

The second point to which I wish to draw attention in the comparison of quantum and pre-quantum theories concerns the significance of transformations of invariance, such as reflections, which cannot be generated by infinitesimal elements. These had very little role in the classical theory but prove their value both in the discussion of fundamental equations, and also in the attempts to solve these. Into the former category belongs for instance the observation that the theory[5] which identifies the neutrino with the antineutrino, by attributing to the inversion of space coordinates a non-linear operation involving transition to the conjugate complex wave function, cannot be welded into a theory which describes also particles of the conventional type.[6] The applications of the reflection invariance for facilitating the solution of the fundamental equations are even more obvious. They lead for instance to the concept of Laporte's parity quantum number—one of the most important concepts of spectroscopy.

Less specifically, but perhaps not less accurately, one can speak of the general impression of quantum mechanics, and the theory of the invariance of its equations, forming an inseparable entity, almost to the degree to which this is true in the general theory of relativity. Schwinger's quantum electrodynamics gives the latest and starkest

[5] Cf. H. Weyl, "Elektron und Gravitation I," *Z. Physik*, 56, 330 (1929).
[6] Another very interesting set of examples has been given recently by T. Okayama, "On the Mesic Charge," *Phys. Rev.*, 75, 308 (1949).

manifestation of this situation: his theory cannot be formulated at all without developing, unified with it, its theory of invariance. Furthermore, one is inclined to believe that this union is the most important success of the theory; that even the explanation of definite and previously unexpected experimental phenomena is less important to us than the knowledge that we can, in general, carry out our calculations of physical phenomena in an invariant fashion, obtaining the same results if we start with only irrelevantly different initial conditions.

Conservation of Electrical Charge

My account of the role of invariance in quantum mechanics would remain grossly incomplete if I did not mention a dissonant sound in the harmony of quantum mechanics and the older theorems of invariance. This is the conservation law for the electrical charge. While the conservation laws for all other quantities, such as energy or angular momentum, follow in a natural way from the principles of invariance, the conservation law for electric charge so far has defied all attempts to place it on an equally general basis. The situation was, of course, the same in classical mechanics but the simplicity of the connection between invariance and the ordinary conservation laws makes the situation even more conspicuous in quantum mechanics.

A short description of the derivation of the usual conservation laws will make this perhaps more evident than an abstract discussion. In order to derive the conservation law for linear momentum, one first constructs a state in which one component, say the x component of the linear momentum, has a definite value p. For this purpose, one chooses an arbitrary state φ_0 of the system for which one wishes to show the conservation theorem and constructs all states φ_a obtained by displacing the system in the state φ_0 by a in the x direction. One then considers the superposition of the states φ_a with the coefficients e^{-ipa}:

$$\Phi_p = \int_{-\infty}^{\infty} \varphi_a e^{-ipa} da.$$

This state has the property that a further displacement by b,

$$\int_{-\infty}^{\infty} \varphi_{a+b} e^{-ipa} da = \int_{-\infty}^{\infty} \varphi_c e^{-ip(c-b)} dc = e^{ipb} \Phi_p,$$

just multiplies it with e^{ipb}. It is called a pure state with momentum component p in the x direction. The property of Φ_p, of being multiplied by e^{ipb} upon displacement by b, will not be lost in time: if φ_0 goes over, after some time, into ψ_0, the state φ_a will go over into the ψ_a which results from ψ_0 by displacement by a. This follows from the invariance of the equations of motion with respect to displacements. As a result of this and the linearity of the equations of motion, Φ_p will go over at the time in question into

$$\Psi_p = \int_{-\infty}^{\infty} \psi_a e^{-ipa} da,$$

which also is multiplied by e^{ipb} upon displacement by b. This property, which characterizes the state with momentum p, is not lost in the course of time, and this constitutes the principle of conservation of linear momentum.

Similar considerations involving the other principles of invariance lead to the other conservation laws. Furthermore, the quantization and the possible values of the quantized quantities also emerge naturally from the above consideration. Thus the quantization of the angular momentum is the result of the condition that rotation by 2π always restores the system to its original state.

No consideration similar in generality and simplicity to the above one is known which would explain the conservation law for electric charges. One can borrow the following argument from classical theory[7]: Suppose we could create charges by some process in a closed system. Let us put then this closed system into a Faraday cage, charge the cage, and create the charge in the closed system. A certain energy E will be necessary for this process. However, inasmuch as no physical phenomenon depends on the absolute value of the potential, the amount of energy E cannot depend on the potential of the Faraday cage inside of which the charge is created. Let us then take our closed system out of the Faraday cage and move it away from it, thereby obtaining a certain amount of work W. Let us then reverse the process which led to the creation of the charge and gain an amount E of energy which is equal to the amount of energy expended in the first place, since the process in a closed system must not depend on the absolute value of the electric potential at which that system is. We now can replace the discharged system into the Faraday cage without the expenditure of any work and have carried out a cycle which resulted in a net gain W of work. This is impossible according to the first law and shows that one of our assumptions must

[7] This point was emphasized by J. R. Oppenheimer during the discussion which followed the presentation of this paper.

have been faulty. It is the assumption that electric charges can be created in a closed system.

The above argument shows the connection between the conservation law for electric charges and the assumption of the irrelevance of the absolute magnitude of the electric potential. It has been translated into quantum mechanics and has been given a much more elegant and general form.[8] Nevertheless, it remains less convincing than the consideration leading to the other conservation laws and, certainly, in it fails to account for the quantization of the electric charge.

The lack of full clarity concerning the foundation of the conservation law for charges raises several important points. Is our present scheme of quantum mechanics incomplete in some fundamental respect? In particular, is the Hilbert space with complex coordinates the proper framework for describing state vectors? Would the use of more general hypercomplex wave functions give essentially different results? But the most important question is, undoubtedly: is the existence of a conservation law a particular feature of the electromagnetic type of interaction or are we going to encounter, or perhaps have we already encountered,[9] similar conservation laws for other types of interactions?

[8] F. London, "Quantenmechanische Deutung der Theorie von Weyl," Z. *Physik*, 42, 375 (1927); Cf. also H. Weyl, *loc. cit.*

[9] It is conceivable, for instance, that a conservation law for the number of heavy particles (protons and neutrons) is responsible for the stability of the protons in the same way as the conservation law for charges is responsible for the stability of the electron. Without the conservation law in question, the proton could disintegrate, under emission of a light quantum, into a positron, just as the electron could disintegrate, were it not for the conservation law for the electric charge, into a light quantum and a neutrino. The Gedanken experiment which led to the conservation law for charges would assume the following, admittedly somewhat vague form, if one wanted to prove a conservation law for the number of nucleons: Assuming that there is no such conservation law, two nucleons could first be created at a distance from each other which is large compared with the range of nuclear forces. An amount E of energy would be needed for this. The nucleons then could be permitted to approach each other, furnishing the amount W of work. Finally, they would be permitted to annihilate, which would again release the energy E first expended. A net gain W in energy would result. The impossibility to perform the above operations may, of course, be connected with many physical phenomena, such as the impossibility of localizing sufficiently accurately the systems in which the nucleons are to be created (i.e., the existence of a fundamental length). The impossibility may also be the consequence of the dependence of the energy E, which is necessary to create the nucleons, on the absolute value of the nuclear potential. The point of view which we wish to represent is, however, that the impossibility of the creation of nucleons (without creating antinucleons) is the real resolution of the paradox. It may be mentioned, as a third point of similarity between the two conservation laws, that there is evidence, although contested by some recent experiments, that the "mesonic

Relativity theory, to the celebration of which the present paper is intended to contribute, has enriched physics in two ways. It has resolved acute difficulties, presented by the Michelson-Morley, the Fizeau, the Trouton-Noble, and other experiments. It has done this by a profound analysis of the space-time concept, and its results in this connection are part of the store of knowledge of all physicists. Even more lasting and more subtle is probably the contribution which relativity theory has made indirectly. Most important among the indirect contributions of the theory of relativity was its demonstration for the need and of the fruitfulness of the analysis of apparently well established concepts, concepts which have formed a habit of thought for many generations. Its fostering the emergence of the importance of the concept of invariance, its enlarging the scope of this concept, can, I believe, justly claim second position.

It is a pleasure to acknowledge Dr. V. Bargmann's critical comments and remarks on the present paper.

---

charge" of all nucleons is the same. If this should prove to be true, it would be evidence for the quantization of the mesonic charge. This quantization would be analogous to the well known quantization of the electric charge.

2

Symmetry and Conservation Laws

Introduction

Symmetry and invariance considerations, and even conservation laws, undoubtedly played an important role in the thinking of the early physicists, such as Galileo and Newton, and probably even before them. However, these considerations were not thought to be particularly important and were articulated only rarely. Newton's equations were not formulated in any special coordinate system and thus left all directions and all points in space equivalent. They were invariant under rotations and displacements, as we now say. The same applies to his gravitational law. There was little point in emphasizing this fact, and in conjuring up the possibility of laws of nature which show a lower symmetry. As to the conservation laws, the energy law was useful and was instinctively recognized in mechanics even before Galileo.[1] The momentum and angular momentum conservation theorems in their full generality were not very useful even though in the special case of central motion they give, of course, one of Kepler's laws. Most books on mechanics, written around the turn of the century and even later, do not mention the general theorem of the conservation of angular momentum.[2] It must have

Reprinted by permission from the *Proceedings of the National Academy of Sciences,* Vol. 51, No. 5 (May, 1964).

[1] G. Hamel, in his *Theoretische Mechanik* (Stuttgart: B. G. Teubner, 1912) mentions (p. 130) Jordanus de Nemore (~1300) as having recognized essential features of what we now call mechanical energy and Leonardo da Vinci as having postulated the impossibility of the Perpetuum Mobile.

[2] F. Cajori's *History of Physics* (New York: Macmillan Company, 1929) gives exactly half a line to it (p. 108).

been known quite generally because those dealing with the three-body problem, where it is useful, write it down as a matter of course. However, people did not pay very much attention to it.

This situation changed radically, as far as the invariance of the equations is concerned, principally as a result of Einstein's theories. Einstein articulated the postulates about the symmetry of space, that is, the equivalence of directions and of different points of space, eloquently.[3] He also re-established, in a modified form, the equivalence of coordinate systems in motion and at rest. As far as the conservation laws are concerned, their significance became evident when, as a result of the interest in Bohr's atomic model, the angular momentum conservation theorem became all-important. Having lived in those days, I know that there was universal confidence in that law as well as in the other conservation laws. There was much reason for this confidence because Hamel, as early as 1904, established the connection between the conservation laws and the fundamental symmetries of space and time.[4] Although his pioneering work remained practically unknown, at least among physicists, the confidence in the conservation laws was as strong as if it had been known as a matter of course to all. This is yet another example of the greater strength of the physicist's intuition than of his knowledge.

Since the turn of the century, our attitude toward symmetries and conservation laws has turned nearly full circle. Few articles are written nowadays on basic questions of physics which do not refer to invariance postulates, and the connection between conservation laws and invariance principles has been accepted, perhaps too generally.[5] In addition, the concept of symmetry and invariance has been extended into a new area—an area where its roots are much less close to direct experience and observation than in the classical area of space-time symmetry. It may be useful, therefore, to discuss first the relations of phenomena, laws of nature, and invariance principles to each other. This relation is not quite the same for the classical invariance principles, which will be called geometrical, and the new ones, which will be called dynamical.

[3] See, for instance, his semipopular booklet *Relativitätstheorie* (Braunschweig: Friedr. Vieweg und Sohn, various editions, 1916-1956).

[4] G. Hamel, *Z. Math. Phys.*, 50, 1 (1904); F. Engel, *Ges. d. Wiss. Göttingen*, 270 (1916).

[5] See the present writer's article, *Progr. Theoret. Phys.*, 11, 437 (1954); also Y. Murai, *Progr. Theoret. Phys.*, 11, 441 (1954); and more recently D. M. Greenberg, *Ann. Phys.* (N.Y.), 25, 290 (1963).

Finally, I would like to review, from a more elementary point of view than customary, the relation between conservation laws and invariance principles.

Events, Laws of Nature, Invariance Principles

The problem of the relation of these concepts is not new; it has occupied people for a long time, first almost subconsciously. It may be of interest to review it in the light of our greater experience and, we hope, more mature understanding.

From a very abstract point of view, there is a great similarity between the relation of the laws of nature to the events on one hand, and the relation of symmetry principles to the laws of nature on the other. Let me begin with the former relation, that of the laws of nature to the events.

If we knew what the position of a planet will be at any given time, there would remain nothing for the laws of physics to tell us about the motion of that planet. This is true also more generally: if we had a complete knowledge of all events in the world, everywhere and at all times, there would be no use for the laws of physics, or, in fact, of any other science. I am making the rather obvious statement that the laws of the natural sciences are useful because without them we would know even less about the world. If we already knew the position of the planet at all times, the mathematical relations between these positions which the planetary laws furnish would not be useful but might still be interesting. They might give us a certain pleasure and perhaps amazement to contemplate, even if they would not furnish us new information. Perhaps also, if someone came who had some different information about the positions of that planet, we would more effectively contradict him if his statements about the positions did not conform with the planetary laws— assuming that we have confidence in the laws of nature which are embodied in the planetary law.

Let us turn now to the relation of symmetry or invariance principles to the laws of nature. If we know a law of nature, such as the equations of electrodynamics, the knowledge of the subtle properties of these equations does not add anything to the content of these equations. It may be interesting to note that the correlations between events which the equations predict are the same no matter whether the events are viewed by an observer at rest, or an observer in uniform motion. However, all the correlations between events are already given by the equations themselves, and the aforementioned observation of the invariance of the equations does not augment the number or change the character of the correlations.

More generally, if we knew all the laws of nature, or the ultimate law of nature, the invariance properties of these laws would not furnish us new information. They might give us a certain pleasure and perhaps amazement to contemplate, even though they would not furnish new information. Perhaps also, if someone came around to propose a different law of nature, we could more effectively contradict him if his law of nature did not conform with our invariance principle—assuming that we have confidence in the invariance principle.

Evidently, the preceding discussion of the relation of the laws of nature to the events, and of the symmetry or invariance principles to the laws of nature is a very sketchy one. Many, many pages could be written about both. As far as I can see, the new aspects which would be dealt with in these pages would not destroy the similarity of the two relations—that is, the similarity between the relation of the laws of nature to the events, and the relation of the invariance principles to the laws of nature. They would, rather, support it and confirm the function of the invariance principles to provide a structure or coherence to the laws of nature just as the laws of nature provide a structure and coherence to the set of events.

Geometrical and Dynamical Principles of Invariance

What is the difference between the old and well-established geometrical principles of invariance, and the novel, dynamical ones? The geometrical principles of invariance, though they give a structure to the laws of nature, are formulated in terms of the events themselves. Thus, the time-displacement invariance, properly formulated, is: the correlations between events depend only on the time intervals between the events, not on the time at which the first event takes place. If P_1, P_2, P_3 are positions which the aforementioned planet can assume at times t_1, t_2, t_3, it could assume these positions also at times $t_1 + t$, $t_2 + t$, $t_3 + t$, where t is quite arbitrary. On the other hand, the new, dynamical principles of invariance are formulated in terms of the laws of nature. They apply to specific types of interaction, rather than to any correlation between events. Thus, we say that the electromagnetic interaction is gauge invariant, referring to a specific law of nature which regulates the generation of the electromagnetic field by charges, and the influence of the electromagnetic field on the motion of the charges.

It follows that the dynamical types of invariance are based on the existence of specific types of interactions. We all remember having read that, a long time ago, it was hoped that all interactions could be derived from mechanical interactions. Some of us still remember that, early in this century, the electromagnetic interactions were considered to be the source of all others. It was necessary, then, to explain away the gravitational interaction, and in fact this could be done quite successfully. We now recognize four or five distinct types of interactions: the gravitational, the electromagnetic, one or two types of strong (that is, nuclear) interactions, and the weak interaction responsible for beta decay, the decay of the μ meson, and some similar phenomena. Thus, we have given up, at least temporarily, the hope of one single basic interaction. Furthermore, every interaction has a dynamical invariance group, such as the gauge group for the electromagnetic interaction.

This is, however, the extent of our knowledge. Otherwise, let us not forget, the problem of interactions is still a mystery. Utiyama[6] has stimulated a fruitful line of thinking about how the interaction itself may be guessed once its group is known. However, we have no way of telling the group ahead of time; we have no way of telling how many groups and hence how many interactions there are. The groups seem to be quite disjointed, and there seems to be no connection between the various groups which characterize the various interactions or between these groups and the geometrical symmetry group, which is a single, well-defined group with which we have been familiar for many, many years.

Geometrical Principles of Invariance and Conservation Laws

Since it is good to stay on *terra cognita* as long as possible, let us first review the geometrical principles of invariance. These were recognized by Poincaré first, and I like to call the group formed by these invariables the Poincaré group.[7] The true meaning and importance of these prin-

---

[6] R. Utiyama, *Phys. Rev.*, 101, 1597 (1956); also C. N. Yang and R. L. Mills, *Phys. Rev.*, 96, 191 (1954).

[7] H. Poincaré, *Compt. Rend.*, 140, 1504 (1905); *Rend. Circ. Mat. Palermo*, 21, 129 (1906).

ciples were brought out only by Einstein, in his special theory of relativity. The group contains, first, displacements in space and time. This means that the correlations between events are the same everywhere and at all times, that the laws of nature—the compendium of the correlations—are the same no matter when and where they are established. If this were not so, it might have been impossible for the human mind to find laws of nature.

It is good to emphasize at this point the fact that the laws of nature, that is, the correlations between events, are the entities to which the symmetry laws apply, not the events themselves. Naturally, the events vary from place to place. However, if one observes the positions of a thrown rock at three different times, one will find a relation between those positions, and this relation will be the same at all points of the Earth.

The second symmetry is not at all as obvious as the first one: it postulates the equivalence of all directions. This principle could be recognized only when the influence of the Earth's attraction was understood to be responsible for the difference between up and down. In other words, contrary to what was just said, the events between which the laws of nature establish correlations are not the three positions of the thrown rock, but the three positions of the rock with respect to the Earth.

The last symmetry—the independence of the laws of nature from the state of motion in which it is observed as long as this is uniform—is not at all obvious to the unpreoccupied mind.[8] One of its consequences is that the laws of nature determine not the velocity but the acceleration of a body: the velocity is different in coordinate systems moving with different speeds; the acceleration is the same as long as the motion of the coordinate systems is uniform with respect to each other. Hence, the principle of the equivalence of uniformly moving coordinate systems, and their equivalence with coordinate systems at rest, could not be established before Newton's second law was understood; it was at once recognized then, by Newton himself. It fell temporarily into dis-

[8] Thus, Aristotle's physics postulated that motion necessarily required the continued operation of a cause. Hence, all bodies would come to an absolute rest if they were removed from the cause which imparts them a velocity. [Cf., e.g., A. C. Crombie's *Augustine to Galileo* (London: Falcon Press, 1952), p. 82 or 244.] This cannot be true for coordinate systems moving with respect to each other. The coordinate systems with respect to which it is true then have a preferred state of motion.

repute as a result of certain electromagnetic phenomena until Einstein re-established it in a somewhat modified form.

It was mentioned already that the conservation laws for energy and for linear and angular momentum are direct consequences of the symmetries just enumerated. This is most evident in quantum-mechanical theory, where they follow directly from the kinematics of the theory, without making use of any dynamical law, such as the Schrödinger equation. This will be demonstrated at once. The situation is much more complex in classical theory, and, in fact, the simplest proof of the conservation laws in classical theory is based on the remark that classical theory is a limiting case of quantum theory. Hence, any equation valid in quantum theory, for any value of Planck's constant h, is valid also in the limit $h = 0$. Traces of this reasoning can be recognized also in the general considerations showing the connection between conservation laws and space-time symmetry in classical theory. The conservation laws can be derived also by elementary means, using the dynamical equation, that is, Newton's second law, and the assumption that the forces can be derived from a potential which depends only on the distances between the particles. Since the notion of a potential is not a very natural one, this is not the usual procedure. Mach, for instance, assumes that the force on any particle is a sum of forces, each due to another particle.[9] Such an assumption is implicit also in Newton's third law, otherwise the notion of counterforce would have no meaning. In addition, Mach assumes that the force depends only on the positions of the interacting pair, not on their velocities. Some such assumption is indeed necessary in classical theory.[10] Under the assumptions just mentioned, the conservation law for linear momentum follows at once from Newton's third law, and, conversely, this third law is also necessary for the conservation of linear momentum. All this was recognized already by Newton. For the conservation law of angular momentum, which was, in its general form, discovered almost 60 years after the *Principia* by Euler, Bernouilli, and d'Arcy, the significance of the isotropy of space is evident. If the direction of the force between a pair of particles were not directed along the line from one particle to the other, it would not be invariant under rotations about that line. Hence, under the assump-

---

[9] E. Mach, *The Science of Mechanics* (Chicago: Open Court Publ. Co., various editions), Chap. 3, Sec. 3.

[10] See footnote 5.

tions made, only central forces are possible. Since the torque of such forces vanishes if they are oppositely equal, the angular momentum law follows. It would not follow if the forces depended on the positions of three particles or more.

In quantum mechanics, as was mentioned before, the conservation laws follow already from the basic kinematical concepts. The point is simply that the states in quantum mechanics are vectors in an abstract space, and the physical quantities, such as position, momentum, etc., are operators on these vectors. It then follows, for instance, from the rotational invariance that, given any state ϕ, there is another state ϕ_α which looks just like ϕ in the coordinate system that is obtained by a rotation α about the Z axis. Let us denote the operator which changes ϕ into ϕ_α by Z_α. Let us further denote the state into which ϕ goes over in the time interval τ by $H_\tau\phi$ (for a schematic picture, cf. Fig. 1). Then,

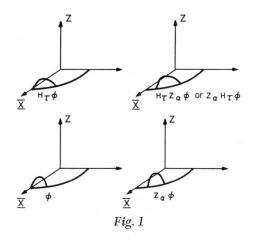

Fig. 1

because of the rotational invariance, ϕ_α will go over, in the same time interval, into the state $H_\tau\phi_\alpha$, which looks, in the second coordinate system, just like $H_\tau\phi$. Hence, it can be obtained from $H_\tau\phi$ by the operation Z_α. It follows that

$$H_\tau Z_\alpha\phi = Z_\alpha H_\tau\phi, \tag{1}$$

and since this is valid for any ϕ,

$$H_\tau Z_\alpha = Z_\alpha H_\tau. \tag{2}$$

Thus the operator Z_α commutes with H_τ, and this is the condition for its being conserved. Actually, the angular momentum about the Z axis is the limit of $(1/\alpha)(Z_\alpha - 1)$ for infinitely small α. The other conservation laws are derived in the same way. The point is that *the transformation operators, or at least the infinitesimal ones among them, play a double role and are themselves the conserved quantities.*

This will conclude the discussion of the geometrical principles of invariance. You will note that reflections which give rise *inter alia* to the concept of parity were not mentioned, nor did I speak about the apparently much more general geometric principle of invariance which forms the foundation of the general theory of relativity. The reason for the former omission is that I will have to consider the reflection operators at the end of this discussion. The reason that I did not speak about the invariance with respect to the general coordinate transformations of the general theory of relativity is that I believe that the underlying invariance is not geometric but dynamic. Let us consider, hence, the dynamic principles of invariance.

Dynamic Principles of Invariance

When we deal with the dynamic principles of invariance, we are largely on *terra incognita*. Nevertheless, since some of the attempts to develop these principles are both ingenious and successful, and since the subject is at the center of interest, I would like to make a few comments. Let us begin with the case that is best understood, the electromagnetic interaction.

In order to describe the interaction of charges with the electromagnetic field, one first introduces new quantities to describe the electromagnetic field, the so-called electromagnetic potentials. From these, the components of the electromagnetic field can be easily calculated, but not conversely. Furthermore, the potentials are not uniquely determined by the field; several potentials (those differing by a gradient) give the same field. It follows that the potentials cannot be measurable, and, in fact, only such quantities can be measurable which are invariant under the transformations which are arbitrary in the potential. This invariance is, of course, an artificial one, similar to that which we could obtain by introducing into our equations the location of a ghost. The equations then must be invariant with respect to changes of the coordinate of that ghost. One does not see, in fact, what good the introduction of the coordinate of the ghost does.

So it is with the replacement of the fields by the potentials, as long as one leaves everything else unchanged. One postulates, however, and this is the decisive step, that in order to maintain the same situation, one has to couple a transformation of the matter field with every transition from a set of potentials to another one which gives the same electromagnetic field. The combination of these two transformations, one on the electromagnetic potentials, the other on the matter field, is called a gauge transformation. Since it leaves the physical situation unchanged, every equation must be invariant thereunder. This is not true, for instance, of the unchanged equations of motion, and they would have, if left unchanged, the absurd property that two situations which are completely equivalent at one time would develop, in the course of time, into two distinguishable situations. Hence, the equations of motion have to be modified, and this can be done most easily by a mathematical device called the modification of the Lagrangian. The simplest modification that restores the invariance gives the accepted equations of electrodynamics which are well in accord with all experience.

Let me state next, without giving all the details, that a similar procedure is possible with respect to the gravitational interaction. Actually, this has been hinted at already by Utiyama.[11] The unnecessary complication that one has to introduce in this case is, instead of potentials, generalized coordinates. The equations then have to be invariant with respect to all the coordinate transformations of the general theory of relativity. This would not change the content of the theory but would only amount to the introduction of a more flexible language in which there are several equivalent descriptions of the same physical situation. Next, however, one postulates that the matter field also transforms as the metric field so that one has to modify the equations in order to preserve their invariance. The simplest modification, or one of the simplest ones, leads to Einstein's equations.

The preceding interpretation of the invariance of the general theory of relativity does not interpret it as a geometrical invariance. That this should not be done had already been pointed out by the Russian physicist Fock.[12] With a slight oversimplification, one can say that a geometrical invariance postulates that two physically different situations, such as

[11] See footnote 6.
[12] V. Fock, *The Theory of Space, Time and Gravitation* (New York: Pergamon Press, 1959). See also A. Kretschman, *Ann. Phys.*, 53, 575 (1917).

those in Figure 1, should develop, in the course of time, into situations which differ in the same way. This is not the case here: the postulate· is merely that two different descriptions of the same situation should develop, in the course of time, into two descriptions which also describe the same physical situation. The similarity with the case of the electro-magnetic potentials is obvious.

Unfortunately, the situation is by no means the same in the case of the other interactions. One knows very little about the weaker one of the strong interactions. The strong one, as well as the weak interaction, has a group which is, first of all, very much smaller than the gauge group or the group of general coordinate transformations.[13] Instead of the infinity of generators of the gauge and general transformation groups, they have only a finite number, that is, eight, generators. They do suffice, nevertheless, to a large extent to determine the form of the interaction, as well as to derive some theorems, similar to those of spectroscopy, which give approximate relations between reaction rates and between energies, that is, masses. Figure 2 shows the octuplet of heavy masses—its members are joined to each other by the simplest nontrivial representation of the underlying group which is equivalent to its conjugate complex.

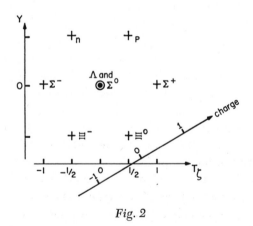

Fig. 2

[13] For the strong interaction, cf. Y. Ne'eman, *Nucl. Phys.*, 26, 222 (1961), and M. Gell-Mann, *Phys. Rev.*, 125, 1067 (1962). For the weak interaction, R. P. Feyn-man and M. Gell-Mann, *Phys. Rev.*, 109, 193 (1958), and E. C. G. Sudarshan and R. E. Marshak, *Phys. Rev.*, 109, 1960 (1958); also J. J. Sakurai, *Nuovo Cimento*, 7, 649 (1958), and G. S. Gershtin and A. B. Zeldovitch, *J. Exptl. Theoret. Phys. USSR*, 29, 698 (1955).

Another difference between the invariance groups of electromagnetism and gravitation on one hand, and at least the invariance group of the strong interaction on the other hand, is that the operations of the former remain valid symmetry operations even if the existence of the other types of interactions is taken into account. The symmetry of the strong interaction, on the other hand, is "broken" by the other interactions, i.e., the operations of the group of the strong interaction are valid symmetry operations only if the other types of interactions can be disregarded. The symmetry group helps to determine the interaction operator in every case. However, whereas all interactions are invariant under the groups of the electromagnetic and gravitational interactions, only the strong interaction is invariant under the group of that interaction.

We have seen before that the operations of the geometric symmetry group entail conservation laws. The question naturally arises whether this is true also for the operations of the dynamic symmetry groups. Again, there seems to be a difference between the different dynamic invariance groups. It is common opinion that the conservation law for electric charge can be regarded as a consequence of gauge invariance, i.e., of the group of the electromagnetic interaction. On the other hand, one can only speculate about conservation laws which could be attributed to the dynamic group of general relativity. Again, it appears reasonable to assume that the conservation laws for baryons and leptons can be deduced by means of the groups of the strong and of the weak interaction.[14] If true, this would imply that the proper groups of these interactions have not yet been recognized. One can adduce two pieces of evidence for the last statement. First, so far, the conservation laws in question[15] could not be deduced from the symmetry properties of these interactions, and it is unlikely that they can be deduced from

[14] For the baryon conservation law and the strong interaction, this was suggested by the present writer, *Proc. Am. Phil. Soc.*, 93, 521 (1949), and these *Proceedings*, 38, 449 (1952). The baryon conservation law was first postulated by E. C. G. Stueckelberg, *Helv. Phys. Acta*, 11, 299 (1938).

[15] For the experimental verification of these and the other conservation laws, see G. Feinberg and M. Goldhaber, these *Proceedings*, 45, 1301 (1959). The conservation law for leptons was proposed by G. Marx in *Acta Phys. Hung.*, 3, 55 (1953); also A. B. Zeldovitch, *Dokl. Akad. Nauk USSR*, 91, 1317 (1953), and E. J. Konopinski and H. M. Mahmoud, *Phys. Rev.*, 92, 1045 (1953). It seemed to be definitely established by T. D. Lee and C. N. Yang, *Phys. Rev.*, 105, 1671 (1957). See also Fermi's observation mentioned by C. N. Yang and J. Tiomno, *Phys. Rev.*, 79, 497 (1950).

them.[16] Second, the symmetry properties in question are not rigorous but are broken by the other interactions. It is not clear how rigorous conservation laws could follow from approximate symmetries—and all evidence indicates that the baryon and lepton conservation laws are rigorous.[17] Again, we are reminded that our ideas on the dynamical principles of invariance are not nearly as firmly established as those on the geometrical ones.

Let me make a last remark on a principle which I would not hesitate to call a symmetry principle and which forms a transition between the geometrical and dynamical principles. This is given by the crossing relations.[18] Let us consider the amplitude for the probability of some collision, such as

$$A + B + \ldots \to X + Y + \ldots. \tag{3}$$

This will be a function of the invariants which can be formed from the momenta four-vectors of the incident and emitted particles. It then follows from one of the reflection principles which I did not discuss, the "time reversal invariance," that the amplitude of (3) determines also the amplitude of the inverse reaction

$$X + Y + \ldots \to A + B + \ldots \tag{4}$$

in a very simple fashion. If one reverses all the velocities and also interchanges past and future (which is the definition of "time reversal"), (4) goes over into (3) so that the amplitudes for both are essentially equal. Similarly, if we denote the antiparticle of A by $\overline{A}$, that of B by $\overline{B}$, and so on, and consider the reaction

$$\overline{A} + \overline{B} + \ldots \to \overline{X} + \overline{Y} + \ldots, \tag{5}$$

its amplitude is immediately given by that of (3) because (according to the interpretation of Lee and Yang), the reaction (5) is obtained from (3) by space inversion. The amplitudes for

$$\overline{X} + \overline{Y} + \ldots \to \overline{A} + \overline{B} + \ldots \tag{6}$$

[16] For the baryon conservation and strong interaction, this was emphatically pointed out in a very interesting article by J. J. Sakurai, *Ann. Phys.* (N.Y.), 11, 1 (1960). Concerning the conservation of lepton members, see G. Marx, *Z. Naturforsch.*, 9a, 1051 (1954).

[17] See footnote 15.

[18] M. L. Goldberger, *Phys. Rev.*, 99, 979 (1955); M. Gell-Mann, and M. L. Goldberger, *Phys. Rev.*, 96, 1433 (1954). See M. L. Goldberger and K. M. Watson, *Collision Theory* (New York: John Wiley and Sons, 1964), chap. 10.

can be obtained in a similar way. The relations between the amplitudes of reactions (3), (4), (5), and (6) are consequences of geometrical principles of invariance.

However, one can go further. The crossing relations tell us how to calculate, for instance, the amplitude of

$$\overline{X} + B + \ldots \rightarrow \overline{A} + Y + \ldots \tag{7}$$

from the amplitude system of (3). To be sure, the calculation, or its result, is not simple any more. One has to consider the dependence of the reaction amplitude for (3) as an analytic function of the invariants formed from the momenta of the particles in (3), and extend this analytic function to such values of the variables which have no physical significance for the reaction (3) but which give the amplitude for (7). Evidently there are several other reactions the amplitudes of which can be obtained in a similar way; they are all obtained by the analytic continuation of the amplitude for (3), or any of the other reactions. Thus, rather than exchanging A and X to obtain (7), A and Y could be exchanged, and so on.

The crossing relations share two properties of the geometrical principles of invariance: they do not refer to any particular type of interaction and most of us believe that they have unlimited validity. On the other hand, though they can be formulated in terms of events, their formulation presupposes the establishment of a law of nature, namely, the mathematical, in fact analytic, expression for the collision amplitude for one of the aforementioned reactions. One may hope that they will help to establish a link between the now disjoint geometrical and dynamical principles of invariance.

3

The Role of Invariance Principles in Natural Philosophy

What Is the Role and Proper Place of Invariance Principles in the Framework of Physical Sciences?

A large part of my scientific work has been devoted to the study of symmetry principles in physics and I was therefore not only flattered but also greatly pleased at Professor Bernardini's invitation to speak at this anniversary on the philosophical and epistemological role of these principles. I would like to review the role of symmetry and invariance principles from a somewhat more general point of view than that of the physicist and appreciate the opportunity also to relate to you some of the conclusions at which Drs. Houtappel, van Dam, and I arrived in a series of long discussions.

There is a strange hierarchy in our knowledge of the world around us. Every moment brings surprises and unforseeable events—truly the future is uncertain. There is, nevertheless, a structure in the events around us, that is, correlations between the events of which we take cognizance. It is this structure, these correlations, which science wishes to discover, or at least the precise and sharply defined correlations. They are refinements and extensions of our everyday knowledge, in some cases so far-reaching that we do not recognize their origin. In some cases they permit

Address at the 10th anniversary of the Scuola Internationale di Fisica "Enrico Fermi," July 14, 1963, Varenna. Reprinted by permission from the *Proceedings of the International School of Physics* "Enrico Fermi," vol. 29, p. 40 (Academic Press, 1964). Copyright by the Italian Physical Society, Bologna, Italy.

us to foresee some events with certainty. Part of the art and skill of the engineer and of the experimental physicist is to create conditions in which certain events are sure to occur. Nevertheless, there are always events which are unforseeable.

If we look a little deeper into this situation we realize that we would not live in the same sense we do if the events around us had no structure. Even if our bodily functions remained unaltered, our consciousness could hardly differ from that of plants if we were unable to influence the events, and if these had no structure or if we were not familiar with some of this structure, we could not influence them. There would be no way our volition could manifest itself and there would be no such thing as that which we call life. This does not mean, of course, that life depends on the existence of the unbelievable precision and accuracy of the correlations between events which our laws of nature express, and indeed the precision of these laws has all the elements of a miracle that one can think of.

We know many laws of nature and we hope and expect to discover more. Nobody can foresee the next such law that will be discovered. Nevertheless, there is a structure in the laws of nature which we call the laws of invariance. This structure is so far-reaching in some cases that laws of nature were guessed on the basis of the postulate that they fit into the invariance structure.

It is not necessary to look deeper into the situation to realize that laws of nature could not exist without principles of invariance. This is explained in many texts of elementary physics even though only few of the readers of these texts can be expected to have the maturity necessary to appreciate these explanations. If the correlations between events changed from day to day, and would be different for different points of space, it would be impossible to discover them. Thus the invariances of the laws of nature with respect to displacements in space and time are almost necessary prerequisites that it be possible to discover, or even catalogue, the correlations between events which are the laws of nature. This does not mean, of course, that either the precision or the scope of the principles of invariance which we accept at present are necessary prerequisites for the existence of laws of nature. Both are very surprising indeed, even if not quite as amazing as the precision of some laws of nature which I am always tempted to add to Kant's starred sky above us, and the categorical imperative within us.

This then, the progression from events to laws of nature, and from laws of nature to symmetry or invariance principles, is what I meant by the hierarchy of our knowledge of the world around us.

There are only two points which I feel should be added to the preceding discussion. The first of these amounts to admitting a certain amount of oversimplification. It concerns the way we take cognizance of the events around us—the events between which we wish to establish correlations. Some of these events, such as the rising and the setting of the sun, we perceive directly—though of course it would lead far and would also be difficult to explain what we mean by direct perception. Other events, such as the motion of an α-particle, we perceive only by means of rather complicated machinery, such as a cloud or a spark chamber. We believe, in such cases, that the established laws of nature tell us how the machinery which we employed functions and that we can consider the information obtained by *interpreting* the sense-data furnished by the machinery on a par with the sense-data the interpretation of which we learned during our childhood.

What I am admitting is that the perception of events, as we practice it in physics, is not independent of our knowledge of the laws of nature. This knowledge interprets for us, for instance, what we directly see in the cloud chamber. Hence the separation of our perceptions from the laws of nature is an oversimplification, though we believe a harmless oversimplification. Nevertheless, I felt that this point should not be suppressed.

The second point which I wish to add to the preceding discussion pertains more directly to our subject. It concerns my reference to *laws* of nature rather than one universal *law* of nature. In fact, if the universal law of nature should be discovered, invariance principles would become merely mathematical transformations which leave that law invariant. They would remain, perhaps, useful tools for deriving consequences of the universal law, much as they were used to derive the qualitative rules of spectroscopy from the laws of quantum mechanics. However, if the universal law of nature should be discovered, the principles of invariance would lose their place in the hierarchy described before. Of course, we all try to discover the universal law and some of us believe that it will be discovered one day. Many others believe that our knowledge of the laws of nature will never be complete. Naturally, even the latter alternative only makes the continued significance of invariance principles possible, it does not guarantee it. Let me remark, though, right here that a similar situation exists with respect to the laws of nature. If we had a complete description of all the events with which we shall ever come into contact, the correlations between these events, that is the laws of nature, would have a reduced significance, similar to that of the invariance principles when the universal law of nature is known. However, few if any of us believe in the possibility of the Laplaceian spirit which knows all the events, so that the significance of the laws of nature is more assured than that of the invariance principles.

Let us turn now to two other subjects: first, the nature and development of invariance principles and, second, their continued significance in a possible, and I hope foreseeable, union of the physical sciences with the other areas of human knowledge.

The Nature and Development of Invariance Principles

The classic invariance or symmetry principles are one rung of the ladder removed from direct observations. Nevertheless, they are, and should be, formulated in terms of direct observations. Thus the time-displacement invariance, properly formulated, reads: the correlations between events depend only on the time intervals between those events; they do not depend on the time when the first of them takes place. Thus, if the same relevant conditions are realized at different times, the expectations of further events will be the same, no matter when these relevant conditions were realized. I realize and wish to admit that the qualification "relevant" of the conditions is ill-defined and unprecise. This is unavoidable as long as we expect discoveries of new agents or of new effects of agents with which we are already familiar. In spite of this lack of precision, it remains true that invariance principles are formulated, jumping down over one rung of the ladder, directly in terms of observations. Only in this way can they be general enough to serve as guides to the formulation and testing of new laws of nature. It is in conformity with the formulation of invariance principles directly in terms of observations that invariance principles are also best refuted directly, in terms of observations. Thus the parity principle was refuted by creating a system with reflection symmetry which showed, subsequently, a departure from that symmetry. Only very elementary theory was necessary to see that Wu's experiment was in conflict with the parity principle.

However, even though the classic invariance principles are formulated directly in terms of observations, they are rarely used directly to forecast the future. Rather, they are used to test a theory or law of nature—that is, the nearest rung of the ladder—in order to ascertain whether its consequences will be necessarily in conformity with the invariance principle. Such a test often involves mathematical and conceptual operations of some complexity, using the often elaborate machinery in terms of which the law of nature is formulated. This explains the often erudite nature of some of the considerations in the theory of invariance.

It was mentioned before that it would have been difficult to establish any laws of nature if these were not invariant with respect to displacements in space and time. The same holds, pretty nearly, of rotational invariance, and these invariances were taken for granted even before the concept of the laws of nature had clearly emerged. It is nevertheless very difficult to verify the invariance with respect to rotations—the isotropy of physical space—by direct experiment: there seems to be an obvious difference between up and down and sidewise. However, Newton's theory of gravitation and his equations of motion are consistent with this invariance and they adequately explain the abovementioned differences as due to the attraction by the Earth. Here is then a case in which laws of nature and invariance principles, the two adjoining rungs of the ladder, mutually support each other. The concluding invariance with respect to Galilei transformations, or their modification, that is Lorentz transformations, was not at all anticipated before it was recognized by Galilei and Newton. The symmetry of the laws of nature with respect to reflections in space and time was taken for granted from about the same time on but the effectiveness and value of these symmetries in quantum mechanics was a surprise to everyone. The same applies though, albeit perhaps to a lesser degree, to the other classical symmetries also.

I have spoken so far about the classical symmetries, which are symmetries of the physical space-time continuum, similar to Klein's symmetries of geometrical space. These are, however, not the only invariances of physics any more—the laws of nature may be time-displacement invariant, the concept of invariance does not seem to be. It may not have been desirable to use the same word for the classical and the new invariances—the invariances which will be considered next. However, this is clearly a question of semantics. What was called here "new invariances" would better be called, perhaps, nongeometrical invariances, and they include the electromagnetic gauge-invariance, the Ne'eman-Gell-Mann eightfold way, and several others. We all feel that there is a qualitative difference between, let us say, rotational invariance on the one hand, and gauge invariance on the other. Even though we all sense the character of the difference involved, it may be worth while to articulate it and to formulate it as generally in terms of the underlying concepts as I can.

The principal difference is, to put it briefly, that the new invariances are invariances of expressions for specific interactions, not for all laws of nature.

This implies, first, the existence of specific types of interactions, such as gravitational, weak, electromagnetic, and, possibly, two kinds of strong interactions. It implies, second, that the new or nongeometrical types of invariances cannot be formulated directly in terms of correlations between observations, as I emphasized the classical or geometrical invariances are. If they could, they each would have the same relevance for all interactions, as do the classical ones. This is not the case.

The emergence of specific types of interactions as separate and well distinguishable entities is one of the most striking results of the last decade. If a malicious remark be permitted at this point, their number shows an alarming tendency to increase. It is equally striking that each of them is invariant under a specific group. This is the SU_3 group for the strong interaction, the gauge group for the electromagnetic interaction, the somewhat more complex group of the $V - A$ expression for the weak interaction, and, I believe, the general group of co-ordinate transformations for the gravitational interaction. In each case, the invariance group permits the determination of the expression for the interaction by means of a few additional assumptions implying the simplicity of the final equation. If my remark concerning the gravitational interaction is correct, Fock's observation must be interpreted as classifying the invariance with respect to the general co-ordinate transformation of relativity theory as a nongeometrical type of invariance, not a classical one.

Nevertheless, there are very great differences between the relations of the five types of interactions to the corresponding groups—so large that one may be quite uncertain whether we already know the proper group in every case. There must be also a deeper principle which explains the existence of separate types of interactions and the distinct groups which correspond to them.

Let us consider the oldest nonclassical invariance, that of the gauge invariance of electromagnetic interaction. It appears that in order to describe the interaction between electric charges and the electromagnetic field, the introduction of a new concept, that of the electromagnetic potentials, is pretty nearly unavoidable. It is not entirely unavoidable—the use of every concrete concept can be circumvented—and Mandelstam in particular has shown how this can be done in the present case. It is unquestionable, however, that the electromagnetic interaction can be expressed much more simply using the potentials. The potentials are redundant for describing the field, that is, an infinite set of potentials corresponds to the same physical situation. In other words, the physical situation, that is, all observable properties, are invariant under certain transformations of the potentials and, conversely, only those expressions in terms of the potentials are observable which are invariant under these so-called gauge transformations. Up to this point, the electromagnetic potential only appears as an awkward but harmlessly awkward concept for describing the electromagnetic field. Next, one postulates, however, that in order to maintain the same physical situation, every transformation of the electromagnetic potentials to equivalent potentials must be coupled with a certain transformation of the field with which they interact, that is, of the matter field. This is the decisive step. As a result, many expressions in terms of the matter field alone become unobservable because they are no longer invariant under gauge transformations. In order to make them invariant one has to modify them. Furthermore, two different matter-field potential combinations, which can be obtained from each other by a gauge transformation and which are therefore physically equivalent, would change in time into matter-field potential combinations which are not physically equivalent if the unchanged field equations are used to calculate their time-dependence. This would be absurd and it follows that the field equations, determining the time-dependence of the matter-field and of the potentials, must also be modified. Such a modification entails an interaction between the two fields and it appears that the simplest modification which guarantees that equivalent fields remain equivalent throughout the passage of time leads to an accurate description of the electromagnetic interaction.

Hence, the expression for the electromagnetic interaction could be guessed by a rather artificial device. First, redundant quantities for the field can be introduced, namely, the potentials. Second, it can be postulated that the transformations which change a potential into an equivalent one should affect the other physical quantities, namely, the matter-field, also; and an assumption made what their effect should be. Lastly, the field equations are so modified that they become consistent with the equivalence of the several possible descriptions of the same physical situation. One will recognize a strong similarity between this procedure and that which leads to Einstein's equations of gravitation. There also, one can start from a co-ordinate system which satisfies Fock's requirements, so that the divergence of the metric field is zero. One can then introduce an awkward or redundant field for which the divergence is not zero and postulate that only those quantities are meaningful, that is, observable, which are the same in all these co-ordinate systems. These are the invariants. The decisive step is, in this case, the postulate that all physical quantities, in particular the stress-energy tensor, transform in the same way as the metric field, that is, as tensors. One then has all the postulates of the Riemannian geometry which Einstein used for deriving his equations of gravitation.

One recognizes, on the other hand, also the great difference between the relation of electromagnetic and gravitational interactions with their groups on one hand, and the relation of the weak and the strong interactions with their groups on the other. The latter relations and groups are much more simple and direct. It is possible, of course, that we shall one day understand the reasons for this difference. It is, perhaps, also possible that gradual modifications of the theory will eliminate these differences and also provide us with a more coherent view of the different types of interactions. This is the objective of Utiyama's proposal.

Whereas one may hope that the nonclassical or nongeometric invariances will acquire a common structure and they may even coalesce into a single deeper entity, the difference between classic and nonclassic invariances appears to be much deeper. If one wishes to bring the fact of Lorentz invariance into the form just discussed for gauge invariance, one must look, first, for redundant quantities in the theory. One can say that the usual absolute co-ordinates are redundant in this way, that their use instead of the distances between particles, or the co-ordinates with respect to the center of mass, is in itself "awkward but harmless."

However, the usual absolute co-ordinates can be observed by reference to other physical systems which are too distant to influence the system in question but provide a meaning to the absolute co-ordinates of its constituents. No similar meaning can be attached to the absolute potentials and they are truly redundant.

Outlook to the Future

Our discussion started with pointing to the uncertainty of the future, to the surprises that every moment brings us. I am on uncertain grounds indeed when speaking about the future role of the invariance principles. However, I can perhaps excuse my concluding sentences by pointing out that what one means when speaking about the outlook to the future is not so much a forecast what the future will bring as a visualization of a possible future.

As far as the physical sciences are concerned, the role of invariance principles does not seem to be near exhaustion. We still seem to be far from the "universal law of nature." We seem to be far from it, if indeed it exists, and, to paraphrase Poincaré, the present picture of four or five different types of interactions, with widely divergent properties, is not such as to permit the human mind to rest contented. Hence, invariance principles, giving a structure to the laws of nature, can be expected to act as guides also in the future and to help us to refine and unify our knowledge of the inanimate world.

One is less inclined to optimism if one considers the question whether the physical sciences will remain separate and distinct from the biological sciences and, in particular, the sciences of the mind. There are many signs which portend that a more profound understanding of the phenomena of observation and cognition, together with an appreciation of the limits of our ability to understand, is a not too distant future step. At any rate, it should be the next decisive step toward a more integrated understanding of the world. On the path toward such understanding, we shall not have to treat physical phenomena and phenomena of the mind in such a way that we forget about the tools used for the consideration of one when thinking about the problems of the other. I confess that I have no conception what the structure of this more integrated science may be and it would be surprising if it continued to contain a hierarchy similar to the one described before, in which invariance and symmetry principles have definite places. That a higher integration of science is needed is perhaps best demonstrated by the observation that the basic entities of intuitionistic mathematics are the physical objects, that the basic concept in the epistemological structure of physics is the concept of observation, and that psychology is not yet ready for providing concepts and idealizations of such precision as are expected in mathematics or even physics. Thus this passing of responsibility from mathematics to physics, and hence to the science of cognition ends nowhere. This state of affairs should be remedied by a closer integration of the now separate disciplines.

4

Events, Laws of Nature, and
Invariance Principles

It is a great and unexpected honor to have the opportunity to speak here today. Six years ago, Yang and Lee spoke here, reviewing symmetry principles in general and their discovery of the violation of the parity principle in particular.[1] There is little point in repeating what they said on the history of the invariance principles, or on my own contribution to these, which they, naturally, exaggerated. What I would like to discuss instead is the general role of symmetry and invariance principles in physics, both modern and classical. More precisely, I would like to discuss the relation between three categories which play a fundamental role in all natural sciences: events, which are the raw materials for the second category, the laws of nature, and symmetry principles, for which I would like to support the thesis that the laws of nature form the raw material.

Events and Laws of Nature

It is often said that the objective of physics is the explanation of nature, or at least of inanimate nature. What do we mean by explanation? It is the establishment of a few simple principles which describe

[1] See the articles of C. N. Yang and of T. D. Lee in *Les Prix Nobel en 1957* (Stockholm: Nobel Foundation, 1958). [Reprinted in *Science*, 127, 565, 569 (1958).]

the properties of what is to be explained. If we understand something, its behavior—that is, the events which it presents—should not produce any surprises for us. We should always have the impression that it could not be otherwise.

It is clear that, in this sense, physics does not endeavor to explain nature. In fact, the great success of physics is due to a restriction of its objectives: it only endeavors to explain the regularities in the behavior of objects. This renunciation of the broader aim, and the specification of the domain for which an explanation can be sought, now appears to us an obvious necessity. In fact, the specification of the explainable may have been the greatest discovery of physics so far. It does not seem easy to find its inventor, or to give the exact date of its origin. Kepler still tried to find exact rules for the magnitude of the planetary orbits, similar to his laws of planetary motion. Newton already realized that physics would deal, for a long time, only with the explanation of those of the regularities discovered by Kepler which we now call Kepler's laws.[2]

The regularities in the phenomena which physical science endeavors to uncover are called the laws of nature. The name is actually very appropriate. Just as legal laws regulate actions and behavior under certain conditions but do not try to regulate all actions and behavior, the laws of physics also determine the behavior of its objects of interest only under certain well-defined conditions but leave much freedom otherwise. The elements of the behavior which are not specified by the laws of nature are called initial conditions. These, then, together with the laws of nature, specify the behavior as far as it can be specified at all: if a further specification were possible, this specification would be considered as an added initial condition. As is well known, before the advent of quantum theory it was believed that a complete description of the behavior of an object is possible so that, if classical theory were valid, the initial conditions and the laws of nature together would completely determine the behavior of an object.

The preceding statement is a definition of the term "initial condition." Because of its somewhat unusual nature, it may be worthwhile to illustrate this on an example. Suppose we did not know Newton's equation for the motion of stars and planets,

---

[2] See, for instance, A. C. Crombie, *Augustine to Galileo* (London: Falcon, 1952), pp. 316 ff. The growth of the understanding of the realm of the explainable, from the end of the 13th century on, can be traced through almost every chapter of this book.

$$\ddot{\mathbf{r}}_i = G \, \Sigma' \, M_j \frac{\mathbf{r}_{ij}}{r^3_{ij}} \qquad \mathbf{r}_{ij} = \mathbf{r}_j - \mathbf{r}_i, \tag{1}$$

but had found only the equation determining the third derivative of the position

$$\dddot{\mathbf{r}}_i = G \, \Sigma' \, M_j \times \frac{\dot{\mathbf{r}}_{ij}(\mathbf{r}_{ij} \cdot \mathbf{r}_{ij}) - 3\mathbf{r}_{ij}(\dot{\mathbf{r}}_{ij} \cdot \mathbf{r}_{ij})}{r^5_{ij}} \,. \tag{2}$$

More generally, if the forces F_i are nongravitational, one would have written

$$M_i \dddot{\mathbf{r}}_i = (\dot{\mathbf{r}}_i \, \mathrm{grad}) \, \mathbf{F}_i + \dot{\mathbf{F}}_i. \tag{2a}$$

The initial conditions then would contain not only all the $\mathbf{r}_i$ and $\dot{\mathbf{r}}_i$, but also the $\ddot{\mathbf{r}}_i$. These data, together with the "equation of motion" (Eq. 2), would then determine the future behavior of the system just as $\mathbf{r}_i$, $\dot{\mathbf{r}}_i$, and Eq. 1 determine it. The fact that initial conditions and laws of nature completely determine the behavior is similarly true in any causal theory.

The surprising discovery of Newton's age is just the clear separation of laws of nature on the one hand and initial conditions on the other. The former are precise beyond anything reasonable; we know virtually nothing about the latter. Let us pause for a minute at this last statement. Are there really no regularities concerning what we just called initial conditions?

The last statement would certainly not be true if as laws of nature Eqs. 2 and 2a were adopted, that is, if we considered the $\ddot{\mathbf{r}}_i$ as part of the initial conditions. In this case, there would be a relation, in fact the precise relation of Eq. 1, between the elements of the initial conditions. The question, therefore, can be only: are there any relations between what we really do consider as initial conditions? Formulated in a more constructive way: how can we ascertain that we know all the laws of nature relevant to a set of phenomena? If we do not, we would determine unnecessarily many initial conditions in order to specify the behavior of the object. One way to ascertain this would be to prove that all the initial conditions can be chosen arbitrarily—a procedure which is, however, impossible in the domain of the very large (we cannot change the orbits of the planets) or the very small (we cannot precisely control atomic particles). No other equally unambiguous criterion is known to me, but there is a distinguishing property of the correctly chosen—that is, minimal—set of initial conditions which is worth mentioning.

The minimal set of initial conditions not only does not permit any exact relation between its elements; on the contrary, there is reason to contend that these are, or at some time have been, as random as the externally imposed, gross constraints allow. I wish to illustrate this point, first, on an example which, at first, seems to contradict the thesis because this example shows the power, and also the weakness of the assertion, best.

Let us consider for this purpose again our planetary system. It was mentioned before that the approximate regularities in the initial conditions, that is, the determinants of the orbits, led Kepler to the considerations which were then left by the wayside by Newton. These regularities form the apparent counterexample to the aforementioned thesis. However, the existence of the regularities in the initial conditions is considered so unsatisfactory that it is felt necessary to show that the regularities are but a consequence of a situation in which there were *no* regularities. Perhaps von Weizsäcker's attempt in this direction[3] is most interesting: he assumes that originally the solar system consisted of a central star, with a gas in rotation, but otherwise in random motion, around it. He then deduces the aforementioned regularities of the planetary system, now called Bode's law, from his assumption. More generally, one tries to deduce almost all "organized motion," even the existence of life, in a similar fashion. It must be admitted that few of these explanations have been carried out in detail,[4] but the fact that such explanations are attempted remains significant.

The preceding paragraph dealt with cases in which there is at least an apparent evidence against the random nature of the uncontrolled initial conditions. It attempted to show that the apparently organized nature of these initial conditions was preceded by a state in which the uncontrolled initial conditions were random. These are, on the whole, exceptional situations. In most cases, there is no reason to question the random nature of the noncontrolled, or nonspecified, initial conditions,

[3] C. F. von Weizsäcker, *Z. Astrophys.*, 22, 319 (1944); S. Chandrasekhar, *Rev. Mod. Phys.*, 18, 94 (1946).

[4] An interesting and well-understood case is that of "focusing collisions" in which neutrons, having velocities which are rather high but with random orientation, are converted into lower-velocity neutrons but with preferential directions of motion. See R. H. Silsbee, *J. Appl. Phys.*, 28, 1246 (1957); C. Lehmann and G. Leibfried, *Z. Physik*, 172, 465 (1963).

and the random nature of these initial conditions is supported by the validity of the conclusions arrived at on the basis of the assumption of randomness. One encounters such situations in the kinetic theory of gases and, more generally, whenever one describes processes in which the entropy increases. Altogether, then, one obtains the impression that, whereas the laws of nature codify beautifully simple regularities, the initial conditions exhibit, as far as they are not controlled, equally simple and beautiful irregularity. Hence there is perhaps little chance that some of the former remain overlooked.

The preceding discussion characterized the laws of nature as regularities in the behavior of an object. In quantum theory, this is natural: the laws of quantum mechanics can be suitably formulated as correlations between subsequent observations on an object. These correlations are the regularities given by the laws of quantum mechanics.[5] The statements of classical theory, its equations of motion, are not customarily viewed as correlations between observations. It is true, however, that their purpose and function is to furnish such correlations and that they are, in essence, nothing but a shorthand expression for such correlations.

Laws of Nature and Invariance

We have ceased to expect from physics an explanation of all events, even in the gross structure of the universe, and we aim only at the discovery of the laws of nature, that is, the regularities of the events. The preceding section gives reason for the hope that the regularities form a sharply defined set and are clearly separable from what we call initial conditions, in which there is a strong element of randomness. However, we are far from having found that set. In fact, if it is true that there are precise regularities, we have reason to believe that we know only an infinitesimal fraction of these. The best evidence for this statement derives perhaps from a fact which was mentioned here by Yang 6 years ago: the multiplicity of the types of interactions. Yang mentioned four of them—gravitational, weak, electromagnetic, and strong, and it now seems that there are two types of strong interactions. All these play a role in every process, but it is hard, if not impossible, to believe that the laws of nature should have such complexity as implied

[5] See, for instance, the section, "What is the state vector?" in E. Wigner, *Am. J. Phys.*, 31, 6 (1963), reprinted in this volume.

by four or five different types of interactions between which no connection, no analogy, can be discovered.

It is natural, therefore, to ask for a superprinciple which is in a similar relation to the laws of nature as these are to the events. The laws of nature permit us to foresee events on the basis of the knowledge of other events; the principles of invariance should permit us to establish new correlations between events, on the basis of the knowledge of established correlations between events. This is exactly what they do. If it is established that the existence of the events *A, B, C,* . . . necessarily entails the occurrence of *X*, then the occurrence of the events *A', B', C',* . . . also necessarily entails *X'*, if *A', B', C',* . . . and *X'* are obtained from *A, B, C,* . . . and *X* by one of the invariance transformations. There are three categories of such invariance transformations:

a) Euclidean transformations: the primed events occur at a different location in space, but in the same relation to each other, as the unprimed events.

b) Time displacements: the primed events occur at a different time, but separated by the same time intervals from each other as the unprimed ones.

c) Uniform motion: the primed events appear to be the same as the unprimed events from the point of view of a uniformly moving coordinate system.

The first two categories of invariance principles were always taken for granted. In fact, it may be argued that laws of nature could not have been recognized if they did not satisfy some elementary invariance principles such as those of categories a and b—if they changed from place to place, or if they were also different at different times. The principle c is not so natural. In fact, it has often been questioned, and it was an accomplishment of extraordinary magnitude on the part of Einstein to have re-established it in his special theory of relativity. However, before discussing this point further, it may be useful to make a few general remarks.

The first remarkable characteristic of the invariance principles which were enumerated is that they are all geometric, at least if four-dimensional space-time is the underlying geometrical space. By this I mean that the invariance transformations do not change the events; they only change their location in space and time and their state of motion. One could easily imagine a principle in which, let us say, protons are replaced by electrons and vice versa, velocities by positions, and so on.[6]

The second remarkable characteristic of the preceding principles is that they are invariance rather than covariance principles. This means that they postulate the same conclusion for the primed premises as for the unprimed premises. It is quite conceivable that, if certain events A, B, . . . take place, the events X_1, X_2, X_3 . . . will follow with certain probabilities p_1, p_2, p_3. . . . From the transformed events A', B', C', the transformed consequences X_1', X_2', X_3', . . . *could* follow with changed probabilities such as

$$p_1' = p_1(1 - p_1 + \Sigma p_n{}^2),$$
$$p_2' = p_2(1 - p_2 + \Sigma p_n{}^2),$$
$$\cdots$$

but this is not the case; we always have $p_i' = p_i$.

These two points are specifically mentioned because there are symmetry principles, the so-called crossing relations,[7] which *may be* precisely valid and which surely do not depend on specific types of interactions. In these regards they are, or may be, similar to the geometric invariance principles. They differ from these because they do change the events and they are covariance rather than invariance principles. Thus, from a full knowledge of the cross section for neutron-proton scattering, they permit one to obtain some of the neutron-antiproton collision cross sections. The former events are surely different from the neutron-antiproton collisions, and the cross sections for the latter are not equal to the neutron-proton cross sections but are obtained from these by a rather complicated mathematical procedure. Hence, the crossing relations, even though they do not depend on a specific type of interaction, are not considered to be geometrical symmetry conditions, and they will not be considered here. Similarly, we shall not be

[6] The possibility of an invariance principle in which velocities are replaced by position, and conversely, was studied by M. Born, *Nature*, 141, 327 (1938); *Proc. Roy. Soc.* (London), A165, 291 (1938); *ibid.*, A166, 552 (1938).

[7] The crossing relations were established by M. L. Goldberger, *Phys. Rev.*, 99, 979 (1955); M. Gell-Mann and M. L. Goldberger, *ibid.*, 96, 1433 (1954). For further literature, see, for instance, M. L. Goldberger and K. M. Watson, *Collision Theory* (New York: John Wiley and Sons, 1964), Chap. 10. The relations of the various types of symmetry principles were considered in two recent articles of the present author: *Proceedings of the International School of Physics "Enrico Fermi"* vol. 29, p. 40 (Academic Press, 1964) (reprinted in this volume), and *Phys. Today*, 17, 34 (1964). See also *Progr. Theoret. Phys.*, 11, 437 (1954).

concerned with the dynamic symmetry principles which are symmetries of specific interactions, such as electromagnetic interactions or strong interactions, and are not formulated in terms of events.[8]

As to the geometrical principles, it should be noted that they depend on the dividing line between initial conditions and laws of nature. Thus, the law of nature Eq. 2 or 2a, obtained from Newton's principle by differentiation with respect to time, is invariant also under the transformation to a uniformly accelerated coordinate system

$$\mathbf{r}_i' = \mathbf{r}_i + t^2\mathbf{a} \quad t' = t, \tag{3}$$

where $\mathbf{a}$ is an arbitrary vector. Naturally, this added principle can have no physical consequence because, if the initial conditions $\mathbf{r}_i$, $\dot{\mathbf{r}}_i$, $\ddot{\mathbf{r}}_i$ are realizable (that is, satisfy Eq. 1), the transformed initial conditions $\mathbf{r}_i' = \mathbf{r}_i$, $\dot{\mathbf{r}}_i' = \dot{\mathbf{r}}_i$, $\ddot{\mathbf{r}}_i' = \ddot{\mathbf{r}}_i + 2\mathbf{a}$ cannot be realizable.

The symmetry principles of the preceding discussion are those of Newtonian mechanics or the special theory of relativity. One may well wonder why the much more general, and apparently geometrical, principles of invariance of the general theory have not been discussed. The reason is that I believe, in conformity with the views expressed by V. Fock,[9] that the curvilinear coordinate transformations of the general theory of relativity are not invariance transformations in the sense considered here. These were so-called active transformations, replacing events $A, B, C, \ldots$ by events $A', B', C', \ldots$, and unless active transformations are possible, there is no physically meaningful invariance. However, the mere replacement of one curvilinear coordinate system by another is a "redescription" in the sense of Melvin[10]; it does not change the events and does not represent a structure in the laws of nature. This does not mean that the transformations of the general theory of relativity are not useful tools for finding the correct laws of gravitation; they evidently are. However, as I suggested elsewhere,[11] the principle which they serve to formulate is different from the geometrical invariance principles considered here; it is a dynamical invariance principle.

---

[8] See footnote 7.

[9] V. A. Fock, *The Theory of Space, Time and Gravitation* (New York: Pergamon Press, 1959). The character of the postulate of invariance with respect to general coordinate transformations as a geometrical invariance had already been questioned by E. Kretschman, *Ann. Phys. Leipzig*, 53, 575 (1917).

[10] M. A. Melvin, *Rev. Mod. Phys.*, 32, 477 (1960).

[11] See footnote 7.

The Use of Invariance Principles, Approximate Invariances

The preceding two sections emphasized the inherent nature of the invariance principles as being rigorous correlations between those correlations between events which are postulated by the laws of nature. This at once points to the use of the set of invariance principles which is surely most important at present: to be touchstones for the validity of possible laws of nature. A law of nature can be accepted as valid only if the correlations which it postulates are consistent with the accepted invariance principles.

Incidentally, Einstein's original article which led to his formulation of the special theory of relativity illustrates the preceding point with greatest clarity.[12] He points out in this article that the correlations between events are the same in all coordinate systems in uniform motion with respect to each other, even though the causes attributed to these correlations at that time did depend on the state of motion of the coordinate system. Similarly, Einstein made the most extensive use of invariance principles to guess the correct form of a law of nature, in this case that of the gravitational law, by postulating that this law conforms with the invariance principles which he postulated.[13] Equally remarkable is the present application of invariance principles in quantum electrodynamics. This is not a consistent theory—in fact, not a theory in the proper sense because its equations are in contradiction to each other. However, these contradictions can be resolved with reasonable uniqueness by postulating that the conclusions conform to the theory of relativity.[14] Another approach, even more fundamental, tries to axiomatize quantum field theories, the invariance principles forming the cornerstone of the axioms.[15] I will not further enlarge on this question because it has been

[12] A. Einstein, "Zur Elektrodynamik bewegter Körper," *Ann. Phys. Leipzig,* 17, 891 (1905).

[13] A. Einstein and S. B. Preuss, *Akad. Wiss.,* pp. 778, 799, 844 (1915); *Ann. Phys. Leipzig,* 49, 769 (1916). Similar results were obtained almost simultaneously by D. Hilbert, *Nachr. Kgl. Ges. Wiss. Göttingen,* p. 395 (1915).

[14] J. Schwinger, *Phys. Rev.,* 76, 790 (1949). See also S. S. Schweber, *An Introduction to Relativistic Quantum Field Theory* (New York: Row, Peterson, 1961), Sec. 15, where further references can also be found.

[15] See A. S. Wightman, "Quelques problèmes mathematiques de la théorie quantique relativiste" and numerous other articles in *Les Problèmes Mathematiques de la Théorie Quantique des Champs* (Paris: Centre National de la Recherche Scientifique, 1959).

discussed often and eloquently. In fact, I myself spoke about it but a short time ago.[16]

To be touchstones for the laws of nature is probably the most important function of invariance principles. It is not the only one. In many cases, consequences of the laws of nature can be derived from the character of the mathematical framework of the theory, together with the postulate that the laws—the exact form of which need not be known—conform with invariance principles. The best known example is the derivation of the conservation laws for linear and angular momentum, and for energy, and of the motion of the center of mass, either on the basis of the Lagrangian framework of classical mechanics or the Hilbert space of quantum mechanics, by means of the geometrical invariance principles enumerated before.[17] Incidentally, conservation laws furnish at present the only generally valid correlations between observations with which we are familiar; for those which derive from the geometrical principles of invariance it is clear that their validity transcends that of any special theory—gravitational, electromagnetic, and so forth—which are only loosely connected in present-day physics. Again, the connection between invariance principles and conservation laws—which in this context always include the law of the motion of the center of mass—has been discussed in the literature frequently and adequately.

In quantum theory, invariance principles permit even further-reaching conclusions than in classical mechanics and, as a matter of fact, my original interest in invariance principles was due to this very fact. The reason for the increased effectiveness of invariance principles in quantum theory is due, essentially, to the linear nature of the underlying Hilbert space.[18] As a result, from any two state vectors, ψ_1 and ψ_2, an infinity of new state vectors

$$\psi = a_1 \psi_1 + a_2 \psi_2 \tag{4}$$

[16] See footnote 7.

[17] G. Hamel, *Z. Math. Phys.*, 50, 1 (1904); G. Herglotz, *Ann. Physik*, 36, 493 (1911); F. Engel, *Nachr. Kgl. Ges. Wiss. Göttingen*, p. 207 (1916); E. Noether, *ibid.*, p. 235 (1918); E. Bessel-Hagen, *Math. Ann.*, 84, 258 (1921). The quantum theoretical derivation given by E. Wigner, *Nachr. Kgl. Ges. Wiss. Göttingen*, p. 375 (1927), contains also the parity conservation law which was shown, in reference 1, to be only approximately valid. See also the article of reference 15.

[18] I heard this remark, for the first time, from C. N. Yang, at the centennial celebration of Bryn Mawr College. However, see also my article *Proc. Am. Phil. Soc.*, 93, 521 (1949).

can be formed, a_1 and a_2 being arbitrary numbers. Similarly, several, even infinitely many, states can be superimposed with largely arbitrary coefficients. This possibility of superposing states is by no means natural physically. In particular, even if we know how to bring a system into the states ψ_1 and ψ_2, we cannot give a prescription how to bring it into a superposition of these states. This prescription would have to depend, naturally, on the coefficients with which the two states are superimposed and is simply unknown. Hence, the superposition principle is strictly an existence postulate—but very effective and useful.

To illustrate this point, let us note that in classical theory, if a state, such as a planetary orbit, is given, another state, that is, another orbit, can be produced by rotating the initial orbit around the center of attraction. This is interesting but has no very surprising consequences. In quantum theory the same is true. In addition, however, the states obtained from a given one by rotation can be superimposed as a result of the aforementioned principle. If the rotations to which the original state was subjected are uniformly distributed over all directions, and if the states so resulting are superimposed with equal coefficients, the resulting state has necessarily spherical symmetry. This construction of a spherically symmetric state could fail only if the superposition resulted in the null-vector of Hilbert space, in which case one would not obtain any state. In such a case, however, other coefficients could be chosen for the superposition—in the plane case, the coefficients $e^{im\varphi}$, where φ is the angle of rotation of the original state—and the resulting state, though not spherically symmetric, or in the plane case axially symmetric, would still exhibit simple properties with respect to rotation. This possibility, the construction of states which have either full rotational symmetry or at least some simple behavior with respect to rotations, is the one which is fundamentally new in quantum theory. The stationary states of systems at rest have such high symmetries with respect to rotations. Such states play an important role in the theory of simple states such as atoms and the high symmetry of these is also conceptually satisfying.

The superposition principle also permits the exploitation of reflection symmetry. In classical mechanics as well as in quantum mechanics, if a state is possible, the mirror image of that state is also possible. However, in classical theory no significant conclusion can be drawn from this fact. In quantum theory, original-state and mirror image can be superimposed, with equal or oppositely equal coefficients. In the first case the resulting state is symmetric with respect to reflection, in the second case antisymmetric. The great accomplishment of Lee and Yang, which was mentioned earlier,[19] was just a very surprising reinterpretation of the physical nature of one of the reflection operations, that of space reflection, with the additional proof that the old interpretation cannot be valid. The consideration of "time inversion" requires rather special care because the corresponding operator is antiunitary. Theoretically, it does lead to a new quantum number and a classification of particles[20] which, however, has not been applied in practice.

My discussion would be far from complete without some reference to approximate invariance relations. Like all approximate relations, these may be very accurate under certain conditions but fail significantly in others. The critical conditions may apply to the state of the object, or may specify a type of phenomenon. The most important example for the first case is that of low relative velocities. In this case, the magnetic fields are weak, and the direction of the spins does not influence the behavior of the other coordinates. One is led to the Russell-Saunders coupling of spectroscopy.[21] Even more interesting should be the case of very high velocities in which the magnitude of the rest mass becomes unimportant. Unfortunately, this case has not been discussed in full detail, even though there are promising beginnings.[22]

Perhaps the most important case of special phenomena in which there are more invariance transformations than enumerated before is the rather general one of all phenomena, such as collisions between atoms, molecules, and nuclei, in which the weak interaction, which is respon-

[19] See footnote 1.

[20] See E. P. Wigner, "Unitary representations of the inhomogeneous Lorentz group including reflections," in *Elementary Particle Physics*, F. Gürsey, ed. (New York: Gordon and Breach, 1964), for a systematic discussion of the reflection operations.

[21] See E. P. Wigner, *Gruppentheorie und ihre Anwendung auf die Quantummechanik der Atomspektren* (Braunschweig: Friedr. Vieweg, 1931) or the English translation by J. Griffin (New York: Academic Press, 1959).

[22] H. A. Kastrup, *Phys. Rev. Letters*, 3, 78 (1962). The additional invariance operations probably form the conformal group. This was discovered by E. Cunningham [*Proc. London Math. Soc.*, 8, 77 (1909)] and by H. Bateman [*ibid.*, 8, 223 (1910)] to leave Maxwell's equations for the vacuum invariant, that is, the equations which describe light, always propagating at light velocity. For more recent considerations, see T. Fulton, F. Rohrlich, L. Witten, *Rev. Mod. Phys.*, 34, 442 (1962), and Y. Murai, *Progr. Theoret. Phys.*, 11, 441 (1954); these articles contain also more extensive references to the subject.

sible for beta decay, does not play a role. In all these cases, the parity operation is a valid invariance operation. This applies also in ordinary spectroscopy.

In another interesting special type of phenomenon the electromagnetic interaction also plays a subordinate role only. This renders the electric charge on the particles insignificant, and the interchange of proton and neutron, or more generally of the members of an isotopic spin multiplet, becomes an invariance operation. These, and the other special cases of increased symmetry, lead to highly interesting questions which are, furthermore, at the center of interest at present. However, the subject has too many ramifications to be discussed in detail at this occasion.

5

Relativistic Invariance and Quantum Phenomena

Introduction

The principal theme of this discourse is the great difference between the relation of special relativity and quantum theory on the one hand, and general relativity and quantum theory on the other. Most of the conclusions which will be reported on in connection with the general theory have been arrived at in collaboration with Dr. H. Salecker,[1] who has spent a year in Princeton to investigate this question.

The difference between the two relations is, briefly, that while there are no conceptual problems to separate the theory of special relativity from quantum theory, there is hardly any common ground between the general theory of relativity and quantum mechanics. The statement, that there are no conceptual conflicts between quantum mechanics and the special theory, should not mean that the mathematical formulations of the two theories naturally mesh. This is not the case, and it required the very ingenious work of Tomonaga, Schwinger, Feynman, and Dyson[2] to adjust quantum mechanics to the postulates of the special theory and this was so far successful only on the working level. What is meant is, rather, that the concepts which are used in quantum mechanics,

Address of retiring president of the American Physical Society, January 31, 1957. Reprinted by permission from the *Reviews of Modern Physics*, Vol. 29, No. 3 (July, 1957).

[1] This will be reported jointly with H. Salecker in more detail in another journal.

[2] See, e.g., J. M. Jauch and F. Rohrlich, *The Theory of Protons and Electrons* (Cambridge: Addison-Wesley Publishing Co., 1955).

measurements of positions, momenta, and the like, are the same concepts in terms of which the special relativistic postulate is formulated. Hence, it is at least possible to formulate the requirement of special relativistic invariance for quantum theories and to ascertain whether these requirements are met. The fact that the answer is more nearly *no* than *yes*, that quantum mechanics has not yet been fully adjusted to the postulates of the special theory, is perhaps irritating. It does not alter the fact that the question of the consistency of the two theories can at least be formulated, that the question of the special relativistic invariance of quantum mechanics by now has more nearly the aspect of a puzzle than that of a problem.

This is not so with the general theory of relativity. The basic premise of this theory is that coordinates are only auxiliary quantities which can be given arbitrary values for every event. Hence, the measurement of position, that is, of the space coordinates, is certainly not a significant measurement if the postulates of the general theory are adopted: the coordinates can be given any value one wants. The same holds for momenta. Most of us have struggled with the problem of how, under these premises, the general theory of relativity can make meaningful statements and predictions at all. Evidently, the usual statements about future positions of particles, as specified by their coordinates, are not meaningful statements in general relativity. This is a point which cannot be emphasized strongly enough and is the basis of a much deeper dilemma than the more technical question of the Lorentz invariance of the quantum field equations. It pervades all the general theory, and to some degree we mislead both our students and ourselves when we calculate, for instance, the mercury perihelion motion without explaining how our coordinate system is fixed in space, what defines it in such a way that it cannot be rotated, by a few seconds a year, to follow the perihelion's apparent motion. Surely the x axis of our coordinate system could be defined in such a way that it pass through all successive perihelions. There must be some assumption on the nature of the coordinate system which keeps it from following the perihelion. This is not difficult to exhibit in the case of the motion of the perihelion, and it would be useful to exhibit it. Neither is this, in general, an academic point, even though it may be academic in the case of the mercury perihelion. A difference in the tacit assumptions which fix the coordinate system is increasingly recognized to be at the bottom of many conflicting results arrived at in calculations based on the general theory of relativity. Expressing our results in terms of the values of coordinates became a habit with us to such a degree that we adhere to this habit also in general relativity, where values of coordinates are not *per se* meaningful. In order to make them meaningful, the mollusk-like coordinate system must be somehow anchored to space-time events and this anchoring is often done with little explicitness. If we want to put general relativity on speaking terms with quantum mechanics, our first task has to be to bring the statements of the general theory of relativity into such form that they conform with the basic principles of the general relativity theory itself. It will be shown below how this may be attempted.

Relativistic Quantum Theory of Elementary Systems

The relation between special theory and quantum mechanics is most simple for single particles. The equations and properties of these, in the absence of interactions, can be deduced already from relativistic invariance. Two cases have to be distinguished: the particle either can, or cannot, be transformed to rest. If it can, it will behave, in that coordinate system, as any other particle, such as an atom. It will have an intrinsic angular momentum called J in the case of atoms and spin S in the case of elementary particles. This leads to the various possibilities with which we are familiar from spectroscopy, that is, spins 0, $\frac{1}{2}$, 1, $\frac{3}{2}$, 2, . . . , each corresponding to a type of particle. If the particle cannot be transformed to rest, its velocity must always be equal to the velocity of light. Every other velocity can be transformed to rest. The rest-mass of these particles is zero because a nonzero rest-mass would entail an infinite energy if moving with light velocity.

Particles with zero rest-mass have only two directions of polarization, no matter how large their spin is. This contrasts with the $2S + 1$ directions of polarization for particles with nonzero rest-mass and spin S. Electromagnetic radiation, that is, light, is the most familiar example for this phenomenon. The "spin" of light is 1, but it has only two directions of polarization, instead of $2S + 1 = 3$. The number of polarizations seems to jump discontinuously to two when the rest-mass decreases and reaches the value 0. Bass and Schrödinger[3] followed this out in detail

[3] L. Bass and E. Schrödinger, *Proc. Roy. Soc.* (London), A232, 1 (1955).

for electromagnetic radiation, that is, for S = 1. It is good to realize, however, that this decrease in the number of possible polarizations is purely a property of the Lorentz transformation and holds for any value of the spin.

There is nothing fundamentally new that can be said about the number of polarizations of a particle, and the principal purpose of the following paragraphs is to illuminate it from a different point of view.[4] Instead of the question: "Why do particles with zero rest-mass have only two directions of polarization?" the slightly different question, "Why do particles with a finite rest-mass have more than two directions of polarization?" is proposed.

The intrinsic angular momentum of a particle with zero rest-mass is parallel to its direction of motion, that is, parallel to its velocity. Thus, if we connect any internal motion with the spin, this is perpendicular to the velocity. In case of light, we speak of transverse polarization. Furthermore, and this is the salient point, the statement that the spin is parallel to the velocity is a relativistically invariant statement: it holds as well if the particle is viewed from a moving coordinate system. If the problem of polarization is regarded from this point of view, it results in the question, "Why can't the angular momentum of a particle with finite rest-mass be parallel to its velocity?" or "Why can't a plane wave represent transverse polarization unless it propagates with light velocity?" The answer is that the angular momentum *can* very well be parallel to the direction of motion and the wave *can* have transverse polarization, but these are not Lorentz invariant statements. In other words, even if velocity and spin are parallel in one coordinate system, they do not appear to be parallel in other coordinate systems. This is most evident if, in this other coordinate system, the particle is at rest: in this coordinate system the angular momentum should be parallel to nothing. However, every particle, unless it moves with light velocity, can be viewed from a coordinate system in which it is at rest. In this coordinate system its angular momentum is surely not parallel to its velocity. Hence, the statement that spin and velocity are parallel cannot be universally valid for the particle with finite rest-mass and such a particle must have other states of polarization also.

[4] The essential point of the argument which follows is contained in the present writer's paper, *Ann. Math.*, 40, 149 (1939), and more explicitly in his address at the Jubilee of Relativity Theory, Bern, 1955 (Basel: Birkhauser Verlag, 1956), A. Mercier and M. Kervaire, editors, p. 210.

It may be worthwhile to illustrate this point somewhat more in detail. Let us consider a particle at rest with a given direction of polarization, say the direction of the z axis. Let us consider this particle now from a coordinate system which is moving in the $-z$ direction. The particle will then appear to have a velocity in the z direction and its polarization will be parallel to its velocity (Fig. 1). It will now be shown that

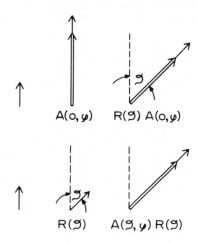

Fig. 1 The short simple arrows illustrate the spin, the double arrows the velocity of the particle. One obtains the same state, no matter whether one first imparts to it a velocity in the direction of the spin, then rotates it $(R(\vartheta)A(0,\varphi))$, or whether one first rotates it, then gives a velocity in the direction of the spin $(A(\vartheta,\varphi)R(\vartheta))$. See Eq. (1.3).

$A(0,\varphi)$ $R(\vartheta)\,A(0,\varphi)$

$R(\vartheta)$ $A(\vartheta,\varphi)\,R(\vartheta)$

this last statement is nearly invariant if the velocity is high. It is evident that the statement is entirely invariant with respect to rotations and with respect to a further increase of the velocity in the z direction. This is illustrated at the bottom of the figure. The coordinate system is first turned to the left and then given a velocity in the direction opposite to the old z axis. The state of the system appears to be exactly the same as if the coordinate system had been first given a velocity in the $-z$ direction and then turned, which is the operation illustrated at the top of the figure. The state of the system appears to be the same not for any physical reason but because the two coordinate systems are identical and they view the same particle (see Appendix I).

Let us now take our particle with a high velocity in the z direction and view it from a coordinate system which moves in the $-y$ direction. The particle now will appear to have a momentum also in the y direction, its velocity will have a direction between the y and z axes (Fig. 2). Its spin, however, will not be in the direction of its motion any more. In the nonrelativistic case, that is, if all velocities are small as compared

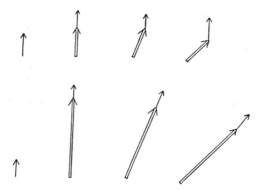

Fig. 2   The particle is first given a small velocity in the direction of its spin, then increasing velocities in a perpendicular direction (upper part of the figure). The direction of the spin remains essentially unchanged; it includes an increasingly large angle with the velocity as the velocity in the perpendicular direction increases. If the velocity imparted to the particle is large (lower part of the figure), the direction of the spin seems to follow the direction of the velocity. See Eqs. (1.8) and (1.7).

with the velocity of light, the spin will still be parallel to z and it will, therefore, enclose an angle with the particle's direction of motion. This shows that the statement that the spin is parallel to the direction of motion is not invariant in the nonrelativistic region. However, if the original velocity of the particle is close to the light velocity, the Lorentz contraction works out in such a way that the angle between spin and velocity is given by

$$\tan (\text{angle between spin and velocity}) = (1 - v^2/c^2)^{1/2} \sin\vartheta, \quad (1)$$

where ϑ is the angle between the velocity v in the moving coordinate system and the velocity in the coordinate system at rest. This last situation is illustrated at the bottom of the figure. If the velocity of the particle is small as compared with the velocity of light, the direction of the spin remains fixed and is the same in the moving coordinate system as in the coordinate system at rest. On the other hand, if the particle's velocity is close to light velocity, the velocity carries the spin with itself and the angle between direction of motion and spin direction becomes very small in the moving coordinate system. Finally, if the particle has light velocity, the statement "spin and velocity are parallel" remains true in every coordinate system. Again, this is not a consequence of any physical property of the spin, but is a consequence of the properties of Lorentz transformations: it is a kind of Lorentz contraction. It is the reason for the different behavior of particles with finite, and particles with zero, rest-mass, as far as the number of states of polarization is concerned. (Details of the calculation are in Appendix I.)

The preceding consideration proves more than was intended: it shows that the statement "spin and velocity are parallel for zero mass particles" is invariant and that, for relativistic reasons, one needs only *one* state of polarization, rather than *two*. This is true as far as proper Lorentz transformations are concerned. The second state of polarization, in which spin and velocity are antiparallel, is a result of the reflection symmetry. Again, this can be illustrated on the example of light: right circularly polarized light appears as right circularly polarized light in all Lorentz frames of reference which can be continuously transformed into each other. Only if one looks at the right circularly polarized light in a mirror does it appear as left circularly polarized light. The postulate of reflection symmetry allows us to infer the existence of left circularly polarized light from the existence of right circularly polarized light—if there were no such reflection symmetry in the real world, the existence of *two* modes of polarization of light, with virtually identical properties, would appear to be a miracle. The situation is entirely different for particles with nonzero mass. For these, the $2S + 1$ directions of polarization follow from the invariance of the theory with respect to proper Lorentz transformations. In particular, if the particle is at rest, the spin will have different orientations with respect to coordinate systems which have different orientations in space. Thus, the existence of all the states of polarization follow from the existence of one, if only the theory is invariant with respect to proper Lorentz transformations. For particles with zero rest-mass, there are only two states of polarization, and even the existence of the second one can be inferred only on the basis of reflection symmetry.

Reflection Symmetry

The problem and existence of reflection symmetry have been furthered in a brilliant way by recent theoretical and experimental research. There is nothing essential that can be added at present to the remarks and conjectures of Lee, Yang, and Oehme, and all that follows has been said, or at least implied, by Salam, Lee, Yang, and Oehme.[5] The sharpness of the break with past concepts is perhaps best illustrated by the cobalt experiment of Wu, Ambler, Hayward, Hoppes, and Hudson.

The ring current—this may be a permanent current in a superconductor—creates a magnetic field. The Co source is in the plane of the current and emits β particles (Fig. 3). The whole experimental arrangement, as shown in Fig. 3, has a symmetry plane and, if the principle of

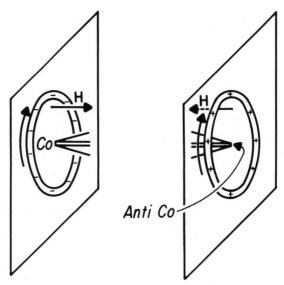

Fig. 3   The right side is the mirror image of the left side, according to the interpretation of the parity experiments,[5a] which maintains the reflection as a symmetry element of all physical laws. It must be assumed that the reflection transforms matter into antimatter: the electronic ring current becomes a positronic ring current, the radioactive cobalt is replaced by radioactive anticobalt.

---

[5] Lee, Yang, and Oehme, *Phys. Rev.*, 106, 340 (1957).

[5a] The interpretation illustrated has been proposed independently by numerous authors, including A. Salam, *Nuovo Cimento*, 5, 229 (1957); L. Landau, *Nucl. Phys.*, 3, 127 (1957), H. D. Smyth and L. Biedenharn (personal communication). Dr. S. Deser has pointed out that the "perturbing possibility" was raised already by Wick, Wightman, and Wigner [*Phys. Rev.*, 88, 101 (1952)] but was held "remote at that time." Naturally, the apparent unanimity of opinion does not prove its correctness.

sufficient cause is valid, the symmetry plane should remain valid throughout the further fate of the system. In other words, since the right and left
sides of the plane had originally identical properties, there is no sufficient
reason for any difference in their properties at a later time. Nevertheless,
the intensity of the β radiation is larger on one side of the plane than
the other side. The situation is paradoxical no matter what the mechanism of the effect is—in fact, it is most paradoxical if one disregards
its mechanism and theory entirely. If the experimental circumstances can
be idealized as indicated, even the principle of sufficient cause seems to
be violated.

It is natural to look for an interpretation of the experiment which
avoids this very far-reaching conclusion and, indeed, there is such an
interpretation.[5a] It is good to reiterate, however, that no matter what
interpretation is adopted, we have to admit that the symmetry of the
real world is smaller than we had thought. However, the symmetry may
still include reflections.

If it is true that a symmetry plane always remains a symmetry plane,
the initial state of the Co experiment could not have contained a symmetry plane. This would not be the case if the magnetic vector were
polar—in which case the electric vector would be axial. The charge
density, the divergence of the electric vector, would then become a
pseudoscalar rather than a simple scalar as in current theory. The mirror
image of a negative charge would be positive, the mirror image of an
electron a positron, and conversely. The mirror image of matter would
be antimatter. The Co experiment, viewed through a mirror, would not
present a picture contrary to established fact: it would present an
experiment carried out with antimatter. The right side of Fig. 3 shows
the mirror image of the left side. Thus, the principle of sufficient cause,
and the validity of symmetry planes, need not be abandoned if one is
willing to admit that the mirror image of matter is antimatter.

The possibility just envisaged would be technically described as the
elimination of the operations of reflection and charge conjugation, as
presently defined, as true symmetry operations. Their product would
still be assumed to be a symmetry operation and proposed to be named,
simply, reflection. A few further technical remarks are contained in
Appendix II. The proposition just made has two aspects: a very appealing one, and a very alarming one.

Let us look first at the appealing aspect. Dirac has said that the number of elementary particles shows an alarming tendency of increasing. One is tempted to add to this that the number of invariance properties also showed a similar tendency. This is not equally alarming because, while the increase in the number of elementary particles complicates our picture of nature, that of the symmetry properties on the whole simplifies it. Nevertheless the clear correspondence between the invariance properties of the laws of nature, and the symmetry properties of space-time, was most clearly breached by the operation of charge conjugation. This postulated that the laws of nature remain the same if all positive charges are replaced by negative charges and vice versa, or more generally, if all particles are replaced by antiparticles. Reasonable as this postulate appears to us, it corresponds to no symmetry of the space-time continuum. If the preceding interpretation of the Co experiments should be sustained, the correspondence between the natural symmetry elements of space-time, and the invariance properties of the laws of nature, would be restored. It is true that the role of the planes of reflection would not be that to which we are accustomed—the mirror image of an electron would become a positron—but the mirror image of a sequence of events would still be a possible sequence of events. This possible sequence of events would be more difficult to realize in the actual physical world than what we had thought, but it would still be possible.

The restoration of the correspondence between the natural symmetry properties of space-time on one hand, and of the laws of nature on the other hand, is the appealing feature of the proposition. It has, actually, two alarming features. The first of these is that a symmetry operation is, physically, so complicated. If it should turn out that the operation of time inversion, as we now conceive it, is not a valid symmetry operation (e.g., if one of the experiments proposed by Treiman and Wyld gave a positive result), we could still maintain the validity of this symmetry operation by reinterpreting it. We could postulate, for instance, that time inversion transforms matter into *meta*-matter which will be discovered later when higher energy accelerators will become available. Thus, maintaining the validity of symmetry planes forces us to a more artificial view of the concept of symmetry and of the invariance of the laws of physics.

The other alarming feature of our new knowledge is that we have been misled for such a long time to believe in more symmetry elements than actually exist. There was ample reason for this and there was ample experimental evidence to believe that the mirror image of a possible event is again a possible event with electrons being the mirror images of electrons and not of positrons. Let us recall in this connection first how the concept of parity, resulting from the beautiful though almost forgotten experiments of Laporte,[6] appeared to be a perfectly valid concept in spectroscopy and in nuclear physics. This concept could be explained very naturally as a result of the reflection symmetry of spacetime, the mirror image of electrons being electrons and not positrons. We are now forced to believe that this symmetry is only approximate and the concept of parity, as used in spectroscopy and nuclear physics, is also only approximate. Even more fundamentally, there is a vast body of experimental information in the chemistry of optically active substances which are mirror images of each other and which have optical activities of opposite direction but exactly equal strength. There is the fact that molecules which have symmetry planes are optically inactive; there is the fact of symmetry planes in crystals.[7] All these facts relate properties of right-handed matter to left-handed *matter*, not of right-handed matter to left-handed *antimatter*. The new experiments leave no doubt that the symmetry plane in this sense is not valid for all phenomena, in particular not valid for β decay, that if the concept of symmetry plane is at all valid for all phenomena, it can be valid only in the sense of converting matter into antimatter.

Furthermore, the old-fashioned type of symmetry plane is not the only symmetry concept that is only approximately valid. Charge conjugation was mentioned before, and we are reminded also of isotopic spin, of the exchange character, that is, multiplet system, for electrons and also of nuclei, which latter holds so accurately that, in practice, parahydrogen molecules can be converted into orthohydrogen molecules only by first destroying them.[8] This approximate validity of laws of symmetry is, therefore, a very general phenomenon—it may be *the* gen-

[6] O. Laporte, Z. *Physik*, 23, 135 (1924). For the interpretation of Laporte's rule in terms of the quantum-mechanical operation of inversion, see the writer's *Gruppentheorie und ihre Anwendungen auf die Quantenmechanik der Atmospektren* (Braunschweig: Friedrich Vieweg und Sohn, 1931), Chap. XVIII.

[7] For the role of the space and time inversion operators in classical theory, see H. Zocher and C. Török, *Proc. Natl. Acad. Sci. U.S.*, 39, 681 (1953), and literature quoted there.

[8] See A. Farkas, *Orthohydrogen, Parahydrogen and Heavy Hydrogen* (New York: Cambridge University Press, 1935).

eral phenomenon. We are reminded of Mach's axiom that the laws of nature depend on the physical content of the universe, and the physical content of the universe certainly shows no symmetry. This suggests—and this may also be the spirit of the ideas of Yang and Lee—that all symmetry properties are only approximate. The weakest interaction, the gravitational force, is the basis of the distinction between inertial and accelerated coordinate systems, the second weakest known interaction, that leading to β decay, leads to the distinction between matter and antimatter. Let me conclude this subject by expressing the conviction that the discoveries of Wu, Ambler, Hayward, Hoppes, and Hudson,[9] and of Garwin, Lederman, and Weinreich,[10] will not remain isolated discoveries. More likely, they herald a revision of our concept of invariance and possibly of other concepts which are even more taken for granted.

Quantum Limitations of the Concepts of General Relativity

The last remarks naturally bring us to a discussion of the general theory of relativity. The main premise of this theory is that coordinates are only labels to specify space-time points. Their values have no particular significance unless the coordinate system is somehow anchored to events in space-time.

Let us look at the question of how the equations of the general theory of relativity could be verified. The purpose of these equations, as of all equations of physics, is to calculate, from the knowledge of the present, the state of affairs that will prevail in the future. The quantities describing the present state are called initial conditions; the ways these quantities change are called the equations of motion. In relativity theory, the state is described by the metric which consists of a network of points in space-time, that is, a network of events, and the distances between these events. If we wish to translate these general statements into something concrete, we must decide what events are, and how we measure distances between *events*. The metric in the general theory of relativity is a metric in space-time, its elements are distances between space-time points, not between points in ordinary space.

[9] Wu, Ambler, Hayward, Hoppes, and Hudson, *Phys. Rev.*, 105, 1413(L) (1957).
[10] Garwin, Lederman, and Weinreich, *Phys. Rev.*, 105, 1415(L) (1957); also, J. L. Friedman and V. L. Telegdi, *ibid.*, 105, 1681(L) (1957).

The events of the general theory of relativity are coincidences, that is, collisions between particles. The founder of the theory, when he created this concept, evidently had macroscopic bodies in mind. Coincidences, that is, collisions between such bodies, are immediately observable. This is not the case for elementary particles; a collision between these is something much more evanescent. In fact, the point of a collision between two elementary particles can be closely localized in space-time only in case of high-energy collisions. (See Appendix III.) This shows that the establishment of a close network of points in space-time requires a reasonable energy density, a dense forest of world lines wherever the network is to be established. However, it is not necessary to discuss this in detail because the measurement of the distances between the points of the network gives more stringent requirements than the establishment of the network.

It is often said that the distances between events must be measured by yardsticks and rods. We found that measurements with a yardstick are rather difficult to describe and that their use would involve a great deal of unnecessary complications. The yardstick gives the distance between events correctly only if its marks coincide with the two events simultaneously from the point of view of the rest-system of the yardstick. Furthermore, it is hard to imagine yardsticks as anything but macroscopic objects. It is desirable, therefore, to reduce all measurements in space-time to measurements by clocks. Naturally, one can measure by clocks directly only the distances of points which are in time-like relation to each other. The distances of events which are in space-like relation, and which would be measured more naturally by yardsticks, will have to be measured, therefore, indirectly.

It appears, thus, that the simplest framework in space-time, and the one which is most nearly microscopic, is a set of clocks which are only slowly moving with respect to each other, that is, with world lines which are approximately parallel. These clocks tick off periods and these ticks form the network of events which we wanted to establish. This, at the same time, establishes the distance of those adjacent points which are on the same world line.

Figure 4 shows two world lines and also shows an event, that is, a tick of the clock, on each. The figure shows an artifice which enables one to measure the distance of space-like events: a light signal is sent out from the first clock which strikes the second clock at event 2. This clock, in turn, sends out a light signal which strikes the first clock at time t' after the event 1. If the first light signal had to be sent out at time t before the first event, the calculation given in Appendix IV shows that the space-like distance of events 1 and 2 is the geometric average of the two measured time-like distances t and t'. This is then a way to measure distances between space-like events by clocks instead of yardsticks.

Fig. 4 Measurement of space-like distances by means of a clock. It is assumed that the metric tensor is essentially constant within the space-time region contained in the figure. The space-like distance between events 1 and 2 is measured by means of the light signals which pass through event 2 and a geodesic which goes through event 1. Explanation in Appendix IV.

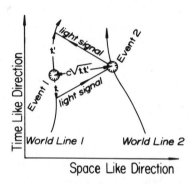

It is interesting to consider the quantum limitations on the accuracy of the conversion of time-like measurements into space-like measurements, which is illustrated in Fig. 4. Naturally, the times t and t' will be well-defined only if the light signal is a short pulse. This implies that it is composed of many frequencies, and, hence, that its energy spectrum has a corresponding width. As a result, it will give an indeterminate recoil to the second clock, thus further increasing the uncertainty of its momentum. All this is closely related to Heisenberg's uncertainty principle. A more detailed calculation shows that the added uncertainty is of the same order of magnitude as the uncertainty inherent in the nature of the best clock that we could think of, so that the conversion of time-like measurements into space-like measurements is essentially free.

We finally come to the discussion of one of the principal problems— the limitations on the accuracy of the clock. It led us to the conclusion that the inherent limitations on the accuracy of a clock of given weight and size, which should run for a period of a certain length, are quite severe. In fact, the result in summary is that a clock is an essentially nonmicroscopic object. In particular, what we vaguely call an atomic clock, a single atom which ticks off its periods, is surely an idealization which is in conflict with fundamental concepts of measurability. This part of our conclusions can be considered to be well established. On the other hand, the actual formula which will be given for the limitation of the accuracy of time measurement, a sort of uncertainty principle, should be considered as the best present estimate.

Let us state the requirements as follows. The watch shall run T seconds, shall measure time with an accuracy of $T/n = t$, its linear extension shall not exceed l, its mass shall be below m. Since the pointer of the watch must be able to assume n different positions, the system will have to run, in the course of the time T, over at least n orthogonal states. Its state must, therefore, be the superposition of at least n stationary states. It is clear, furthermore, that unless its total energy is at least $\hbar/t$, it cannot measure a time interval which is smaller than t. This is equivalent to the usual uncertainty principle. These two requirements follow directly from the basic principles of quantum theory; they are also the requirements which could well have been anticipated. A clock which conforms with these postulates is, for instance, an oscillator, with a period which is equal to the running time of the clock, if it is with equal probability in any of the first n quantum states. Its energy is about n times the energy of the first excited state. This corresponds to the uncertainty principle with the accuracy t as time uncertainty. Broadly speaking, the clock is a very soft oscillator, the oscillating particle moving very slowly and with a rather large amplitude. The pointer of the clock is the position of the oscillating particle.

The clock of the preceding paragraph is still very light. Let us consider, however, the requirement that the linear dimensions of the clock be limited. Since there is little point in dealing with the question in great generality, it may as well be assumed here that the linear dimension shall correspond to the accuracy in time. The requirement $l \approx ct$ increases the mass of the clock by n^3, which may be a very large factor indeed:

$$m > n^3 \hbar t / l^2 \approx n^3 \hbar / c^2 t.$$

For example, a clock, with a running time of a day and an accuracy of 10^{-8} second, must weigh almost a gram—for reasons stemming solely from uncertainty principles and similar considerations.

So far, we have paid attention only to the physical dimension of the clock and the requirement that it be able to distinguish between events which are only a distance t apart on the time scale. In order to make it usable as part of the framework which was described before, it is

necessary to *read* the clock and to start it. As part of the framework to
map out the metric of space-time, it must either register the readings at
which it receives impulses, or transmit these readings to a part of space
outside the region to be mapped out. This point was already noted by
Schrödinger.[11] However, we found it reassuring that, in the most interesting case in which $l = ct$, that is, if space and time inaccuracies are
about equal, the reading requirement introduces only an insignificant
numerical factor but does not change the form of the expression for the
minimum mass of the clock.

The arrangement to map the metric might consist, therefore, of a
lattice of clocks, all more or less at rest with respect to each other.
All these clocks can emit light signals and receive them. They can also
transmit their reading at the time of the receipt of the light signal to the
outside. The clocks may resemble oscillators, well in the nonrelativistic
region. In fact, the velocity of the oscillating particle is about n times
smaller than the velocity of light, where n is the ratio of the *error* in the
time measurement to the *duration* of the whole interval to be measured.
This last quantity is the spacing of the events on the time axis; it is also
the distance of the clocks from each other, divided by the light velocity.
The world lines of the clocks form the dense forest which was mentioned
before. Its branches suffuse the region of space-time in which the metric
is to be mapped out.

We are not absolutely convinced that our clocks are the best possible.
Our principal concern is that we have considered only one space-like
dimension. One consequence of this was that the oscillator had to be a
one-dimensional oscillator. It is possible that the size limitation does
not increase the necessary mass of the clock to the same extent if use is
made of all three spatial dimensions.

The curvature tensor can be obtained from the metric in the conventional way, if the metric is measured with sufficient accuracy. It may be
of interest, nevertheless, to describe a more direct method for measuring the curvature of space. It involves an arrangement, illustrated in
Fig. 5, which is similar to that used for obtaining the metric. There is a
clock, and a mirror, at such a distance from each other that the curvature
of space can be assumed to be constant in the intervening region. The
two clocks need not be at rest with respect to each other; in fact, such

[11] E. Schrödinger, *Ber. Preuss. Akad. Wiss. Phys.-Math. Kl.*, p. 238 (1931).

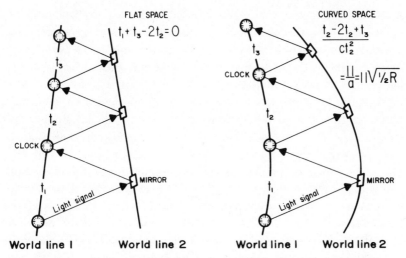

Fig. 5 Direct measurement of the curvature by means of a clock and mirror. Only one space-like dimension is considered and the curvature assumed to be constant within the space-time region contained in the figure. The explanation is given in Appendix V.

a requirement would involve additional measurements to verify it. If the space is flat, the world lines of the clocks can be drawn straight. In order to measure the curvature, a light signal is emitted by the clock, and this is reflected by the mirror. The time of return is read on the clock— it is t_1—and the light signal returned to the mirror. The time which the light signal takes on its second trip to return to the clock is denoted by t_2. The process is repeated a third time, the duration of the last roundtrip denoted by t_3. As shown in Appendix V, the radius of curvature a and the relevant component R_{0101} of the Riemann tensor are given by

$$\frac{t_1 - 2t_2 + t_3}{t_2^2} = \frac{11}{a} = 11(\tfrac{1}{2}R_{0101})^{1/2}. \tag{2}$$

If classical theory would be valid also in the microscopic domain, there would be no limit on the accuracy of the measurement indicated in Fig. 5. If $\hbar$ is infinitely small, the time intervals t_1, t_2, t_3 can all be measured with arbitrary accuracy with an infinitely light clock. Similarly, the light signals between clock and mirror, however short, need carry only an infinitesimal amount of momentum and thus deflect clock and mirror arbitrarily little from their geodesic paths. The quantum phenomena considered before force us, however, to use a clock with a minimum mass if the measurement of the time intervals is to have a given accuracy. In the present case, this accuracy must be relatively high unless the time intervals t_1, t_2, t_3 are of the same order of magnitude as the curvature of space. Similarly, the deflection of clock and mirror from their geodesic paths must be very small if the result of the measurement is to be meaningful. This gives an effective limit for the accuracy with which the curvature can be measured. The result is, as could be anticipated, that the curvature at a *point* in space-time cannot be measured at all; only the average curvature over a finite region of space-time can be obtained. The error of the measurement is inversely proportional to the two-thirds power of the area available in space-time, that is, the area around which a vector is carried, always parallel to itself, in the customary definition of the curvature. The error is also proportional to the cube root of the Compton wavelength of the clock. Our principal hesitation in considering this result as definitive is again its being based on the consideration of only one space-like dimension. The possibilities of measuring devices, as well as the problems, may be substantially different in three-dimensional space.

Whether or not this is the case, the essentially nonmicroscopic nature of the general relativistic concepts seems to us inescapable. If we look at this first from a practical point of view, the situation is rather reassuring. We can note first, that the measurement of electric and magnetic fields, as discussed by Bohr and Rosenfeld,[12] also requires macroscopic, in fact *very* macroscopic, equipment and that this does not render the electromagnetic field concepts useless for the purposes of quantum electrodynamics. It is true that the measurement of space-time curvature requires a finite region of space and there is a minimum for the mass, and even the mass uncertainty, of the measuring equipment. However, numerically, the situation is by no means alarming. Even in interstellar space, it should be possible to measure the curvature in a volume of a light second or so. Furthermore, the mass of the clocks which one will wish to employ for such a measurement is of the order of several micrograms, so that the finite mass of elementary particles does not cause any difficulty. The clocks will contain many particles and there is no need, and there is not even an incentive, to employ clocks which

[12] N. Bohr and L. Rosenfeld, *Kgl. Danske Videnskab. Selskab, Mat.-Fys. Medd.*, 12, No. 8 (1933). See also further literature quoted in L. Rosenfeld's article in *Niels Bohr and the Development of Physics* (London: Pergamon Press, 1955).

are lighter than the elementary particles. This is hardly surprising since the mass which can be derived from the gravitational constant, light velocity, and Planck's constant is about 20 micrograms.

It is well to repeat, however, that the situation is less satisfactory from a more fundamental point of view. It remains true that we consider, in ordinary quantum theory, position operators as observables without specifying what the coordinates mean. The concepts of quantum field theories are even more weird from the point of view of the basic observation that only coincidences are meaningful. This again is hardly surprising because even a 20-microgram clock is too large for the measurement of atomic times or distances. If we analyze the way in which we "get away" with the use of an absolute space concept, we simply find that we do not. In our experiments we surround the microscopic objects with a very macroscopic framework and observe *coincidences* between the particles emanating from the microscopic system, and parts of the framework. This gives the collision matrix, which is observable, and observable in terms of macroscopic coincidences. However, the so-called observables of the microscopic system are not only not observed, they do not even appear to be meaningful. There is, therefore, a boundary in our experiments between the region in which we use the quantum concepts without worrying about their meaning in the face of the fundamental observation of the general theory of relativity, and the surrounding region in which we use concepts which are meaningful also in the face of the basic observation of the general theory of relativity but which cannot be described by means of quantum theory. This appears most unsatisfactory from a strictly logical standpoint.

Appendix I

It will be necessary, in this appendix, to compare various states of the same physical system. These states will be generated by looking at the same state—the standard state—from various coordinate systems. Hence every Lorentz frame of reference will define a state of the system—the state which the standard state appears to be from the point of view of this coordinate system. In order to define the standard state, we choose an arbitrary but fixed Lorentz frame of reference and stipulate that, in this frame of reference, the particle in the standard state be at rest and its spin (if any) have the direction of the z axis. Thus, if we

wish to have a particle moving with a velocity v in the z direction and
with a spin also directed along this axis, we look at the particle in the
standard state from a coordinate system moving with the velocity v in
the $-z$ direction. If we wish to have a particle at rest but with its spin
in the yz plane, including an angle α with the z axis, we look at the standard state from a coordinate system the y and z axes of which include an
angle α with the y and z axes of the coordinate system in which the
standard state was defined. In order to obtain a state in which both
velocity and spin have the aforementioned direction (i.e., a direction in
the yz plane, including the angles α and $\frac{1}{2}\pi-\alpha$ with the y and z axes),
we look at the standard state from the point of view of a coordinate
system in which the spin of the standard state is described as this direction and which is moving in the opposite direction.

Two states of the system will be identical only if the Lorentz frames
of reference which define them are identical. Under this definition, the
relations which will be obtained will be valid independently of the
properties of the particle, such as spin or mass (as long as the mass is
nonzero so that the standard state exists). Two states will be approximately the same if the two Lorentz frames of reference which define
them can be obtained from each other by a very small Lorentz transformation, that is, one which is near the identity. Naturally, all states
of a particle which can be compared in this way are related to each other
inasmuch as they represent the same standard state viewed from various
coordinate systems. However, we shall have to compare only these
states.

Let us denote by $A\,(0,\varphi)$ the matrix of the transformation in which the
transformed coordinate system moves with the velocity $-v$ in the z direction, where $v = c\,\tanh\varphi$:

$$A(0,\varphi)=\left\|\begin{matrix}0 & 0 & 0 \\ 0 & \cosh\varphi & \sinh\varphi \\ 0 & \sinh\varphi & \cosh\varphi\end{matrix}\right\|. \qquad (1.1)$$

Since the x axis will play no role in the following consideration, it is suppressed in (1.1) and the three rows and the three columns of this matrix
refer to the y', z', ct' and to the y, z, ct axes, respectively. The matrix
(1.1) characterizes the state in which the particle moves with a velocity
v in the direction of the z axis and its spin is parallel to this axis.

Let us further denote the matrix of the rotation by an angle ϑ in the
yz plane by

$$R(\vartheta) = \begin{Vmatrix} \cos\vartheta & \sin\vartheta & 0 \\ -\sin\vartheta & \cos\vartheta & 0 \\ 0 & 0 & 1 \end{Vmatrix}. \tag{1.2}$$

We refer to the direction in the yz plane which lies between the y and z axes and includes an angle ϑ with the z axis as the direction ϑ. The coordinate system which moves with the velocity $-v$ in the ϑ direction is obtained by the transformation

$$A(\vartheta, \varphi) = R(\vartheta)A(0, \varphi)R(-\vartheta). \tag{1.3}$$

In order to obtain a particle which moves in the direction ϑ and is polarized in this direction, we first rotate the coordinate system counterclockwise by ϑ (to have the particle polarized in the proper direction) and impart it then a velocity $-v$ in the ϑ direction. Hence, it is the transformation

$$T(\vartheta, \varphi) = A(\vartheta, \varphi)R(\vartheta)$$

$$= \begin{Vmatrix} \cos\vartheta & \sin\vartheta\cosh\varphi & \sin\vartheta\sinh\varphi \\ -\sin\vartheta & \cos\vartheta\cosh\varphi & \cos\vartheta\sinh\varphi \\ 0 & \sinh\varphi & \cosh\varphi \end{Vmatrix}, \tag{1.4}$$

which characterizes the aforementioned state of the particle. It follows from (1.3) that

$$T(\vartheta, \varphi) = R(\vartheta)A(0, \varphi) = R(\vartheta)T(0, \varphi), \tag{1.5}$$

so that the same state can be obtained also by viewing the state characterized by (1.1) from a coordinate system that is rotated by ϑ. It follows that the statement "velocity and spin are parallel" is invariant under rotations. This had to be expected.

If the state generated by $A(0, \varphi) = T(0, \varphi)$ is viewed from a coordinate system which is moving with the velocity u in the direction of the z axis, the particle will still appear to move in the z direction and its spin will remain parallel to its direction of motion, unless $u > v$, in which case the two directions will become antiparallel, or unless $u = v$, in which case the statement becomes meaningless, the particle appearing to be at rest. Similarly, the other states in which spin and velocity are parallel, i.e., the states generated by the transformations $T(\vartheta, \varphi)$, remain such states if viewed from a coordinate system moving in the direction of the particle's velocity, as long as the coordinate system is not moving faster than the particle. This also had to be expected. However, if the state generated by

$T(0,\varphi)$ is viewed from a coordinate system moving with velocity $v' = c\tanh\varphi'$ in the $-y$ direction, spin and velocity will *not* appear parallel any more, *provided the velocity v of the particle is not close to light velocity*. This last proviso is the essential one; it means that the high velocity states of a particle for which spin and velocity are parallel (i.e., the states generated by (1.4) with a large φ) are states of this same nature if viewed from a coordinate system which is not moving too fast in the direction of motion of the particle itself. In the limiting case of the particle moving with light velocity, the aforementioned states become invariant under *all* Lorentz transformations.

Let us first convince ourselves that if the state (1.1) is viewed from a coordinate system moving in the $-y$ direction, its spin and velocity no longer appear parallel. The state in question is generated from the normal transformation

$$A(\tfrac{1}{2}\pi,\varphi')A(0,\varphi)$$

$$= \begin{Vmatrix} \cosh\varphi' & \sinh\varphi\sinh\varphi' & \cosh\varphi\sinh\varphi' \\ 0 & \cosh\varphi & \sinh\varphi \\ \sinh\varphi' & \sinh\varphi\cosh\varphi' & \cosh\varphi\cosh\varphi' \end{Vmatrix}. \qquad (1.6)$$

This transformation does not have the form (1.4). In order to bring it into that form, it has to be multiplied on the right by $R(\epsilon)$, i.e., one has to rotate the spin ahead of time. The angle ϵ is given by the equation

$$\tan\epsilon = \frac{\tanh\varphi'}{\sinh\varphi} = \frac{v'}{v}(1-v^2/c^2)^{\frac{1}{2}} \qquad (1.7)$$

and is called the angle between spin and velocity. For $v \ll c$, it becomes equal to the angle which the ordinary resultant of two perpendicular velocities, v and v', includes with the first of these. However, ϵ becomes very small if v is close to c; in this case it is hardly necessary to rotate the spin away from the z axis before giving it a velocity in the z direction. These statements express the identity

$$A(\tfrac{1}{2}\pi,\varphi')A(0,\varphi)R(\epsilon) = T(\vartheta,\varphi''), \qquad (1.8)$$

which can be verified by direct calculation. The right side represents a particle with parallel spin and velocity, the magnitude and direction of the latter being given by the well-known equations

$$v'' = c\tanh\varphi'' = (v^2+v'^2-v^2v'^2/c^2)^{\frac{1}{2}} \qquad (1.8a)$$

and

$$\tan\vartheta = \frac{\sinh\varphi'}{\tanh\varphi} = \frac{v'}{v(1-v'^2/c^2)^{\frac{1}{2}}} \cdot \qquad (1.8b)$$

Equation (1) given in the text follows from (1.7) and (1.8b) for $v \sim c$.

The fact that the states $T(\vartheta,\varphi)\psi_0$ (where ψ_0 is the standard state and $\varphi \gg 1$) are approximately invariant under all Lorentz transformations is expressed mathematically by the equations

$$R(\vartheta) \cdot T(0,\varphi)\psi_0 = T(\vartheta,\varphi)\psi_0, \qquad (1.5a)$$
$$A(0,\varphi') \cdot T(0,\varphi)\psi_0 = T(0,\varphi' + \varphi)\psi_0, \qquad (1.9a)$$

and

$$A(\tfrac{1}{2}\pi,\varphi') \cdot T(0,\varphi)\psi_0 \rightarrow T(\vartheta,\varphi'')\psi_0, \qquad (1.9b)$$

which give the wave function of the state $T(0,\varphi)\psi_0$, as viewed from other Lorentz frames of reference. Naturally, similar equations apply to all $T(\alpha,\varphi)\psi_0$. In particular, (1.5a) shows that the states in question are invariant under rotations of the coordinate system, (1.9a) that they are invariant with respect to Lorentz transformations with a velocity not too high *in* the direction of motion (so that $\varphi' + \varphi \gg 0$, i.e., φ' not too large a negative number). Finally, in order to prove (1.9b), we calculate the transition probability between the state $A(\tfrac{1}{2}\pi,\varphi') \cdot T(0,\varphi)\psi_0$ and $T(\vartheta,\varphi'')\psi_0$, where ϑ and φ'' are given by (1.8a) and (1.8b). For this, (1.8) gives

$$(A(\tfrac{1}{2}\pi,\varphi') \cdot T(0,\varphi)\psi_0, T(\vartheta,\varphi'')\psi_0$$
$$= (T(\vartheta,\varphi'')R(\epsilon)^{-1}\psi_0, T(\vartheta,\varphi'')\psi_0)$$
$$= (R(\epsilon)^{-1}\psi_0, \psi_0) \rightarrow (\psi_0, \psi_0).$$

The second line follows because $T(\vartheta,\varphi'')$ represents a coordinate transformation and is, therefore, unitary. The last member follows because $\epsilon \rightarrow 0$ as $\varphi \rightarrow \infty$, as can be seen from (1.7) and $R(0) = 1$.

The preceding consideration is not fundamentally new. It is an elaboration of the facts (a) that the subgroup of the Lorentz group which leaves a null-vector invariant is different from the subgroup which leaves a time-like vector invariant and (b) that the representations of the latter subgroup decompose into one dimensional representations if this subgroup is "contracted" into the subgroup which leaves a null-vector invariant.[13]

[13] E. Inonu and E. P. Wigner, *Proc. Natl. Acad. Sci. U.S.*, 39, 510 (1953).

Appendix II

Before the hypothesis of Lee and Yang[14] was put forward, it was commonly assumed that there were, in addition to the symmetry operations of the proper Poincaré group, three further independent symmetry operations. The proper Poincaré group consists of all Lorentz transformations which can be continuously obtained from unity and all translations in space-like and time-like directions, as well as the products of all these transformations. It is a continuous group; the Lorentz transformations contained in it do not change the direction of the time axis and their determinant is 1. The three independent further operations which were considered to be rigorously valid, were

Space inversion I, that is, the transformation $x, y, z \rightarrow -x, -y, -z$, without changing particles into antiparticles.*

Time inversion T, more appropriately described by Lüders[15] as *Umkehr der Bewegungsrichtung*, which replaces every velocity by the opposite velocity, so that the position of the particles at $+t$ becomes the same as it was, without time inversion, at $-t$. The time inversion T (also called time inversion of the first kind by Lüders[16]) does not convert particles into antiparticles either.

Charge conjugation C, that is, the replacement of positive charges by negative charges and more generally of particles by antiparticles, without changing either the position or the velocity of these particles.[17] The quantum-mechanical expressions for the symmetry operations I and C are unitary, that for T is antiunitary.

[14] T. D. Lee and C. N. Yang, *Phys. Rev.*, 104, 254 (1956). See also E. M. Purcell and N. F. Ramsey, *Phys. Rev.*, 78, 807 (1950).

* The usual symbol for this is P at present. (Note added with the proofs of this book.)

[15] G. Lüders, Z. *Physik,* 133, 325 (1952).

[16] G. Lüders, *Kgl. Danske Videnskab. Selskab, Mat.-Fys. Medd.*, 28, No. 5 (1954).

[17] All three symmetry operations were first discussed in detail by J. Schwinger, *Phys. Rev.*, 74, 1439 (1948). See also H. A. Kramers, *Proc. Acad. Sci. Amsterdam,* 40, 814 (1937), and W. Pauli's article in *Niels Bohr and the Development of Physics* (London: Pergamon Press, 1955). The significance of the first two symmetry operations (and their connection with the concepts of parity and the Kramers degeneracy, respectively), were first pointed out by the present writer, Z. *Physik,* 43, 624 (1927), and *Nachr. Akad. Wiss. Göttingen, Math.-Physik,* 1932, 546. See also T. D. Newton and E. P. Wigner, *Rev. Mod. Phys.*, 21, 400 (1949); S. Watanabe, *Rev. Mod. Phys.*, 27, 26 (1945). The concept of charge conjugation is based on the observation of W. Furry, *Phys. Rev.*, 51, 125 (1937).

The three operations I, T, C, together with their products TC (Lüders' time inversion of the second kind), IC, IT, ITC, and the unit operation form a group, and the products of the elements of this group with those of the proper Poincaré group were considered to be the symmetry operations of all laws of physics. The suggestion given in the text amounts to eliminating the operations I and C separately while continuing to postulate their product IC as symmetry operation. The discrete symmetry group then reduces to the unit operation plus

$$IC, T, \text{ and } ICT, \tag{2.1}$$

and the total symmetry group of the laws of physics becomes the proper Poincaré group plus its products with the elements (2.1). This group is isomorphic (essentially identical) with the unrestricted Poincaré group, i.e., the product of *all* Lorentz transformations with all the displacements in space and time. The quantum mechanical expressions for the operations of the proper Lorentz group and its product with IC are unitary, those for T and ICT (as well as for their products with the elements of the proper Poincaré group) antiunitary. Lüders has pointed out that, under certain very natural conditions, ICT belongs to the symmetry group of every *local* field theory.

Appendix III

Let us consider, first, the collision of two particles of equal mass m in the coordinate system in which the average of the sum of their momenta is zero. Let us assume that, at a given time, the wave function of both particles is confined to a distance l in the direction of their average velocity with respect to each other. If we consider only this spacelike direction, and the time axis, the area in space-time in which the two wave functions will substantially overlap is [see Fig. 6(a)]

$$a = l^2/2v_{\min}, \tag{3.1}$$

where $v_{\min}$ is the lowest velocity which occurs with substantial probability in the wave packets of the colliding particles. Denoting the average momentum by $\bar{p}$ (this has the same value for both particles), the half-width of the momentum distribution by δ, then $v_{\min} = (\bar{p} - \delta)(m^2 + (\bar{p} - \delta)^2/c^2)^{-1/2}$. Since l cannot be below $\hbar/\delta$, the area (3.1) is at least

$$\frac{\hbar^2}{2\delta^2}\frac{(m^2 + (\bar{p} - \delta)^2/c^2)^{1/2}}{\bar{p} - \delta} \tag{3.1a}$$

(Note that the area becomes infinite if $\delta > \bar{p}$.) The minimum of (3.1a) is, apart from a numerical factor,

$$a_{\min} \approx \frac{\hbar^2}{\bar{p}^3}(m^2 + \bar{p}^2/c^2)^{1/2} \approx \frac{\hbar^2 c}{E^{1/2}(E + mc^2)^{1/2}}, \tag{3.2}$$

where E is the kinetic energy (total energy minus rest-energy) of the particles.

The kinetic energy E permits the contraction of the wave functions of the colliding particles also in directions perpendicular to the average relative velocity, to an area $\hbar^2 c^2/E(E + 2mc^2)$. Hence, again apart from a numerical factor, the volume to which the collision can be confined in four dimensional space-time becomes

$$V_{\min} = \frac{\hbar^4 c^3}{E^{3/2}(E + mc^2)^{3/2}}. \tag{3.3}$$

E is the average kinetic energy of the particles in the coordinate system in which their center of mass is, on the average, at rest. Equation (3.3) is valid apart from a numerical constant of unit order of magnitude but this constant depends on E/mc^2.

Let us consider now the opposite limiting case, the collision of a particle with finite rest-mass m with a particle with zero rest-mass. The collision is viewed again in the coordinate system in which the average linear momentum is zero. In this case, one will wish to confine the wave function of the particle with finite rest-mass to a narrower region l than that of the particle with zero rest-mass. If the latter is confined to a region of thickness λ [see Fig. 6(b)], its momentum and energy uncertainties will be at least $\hbar/\lambda$ and $\hbar c/\lambda$, and these expressions will also give, apart from a numerical factor, the average values of these quantities. Hence $\bar{p} \approx \hbar/\lambda$. The kinetic energy of the particle with finite rest-mass will be of the order of magnitude

$$\tfrac{1}{2}(m^2 c^4 + (\bar{p} + \hbar/l)^2 c^2)^{1/2} + \tfrac{1}{2}(m^2 c^4 + (\bar{p} - \hbar/l)^2 c^2)^{1/2} - mc^2, \tag{3.4}$$

since $\hbar/l$ is the momentum uncertainty. Since $l \leq \lambda$, one can neglect $\bar{p}$ in (3.4) if one is interested only in the order of magnitude. This gives for the total kinetic energy,

$$E \approx \hbar c/\lambda + (m^2c^4 + \hbar^2c^2/l^2)^{1/2} - mc^2, \tag{3.5}$$

while the area in Fig. 6(b) is of the order of magnitude

$$a = (\lambda/c)(l + \Delta v\lambda/c), \tag{3.6}$$

where Δv is the uncertainty in the velocity of the second particle,

$$\Delta v = \frac{\bar{p} + \hbar/l}{(m^2 + (\bar{p} + \hbar/l)^2/c^2)^{1/2}} - \frac{\bar{p} - \hbar/l}{(m^2 + (\bar{p} - \hbar/l)^2/c^2)^{1/2}}. \tag{3.6a}$$

This can again be replaced by $(\hbar/l)(m^2 + \hbar^2/l^2c^2)^{-1/2}$.

For given E, the minimum value of a is assumed if the *kinetic energies* of the two particles are of the same order of magnitude. The two terms of (3.6) then become about equal and $l/\lambda \approx (E/(mc^2 + E))^{1/2}$. The minimum value of a, as far as order of magnitude is concerned, is again given by (3.2). Similarly, (3.3) also remains valid if one of the two particles has zero rest-mass.

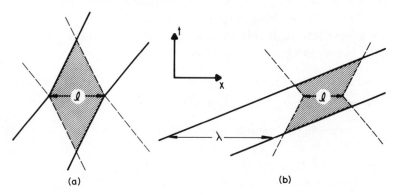

(a)   (b)

Fig. 6a Localization of a collision of two particles of equal mass. The full lines indicate the effective boundaries of the wave packet of the particle traveling to the right, the broken lines the effective boundaries of the wave packet of the particle traveling to the left. The collision can take place in the shaded area of space-time.

Fig. 6b Localization of a collision between a particle with finite mass and a particle with zero rest-mass. The full lines, at a distance λ apart in the x direction, indicate the boundary of the particle with zero rest-mass, the broken lines apply to the wave packet of the particle with nonzero rest-mass. The collision can take place in the shaded area.

The two-dimensional case becomes simplest if both particles have zero rest-mass. In this case the wave packets do not spread at all and (3.2) can be immediately seen to be valid. In the four-dimensional case, (3.3) again holds. However, its proof by means of explicitly constructed wave packets (rather than reference to the uncertainty relations) is by no means simple. It requires wave packets which are confined in every direction, do not spread too fast, and progress essentially only into one half space (one particle going toward the right, the other toward the left). The construction of such wave packets will not be given in detail. They are necessary to prove (3.2) and (3.3) more rigorously also in the case of finite masses; the preceding proofs, based on the uncertainty relations, show only that a and v cannot be *smaller* than the right sides of the corresponding equations. It is clear, in fact, that the limits given by (3.2) and (3.3) would be very difficult to realize, except in the two-dimensional case and for the collision of two particles with zero rest-mass. In all other cases, the relatively low values of a_{min} and V_{min} are predicated on the assumption that the wave packets of the colliding particles are so constituted that they assume a minimum size at the time of the collision. At any rate, (3.2) and (3.3) show that only collisions with a relatively high collision energy, and high energy uncertainty, can be closely localized in space-time.

Appendix IV

Let us denote the components of the vector from event 1 to event 2 by x_i, the components of the unit vector along the world line of the first clock at event 1 by e_i. The components of the first light signal are $x_i + te_i$, that of the second light signal $x_i - t'e_i$. Hence (see Fig. 4)

$$g^{ik}(x_i + te_i)(x_k + te_k) = 0, \tag{4.1}$$

$$g^{ik}(x_i - t'e_i)(x_k - t'e_k) = 0. \tag{4.2}$$

Elimination of the linear terms in t and t' by multiplication of (4.1) with t' and (4.2) with t and addition gives

$$2g^{ik}x_ix_k + 2tt'g^{ik}e_ie_k = 0. \tag{4.3}$$

Since e is a unit vector, $g^{ik}e_ie_k = 1$, and (4.3) shows that the space-like distance between points 1 and 2 is $(tt')^{1/2}$.

Appendix V

Since the measurement of the curvature, described in the text, pre-supposes *constant curvature* over the space-time domain in which the measurement takes place, we use a space with constant curvature, or, rather, part of a space with constant curvature, to carry out the calculation. We consider only one spatial dimension, i.e., a two-dimensional deSitter space. This will be embedded, in the usual way, in a three-dimensional space[18] with coordinates x, y, τ. The points of the deSitter space then form the hyperboloid

$$x^2 + y^2 - \tau^2 = a^2, \tag{5.1}$$

where a is the "radius of the universe." As coordinates of a point we use x and y, or rather the corresponding polar angles r, ϕ. The metric form in terms of these is

$$(ds)^2 = \frac{a^2}{r^2 - a^2} dr^2 - r^2 d\phi^2. \tag{5.2}$$

Two points of deSitter space correspond to every pair r, ϕ (except $r = a$): those with positive and negative $\tau = (r^2 - a^2)^{1/2}$. This will not lead to any confusion as all events take place at positive τ. The null lines (paths of light signals) are the tangents to the $r = a$ circle.

The experiment described in the text can be analyzed by means of Fig. 7. For the sake of simplicity, the clock and mirror are assumed to be "at rest," i.e., their world lines have constant polar angles which will be assumed as 0 and δ, respectively. The first light signal travels from 1 to 1′ and back to 2, the second from 2 to 2′ and back to 3, the third from 3 to 3′ and back to 4. The polar angle of the radius vector which is perpendicular to the first part 22′ of the world line of the second light signal is denoted by ϕ_2. The construction of Fig. 7 shows that angle ϕ_2' which the world line of the mirror includes with the radius vector perpendicular to the second part 2′3 of the second light signal's world line is

$$\phi_2' = \phi_2 + \delta. \tag{5.3}$$

The angles ϕ_1, ϕ_1' ϕ_3, ϕ_3' have similar meanings; they are not indicated

[18] See, e.g., H. P. Robertson, *Rev. Mod. Phys.*, 5, 62 (1933).

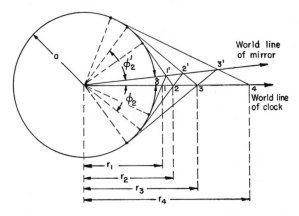

Fig. 7 Analysis of the experiment of Fig. 5. The
figure represents a view of the hyperboloid of deSitter
space, viewed along its axis. Every point of the plane
which is outside the circle corresponds to two points of
the deSitter world with the same spatial coordinate
but with oppositely equal time coordinates. The first
light signal is emitted at 1, reaches the mirror at 1′,
and returns to the clock at 2. The paths of the second
and third light signals are 22′3 and 33′4.

in the figure in order to avoid overcrowding. For reasons similar to
those leading to (5.3), we have

$$\phi_3 = \phi_2' + \delta = \phi_2 + 2\delta, \tag{5.3a}$$

$$\phi_1 = \phi_2 - 2\delta, \tag{5.3b}$$

$$\phi_4 = \phi_3 + 2\delta = \phi_2 + 4\delta. \tag{5.3c}$$

The radial coordinates of the points 1, 2, 3, 4 are denoted by r_1, r_2, r_3, r_4:

$$r_i = a/\cos\phi_i. \tag{5.4}$$

The proper time t, registered by the clock, can be obtained by integrat-
ing the metric form (5.2) along the world line $\phi = 0$ of the clock:

$$t = a \ln[r + (r^2 - a^2)^{1/2}]. \tag{5.5}$$

Hence, the traveling time t_2 of the second light signal becomes

$$t_2 = a \ln \frac{r_3 + (r_3{}^2 - a^2)^{1/2}}{r_2 + (r_2{}^2 - a^2)^{1/2}} = a \ln \frac{\cos\phi_2(1 + \sin\phi_3)}{\cos\phi_3(1 + \sin\phi_2)}. \tag{5.6}$$

Similar expressions apply for the traveling times of the first and third
light signals; all ϕ can be expressed by means of (5.3a), (5.3b), (5.3c) in

terms of ϕ_2 and δ. This allows the calculation of the expression (3). For small δ, one obtains

$$\frac{t_1 - 2t_2 + t_3}{t_2^2} \approx \frac{11}{a}, \tag{5.7}$$

and Riemann's invariant $R = 2/a^2$ is proportional to the square of (5.7). In particular, it vanishes if the expression (2) is zero.

6

On the Structure of Solid Bodies

(1) Physics always develops in two directions. One front pushes forward towards phenomena which do not yet fit into the general picture, and the victories on this front are marked by important changes in our fundamental concepts. On this front to-day the main struggle is for a better understanding of nuclear phenomena by the application of both theory and experimentation. But, in addition to this search for new concepts, there is a constant effort directed toward the deepening and broadening of our knowledge of phenomena which, we believe, *can* be understood on the basis of existing concepts and theories. Doubtless this second front is of less importance. It rarely leads to fundamental discoveries in physics proper but supports rather the studies on the borderline of this science, such as physical chemistry and the applied sciences. Spectroscopy suddenly changed, about six years ago, from the first to the second category, and not much later it became apparent that the study of the solid body belongs also to this second class. In spite of this, it remains one of the most attractive of all fields, since it deals in a scientific way with those subjects with which we must deal in our everyday experience. For example, we are never afraid when dropping a key that it will fly to pieces, as glass would, nor do we fear that a gold coin will dissolve in water or evaporate if left for awhile in the open air.

X-ray studies have revealed that most of the solid bodies in our surroundings are crystalline. This does not necessarily mean that they are

Reprinted by permission from the *Scientific Monthly*, Vol. 42 (January, 1936).

formed by one single crystal—although even this can be true for bodies of such enormous size as icebergs. More commonly, they are polycrystalline, like the metal parts of ordinary tools, i.e., a conglomerate of microscopic crystals of various sizes. Crystalline in this connection does not mean a regularly shaped body of the kind we see in our crystallographic collections, but only that the grains have a regular *inner structure* arising from the arrangement of the atoms in surprisingly regular *lattices.**

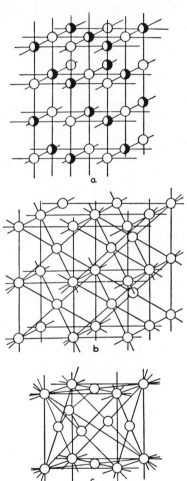

Fig. 1a Part of a KCl lattice. The shadowed spheres denote the positions of the K ions, the empty ones the positions of the Cl ions. The distance between nearest neighbors is .00000031 mm. Ordinary rocksalt has the same lattice with somewhat smaller dimensions.

Fig. 1b Part of the lattice of an alkali metal. The spheres represent the centers of mass of the atoms. The distance between nearest neighbors is .000000372 mm in sodium.

Fig. 1c Unit cell of the diamond lattice. The distance between next neighbors is .000000154 mm. Si has a similar lattice with a distance of .000000234 mm between nearest neighbors.

* Current crystallographic nomenclature uses the word *structure* to designate a regular arrangement of atoms in space. For example, KCl *structure*, diamond *structure*, etc. *Eds.*

Samples of such lattices are shown in Fig. 1. (The circles represent the centers of atoms; the lines have no physical significance and are drawn only in order to facilitate space-vision.) The region over which the regular arrangement has a certain orientation is called a microcrystal and may have a size anywhere from .00001 mm to 1 mm or even more. These microcrystals, generally possessing irregular boundaries, are heaped together in an apparently random manner to form the poly-crystalline body. (Very little is known about how the microcrystals with their different orientations fit and stick together. Some assume a separate very thin noncrystalline phase which "pastes" them together, but there is no definitive evidence for this.)

The crystalline and polycrystalline substances constitute by far the greater part of all solid bodies found in nature. Practically all rocks are conglomerates of crystals, ice is crystalline, and so are all metals. The grains of sand are minute crystals and loam also is crystalline. Apart from the glasses and substances of organic origin, like wood, there are very few non-crystalline solids.

(2) A distinction not necessary in the case of gases or liquids must be made between different kinds of properties of solids.

Evidently, the consideration of a regular lattice is much simpler than that of an irregularly spaced heap of atoms. It is important, therefore, that many of the properties of a polycrystal are the same as those pos-sessed by a perfect single crystal. These properties are connected with phenomena which affect the bulk of the material, like vaporization, fusion, specific gravity, and compressibility. Our understanding of these "insensitive properties" is naturally the farthest advanced, and we shall devote most of our attention to them.

Unfortunately, a great many very important properties belong in a second "sensitive" class. The breaking strength, for instance, is deter-mined by the very weakest part of the crystal; one single imperfection of certain types may suffice to cause rupture under a very low stress, a tenth or even a hundredth of that which a perfect crystal could sup-port. Fig. 2 gives a rough picture of how this can happen: the stress, characterized by the stress lines, concentrates in the neighborhood of the imperfection and attains values which are many times those in the bulk of the material. This highly concentrated stress can widen the notch and finally break the whole body. Thus, the parts of a solid which lie above and below a crack not only do not increase the strength of the material but very definitely weaken it. One can say that the strength of a solid is much smaller than that of its weakest part.

The situation for the electric breakdown of insulators parallels that for the elastic limit (the smallest stress which causes a permanent deformation), and the study of these sensitive properties of crystals involves besides a knowledge of the crystal in bulk, its criminology, i.e., a knowledge of the most dangerous faults and imperfections.

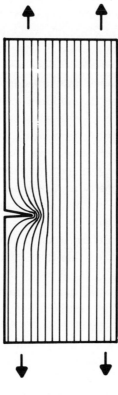

Fig. 2

In addition to these extremes, there are, of course, a number of border-line properties. These are partly connected with the external surface, as, for example, the thermionic emission of electrons, or with the internal boundaries of crystallites, exemplified by the electric conductivity of compressed salts. All these properties are influenced to some extent by small contaminations. With extreme care and sufficient experimental skill reproducible results are sometimes obtainable for these phenomena, and they are then frequently as amenable to theoretical interpretation as the insensitive properties.

(3) Let us return now to the insensitive properties. Even with regard to these, the variety found in solids is much greater than that in gases. From the empirical point of view, four main classes, with many transitions between them, can be distinguished. This classification, which in its essentials goes back to Grimm, contains:

(a) *Molecular lattices.* Inert gases or saturated compounds like He, Ne, A, etc., H_2, N_2, O_2, etc., CH_4, C_2H_6, H_2O, H_2S, etc., and all organic compounds form such crystals. They all have low heats of vaporization and condense only at comparatively low temperatures. They are soft and moderately brittle, are good insulators and are transparent, except in spectral regions in which the building molecules themselves show absorption.

(b) *Metals* have in many respects properties opposite to those of class *a*. The binding forces between the atoms are much higher and the heat of vaporization greater, and they have an increased hardness. Their most remarkable property is, of course, that they are good conductors for electricity and heat. They are opaque and owe many of their important applications in industry to their plasticity; that is to say, they break only after great deformation.[1] Their solubility in each other is considerable (alloys), but they hardly ever dissolve in solids of other classes.

(c) *Valence lattices* (diamond, quartz, carborundum) and

(d) *Ionic lattices* (salts) are rather similar types. They both have high heats of vaporization, strong cohesive forces, are transparent like molecular lattices, are good insulators, and are hard and brittle. The main difference between them is that while the former are formed from neutral atoms, the building stones of the salts are electrically charged ions, held together by the electrical attraction between opposite charges. They dissolve, therefore, in liquids with high dielectric constants like water, which diminish the electrical attraction of the ions down to a small fraction of its original value.

---

[1] This is why they do not break if dropped. The sudden stopping on the ground causes great stresses. In consequence of this, the metal will suffer a plastic deformation which will not cause rupture, however. In consequence of the plastic deformation the metal will act as its own shock absorber by allowing more time for the stopping of the bulk of the material.

This characterization of the four groups of solids should be understood in the same sense as should a similar characterization of a class of plants in botany. It does not give ironclad rules, but rather ideals from which the real cases often deviate; especially is this true for the more complicated compounds. Also various kinds of transitions occur between the four groups. Sometimes inside individual layers we have a lattice of one kind, while the forces *between* the layers are characteristic of another of our classes. There are also cases which are really transitional in all their behavior between two (or even three) groups, especially between valence and ionic lattices.

These exceptions are rare, however. The importance of the four groups becomes most evident, perhaps, if we realize that instinctively we classify into one of these groups all solid bodies of inorganic origin, which happen to fall into our hands. The above characterization of the four groups is the scientific description of what all of us would expect with regard to vaporization, hardness, electric conductivity, and brittleness after some inspection and handling of such substances as condensed CO_2, rhodium, carborundum, and Glauber's salts, even if we had never seen them before. On the other hand, we wouldn't quite know what to expect from transition lattices such as carbide or even graphite.

(4) The enormous differences between the physical properties of different kinds of lattices make it evident that the forces holding the atoms or molecules together are very different in the four cases. In order to understand the origin and nature of these forces, we must first recall the structure of isolated atoms and molecules. This is probably well known to the readers of the *Scientific Monthly*. It is only recently that Professor Eyring gave an excellent review of this subject in these pages.[2] According to Rutherford, the atom contains, first of all, a heavy nucleus, containing all the positive charge and (except for about one part in two thousand) all the mass of the atom. The center of gravity of the atom practically coincides with the nucleus, so that in Fig. 1 the circles may be regarded alternatively as the positions of atoms or nuclei. This nucleus, though small, is full of mysteries, which fortunately are of no importance in understanding the solid state. The negative charges, which exactly compensate the positive charge of the nucleus of a neutral atom, are carried by light particles, the electrons. These electrons surround the nucleus like an enormous cloud with dimensions a hundred

[2] *Scientific Monthly,* 39, 415-419 (November, 1934).

thousand times that of the nucleus, although the cloud is itself only about .0000001 mm thick. Quantum mechanics, created by Heisenberg, Schrödinger, and Dirac, unravelled for us about eight years ago the exact laws of motion of this electron cloud. It is now possible to calculate the density of this cloud at different distances from the nucleus, and from this one would naturally expect to obtain important information concerning the structure of solids, by comparing the density distribution of the electrons for different distances in the lattice. The outermost or valence electrons are responsible for the entire chemical behavior of the atoms. In Fig. 3, the full line represents the density of the valence electrons as a function of the distance from the nucleus. In addition to this, the position of the nearest neighbor is marked on the abscissa, and the density distribution of the valence electron of this neighbor is plotted *in the direction of the first atom* as the dotted line. The first plot is for He, the most characteristic representative of a molecular lattice; the second is for the valence lattice of silicon; the third is for sodium, a typical metal; and the last one is for KCl, which closely resembles ordinary rocksalt.

We realize at once an important difference between the molecular and ionic lattices (first and last pictures) on the one hand, and the metallic and valence lattices on the other. For the former, the overlapping of the electron clouds is small, in the latter ones it is so great that it is impossible to tell to which atom a certain valence electron belongs. In the former cases the constituent atoms or ions, although attracted by their neighbors, have their charge distribution but slightly affected. This is not so for the metals and valence lattices. There is no region between the atoms with a small charge density and consequently no forbidden region for the electrons. The electrons are able to pass from one atom to the next. Thus the valence electrons move freely and are common to the whole lattice. This is of decisive importance for the properties of these substances.

In molecular and ionic lattices, it is possible to consider the constituents as different entities. Born's classical theory of mechanical, electric, and thermal properties, which treats the atoms and ions of the lattice as individuals, attained its great successes for these lattices.

The great differences in the behavior of the two classes are due to the different character of the constituents. These are neutral atoms in the first case; in the ionic lattices they are charged particles. The electric

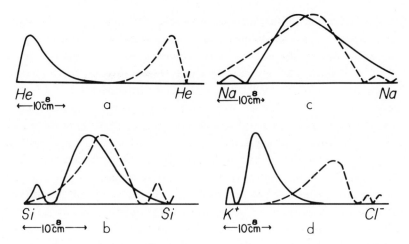

Fig. 3a   Charge distribution of two neighboring He atoms in the lattice.

Fig. 3b   Charge distribution of external electrons in free Si atom (full line). The dotted line is the charge distribution of the valence electrons of another Si atom, placed at the same distance from the first as in the lattice.

Fig. 3c   Charge distribution of the valence electron in free sodium atom (full line). The dotted line is the charge distribution of the valence electron of another sodium atom, placed at the same distance from the first as the nearest neighbor in the lattice.

Fig. 3d   Charge distribution of external electrons in K ion (full line) and Cl ion (dotted line). The distance of the zeros of the two plots is equal to the distance of the nearest ions in the KCl lattice.

forces between ions are very strong, and this makes the cohesive forces, the heat of vaporization, and hardness great. The distances between neighboring ions are given by the charge distribution, as illustrated in Fig. 3. The calculations of ionic radii were carried out by L. Pauling in California and show remarkable agreement with the values derived by Goldschmidt from observations. These lattices are always so constructed that the positive ions are surrounded by negative ions, the negative ions by positive ones. (Cf. the NaCl lattice in Fig. 1.) Since opposite charges attract each other, there are considerable forces holding these lattices together.

The nature of the forces in molecular lattices is not so simple. Van der

Waals was the first to assume that condensation is caused by the same forces which are responsible for the deviation in the behavior of real gases from the ideal gas laws. This proved to be true in the case of molecular lattices, and the laws of these forces have been recognized by London and Wang on the basis of quantum mechanics and called van der Waals' forces.

Of course, there is no attraction due to electric charges in molecular lattices, since the constituents are uncharged. And, indeed, the attraction cannot be understood as long as we consider the electrons as charge clouds. But if we remember their corpuscular nature, we realize that they can form *dipoles* with the nucleus. The direction of this dipole will vary quickly because of the quick motion of the electrons. There will be no force, in the mean, on a dipole of constant orientation, since the attraction for one dipole orientation is as great as the repulsion for the opposite orientation—and all dipole directions are equally probable. But if two variable dipoles face each other, it will be possible that the two attractive configurations *a* and *c* of Fig. 4 will occur more often than the repulsive configurations *b* and *d*, although all the orientations for the *single* dipoles are equally probable. London and Wang have shown that this is actually the situation, and thus laid the foundation not only for a satisfactory theory of molecular lattices but also for a theory of the behavior of real gases.

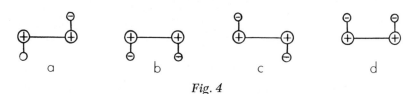

Fig. 4

Naturally, the van der Waals forces are much smaller than the Coulombic forces between ions. Thus, the cohesion in molecular lattices is small, the vaporization easy. Also it is evident that these very small forces will be important only if no other stronger forces are present. Molecular lattices will be formed by saturated compounds and inert gases.

(5) Fig. 3 shows us that the metallic and valence lattices form the more compact modifications of matter, as contrasted with molecular lattices and salts. This gives important information concerning the question

of the behavior of solids under extremely high pressures: according to Bernal, who first emphasized this point, they will go over into metals or valence lattices. A convincing piece of evidence for this point of view, which is quite independent of calculations of charge distribution, is furnished by the phenomenon of *allotropy*. This is the name given the phenomenon of the appearance of the same chemical element in different "modifications" with widely different physical and chemical properties. The ordinary, yellow (white) form of phosphorus forms a somewhat complicated molecular lattice. It is a good insulator, soft, dissolves in organic solvents, and has a density of 1.83. Bridgman at Harvard subjected this element to very high pressures, and the lattice "collapsed." It transformed into *black phosphorus,* which has a density of 2.70, is a fairly good conductor of electricity, and insoluble in organic liquids. And this is the general rule: Whenever an element has two allotropic modifications, the *metallic or valence form has the higher density.* The following table illustrates this point:

As, metallic	5.72	yellow	2.03
diamond	3.51	graphite	2.24
black phosph.	2.70	yellow	1.83
Se, metallic	4.82	red	4.47
Sn, white	7.28	gray	5.76

Calculations made in our laboratory by H. B. Huntington show that metallic hydrogen should also exist, though only under extremely high pressures, and that it should have a density many times higher than that of the usual molecular form.

I shall not go into detail with regard to the next question which naturally arises—the cause of the fundamental difference between valence and metallic lattices. Although both form in the compact modification of matter, apart from the high heat of vaporization and boiling point, they have nothing in common. The reason for this is deeply rooted in the principles of quantum mechanics and has been brought out but lately by considerations of Peierls and Brillouin. According to their investigations, it is essential for a valence lattice that the number of valence electrons be *even,* and this rule holds without exceptions. We owe much valuable information concerning the structure and crystal form of valence lattices to Pauling and Slater, but a review of their work would greatly exceed the scope of this report.

I hope that I have succeeded in imparting to the reader the impression that the foundations for the understanding of the nature of the solid state are laid. Still, it will require much thorough work, perseverance, and many new ideas before we will be able to add the theory of solids as a finished story to the building of physics and before we will be able to apply with success our knowledge in industry.

The progress in the explanation of the properties of solid bodies is due on the theoretical side to the newly developed quantum mechanics, and experimentally mainly to the study of crystal structure by x-rays. Without these tools we would face these problems as helplessly as we still face the problem of liquids, where x-ray studies have proved less efficient so far.

7

On the Development of the Compound Nucleus Model

The Compound Nucleus Model

The compound nucleus model pictures the nuclear reaction as a succession of two events. The first event is the union of the colliding nuclei into a single unit, the so-called compound nucleus. This compound nucleus, although not stable, has many of the properties of stable nuclei. In particular, it has rather well defined energy levels. The second event is the disintegration of the compound nucleus, either into the nuclei from which it was formed, or into another pair of nuclei. In the first case, no reaction, only a scattering process has taken place; the second case corresponds to a real reaction.

The probability of the formation of the compound nucleus is very small unless the energy of the colliding pair coincides very closely with one of the energy levels of the compound nucleus. On the other hand, if the coincidence is perfect, the cross section for the formation of the compound nucleus is very large: its impact parameter corresponds to angular momentum $\hbar$ of the colliding pair about their common center of mass. Hence, the cross section for the formation of the compound nucleus shows sharp maxima but drops to very small values between these. The disintegration of the compound nucleus is subject to probability laws: once the compound nucleus has been formed, the probability

Richtmyer Memorial Lecture, January 28, 1955. Reprinted by permission from the *American Journal of Physics,* Vol. 23, No. 6 (September, 1955).

of a particular mode of disintegration is independent of the mode of formation. As was mentioned before, the different modes of disintegration lead to different reaction products; if the disintegration leads to the same nuclei which formed the compound nucleus, no reaction has taken place.

The model just described was proposed also for chemical reactions,[1] the result of the first step being called in this case the compound molecule. However, certainly not all chemical reactions show a cross section with high maxima and very low values between the maxima. Hence, the compound molecule picture is a valid picture only for a limited class of chemical reactions. Other mechanisms, i.e., other models, are more suitable for the description of other reactions.[2] Whether and in what sense the compound nucleus picture is a general one for all nuclear reactions is one of the questions which I wish to bring up in the course of this discussion.

I do not want to give a detailed history of the origin of the compound nucleus model. Those of us who have read Bohr and Kalckar's paper,[3] for instance, do not need to be reminded of it. The reminder would mean very little for those whose acquaintance with the subject is of later date and who are unfamiliar with the early papers on the subject. Experimental work constituted, in my opinion, the most important step in the development. The experiments of Moon and Tillman, of Bjerge and Westcott, of Szilard, and of several other investigators[4] demonstrated that the slow neutron absorption of many nuclei shows the characteristics of high maxima and low values between the maxima which were known consequences of the compound molecule theory of chemical reactions. It was natural, therefore, to attempt a two stage theory of transformations to describe at least some nuclear reactions.

The process of the formation and subsequent disintegration of a compound is also the customary picture for the description of the scattering

[1] Cf., e.g., M. Polanyi, Z. *Physik*, 2, 90 (1920).

[2] The most useful model for the simplest type of exchange reactions is the adiabatic model. Cf. F. London, *Sommerfeld Festschrift*, p. 104 (Leipzig: S. Hirzel, 1928).

[3] N. Bohr and F. Kalckar, *Kgl. Danske Videnskab. Selskab, Mat.-Fys. Medd.*, 14, 10 (1937).

[4] P. B. Moon and J. R. Tillman, *Nature*, 135, 904 (1935); L. Szilard, *Nature*, 136, 150 (1935); T. Bjerge and C. H. Westcott, *Proc. Roy. Soc.* (London), A150, 709 (1935); E. Amaldi and E. Fermi, *Ricerca Sci.*, 1, 310 (1936); J. R. Dunning, G. B. Pegram, G. A. Fink, and D. P. Mitchell, *Phys. Rev.*, 48, 265 (1935).

and fluorescence of light. The absorption of light leads to an excited state of the absorber; this excited state corresponds to the compound nucleus. The reemission of light by the excited state corresponds to the disintegration of the compound nucleus. Hence, the compound nucleus model shows great formal similarity with the process of light absorption and reemission. The model which had been introduced to explain the absorption of light and its reemission could have been taken over, in fact, verbatim but for one new element. This new element is the energy dependence of the probabilities of the different modes of disintegration of the compound nucleus, in particular the proportionality between the probability of neutron emission and the square root of the energy with which the neutron is to be emitted. Even though the disintegration probabilities of the compound nucleus, at a given energy, do not depend on its mode of formation, they do depend on its energy, sometimes quite critically.

Extensions of the Applications of the Compound Nucleus Model

Even after the compound nucleus model had proved its worth for the description of neutron absorption phenomena, at least at low energies, there were those of us who, mindful of the limited validity of this model in describing chemical reactions, doubted its usefulness as a general framework into which all nuclear reactions could be fitted. The more courageous camp to which we owe most of the extensions of the compound nucleus model, headed principally by Bethe, Breit,[5] and Weisskopf, derived much encouragement from the experiments of Hafstad, Heydenberg and Tuve, and of Herb and his collaborators,[6] who showed, almost simultaneously with the slow neutron experiments which were mentioned before, that reactions induced by protons of about 1 Mev show the same type of resonance structure as exhibited by reactions induced by neutrons of a few ev. This was indeed impressive demonstration of the wide scope of applicability of the com-

[5] H. A. Bethe, *Rev. Mod. Phys.*, 9, 71 (1937); G. Breit, *Phys. Rev.*, 58, 1068 (1940), 69, 472 (1946).
[6] L. R. Hafstad and M. A. Tuve, *Phys. Rev.*, 48, 306 (1935); L. R. Hafstad, N. P. Heydenberg, and M. A. Tuve, *ibid.*, 50, 504 (1936); R. G. Herb, D. W. Kerst, and J. L. McKibben, *ibid.*, 51, 691 (1937); E J. Bernet, R. G. Herb, and D. B. Parkinson, *ibid.*, 54, 398 (1938).

pound nucleus model. The reactions which attracted Weisskopf's attention principally were, however, not these but those in which the resonances were so numerous and their widths so great that they overlapped to give a continuous energy dependence to the cross section. The continuous energy dependence might have been taken as an indication that the compound nucleus model does not apply—it was considered to be such an indication, and rightly so, in the case of chemical reactions—but Weisskopf and Ewing suggested a way to apply the concepts of the compound nucleus theory in the case of overlapping levels.[7] If the levels of the compound nucleus are very closely spaced, it becomes impossible to investigate their properties individually and, in fact, Weisskopf and Ewing's theory deals with joint properties of a very large number of levels of the compound nucleus and, usually, with joint properties of many levels of the product nucleus.

Weisskopf and Ewing's statistical model is one of the most encompassing models that were ever put forward. It gives an expression for virtually every nuclear cross section and it has stimulated experimental work on almost every type of nuclear reaction. It is natural that it contained several important assumptions and it may be useful to test these assumptions separately in the light of our present knowledge of nuclear transformations.

The statistical model is on safest ground in the energy region where the levels of the compound nucleus are sharp enough to be easily distinguishable. This restricts the energy of the incoming particles to a few Mev in heavy nuclei but leaves much more leeway in light nuclei. In this case the only relevant assumption of the statistical model is that when the compound nucleus disintegrates, all possible states of the product nucleus are formed with essentially the same probability. "Essentially the same" means that it is the same if the energy dependence of the disintegration probability, which was mentioned before, is disregarded. Although there are many indications that this assumption is invalid under certain conditions, there are at least equally many indications that it is a useful guide, if not much more.

The statistical theory is on much less safe ground in the energy region in which the levels of the compound nucleus are broad enough to overlap. It was mentioned before that the compound molecule theory of chemical reactions does not apply in such cases. In such a case, even the

[7] V. F. Weisskopf and D. H. Ewing, *Phys. Rev.*, 57, 472, 935 (1940).

concept of the compound nucleus is questionable in the sense that its energy determines its properties, in particular the probabilities of the various modes of its disintegration. Just as a very high energy electron can traverse an atom without much energy loss, a very high energy proton will be able to traverse a nucleus without being much affected by it. This is contrary to the compound nucleus model as used in the statistical theory, which postulates that the emergence of the proton should be just as probable no matter whether the compound nucleus originates from the collision of a very fast proton or of a very fast neutron with the appropriate target nucleus. It is natural to expect, in the second case, that the neutron would emerge from the target. It is clear, therefore, that the validity of not only the statistical model, but also of the original ideas of the compound nucleus theory, is limited toward the high energy region. The statistical theory demands not only that the reaction products depend only on the energy (and angular momentum) of the compound nucleus, it demands further that all energetically possible reaction products appear with essentially the same probabilities.

Many experiments gave strong support to the statistical theory even under the most adverse conditions. However, more recently, the conflicting experiments began to preponderate. They can be brought to a common denominator: the probability of the formation of the product nucleus in its various states of excitation is not equal but there is a definite preference for the formation of states of low excitation. This is directly demonstrated in the experiments of Gugelot and B. Cohen.[8] The preferential emission of protons and α particles, first discovered by the Swiss school,[9] can also be explained in this way.

The question naturally arises whether there is an energy region in which the naive form of the compound nucleus theory remains valid but the specific hypothesis of the statistical theory is invalid. Personally, I am inclined to be doubtful concerning the basic postulate of the statistical theory with respect to the equality of the probabilities of all modes of disintegration of the compound nucleus. Nevertheless, I wish to emphasize that, in my opinion, there is no unequivocal evidence that the statistical theory breaks down before the compound nucleus theory, as

[8] P. Gugelot, *Phys. Rev.*, 93, 425 (1954); B. L. Cohen, *ibid.*, 92, 1245 (1953).
[9] O. Hirzel and H. Waffler, *Helv. Phys. Acta,* 20, 373 (1947); E. B. Paul and R. L. Clarke, *Can. J. Phys.,* 31, 267 (1953).

discussed above, ceases to be valid. Courant's considerations[10] suggest, on the contrary, that the statistical assumption is correct whenever the compound nucleus picture can be used in the form discussed above.

The principal objection to the assumption of equal transition probabilities to all possible states is, however, the same as that to all theories which we inherited, mostly from ourselves, from the years before the War. All these consider all nuclear properties to be smooth functions of the mass and charge numbers and of the energy. As far as the normal states of nuclei are concerned, this view was refuted by the observations of Mayer[11] and of Haxel, Jensen, and Suess[12] and their theories of nuclear shell structure. However, the situation is not too different even as far as nuclear reactions are concerned. The large scattering cross sections of the iron group, the large absorption cross sections of the rare earths, are too systematic to be accidental and have been reinforced by the total cross section measurements of Fields, Russell, Sachs, and Wattenberg.[13] Bohm and Ford[14] tried to interpret these measurements on the basis of the independent particle model. However, the independent particle model which does reproduce the gross structure cannot account for the fine structure, i.e., the resonance character, of the cross section curve. When the empirical situation was fully clarified as a result of the experiments of Barschall and his collaborators,[15] it was

[10] E. D. Courant, *Phys. Rev.*, 82, 703 (1951); H. McManus and W. T. Sharp, *ibid.*, 87, 188 (1952).

[11] M. G. Mayer, *Phys. Rev.*, 74, 235 (1948); also W. Elsasser, *J. Phys. Radium*, 5, 625 (1934).

[12] O. Haxel, J. Jensen, and H. Suess, *Z. Physik*, 128, 295 (1950).

[13] R. Fields, B. Russell, D. Sachs, and A. Wattenberg, *Phys. Rev.*, 71, 508 (1947).

[14] K. W. Ford and D. Bohm, *Phys. Rev.*, 79, 745 (1950).

[15] The information on low energy (50 to 3,000 kev) cross sections was obtained by Barschall and his collaborators as a result of a series of investigations, starting back in 1948. Cf. H. H. Barschall, C. K. Bockelman, and L. W. Seagondollar, *Phys. Rev.*, 73, 659 (1948) (Fe, Ni, Bi); R. K. Adair, H. H. Barschall, C. K. Bockelman, and O. Sala, *ibid.*, 75, 1124 (1949) (Be, O, Na, Ca); C. K. Bockelman, R. E. Peterson, R. K. Adair, and H. H. Barschall, *ibid.*, 76, 277 (1949) (Zr, Ag, In, Sb, I, Ta, Pb); R. E. Peterson, R. K. Adair, and H. H. Barschall, *ibid.*, 79 (1950) (lead isotopes); C. K. Bockelman, D. W. Miller, R. K. Adair, and H. H. Barschall, *ibid.*, 84, 69 (1951) (Li, Be, B, C, O); H. H. Barschall, *ibid.*, 86, 431L (1952) (review); D. W. Miller, R. K. Adair, C. K. Bockelman, and S. E. Darden, *ibid.*, 88, 83 (1952) (review); N. Nereson and S. Darden, *ibid.*, 89, 775 (1953) (higher energies); M. Walt, R. L. Becker, A. Okazaki, R. E. Fields, *ibid.*, 89, 1271 (1953) (Co, Ga, Se, Cd, Te, Pt, Au, Hg, Th); A. Okasaki, S. E. Darden, R. B. Walton, *ibid.*, 93, 461 (1954) (Nd, Sm, Er, Yb, Hf); M. Walt and H. H. Barschall, *ibid.*, 93, 1062 (1954) (angular distributions); cf. also R. K. Adair, *Rev. Mod. Phys.*, 22, 249 (1950); A. Langsdorf, *Phys. Rev.*, 80, 132 (1950).

again Weisskopf, in collaboration with Feshbach and Porter, who gave the solution: the independent particle model—it would be more accurate to say, *an* independent particle model—gives only the average cross section, that is, the gross structure, by determining the product of the density and strength of the levels of the compound nucleus.[16] The reaction, itself, proceeds via the compound nucleus mechanism. In other words, it is not the compound nucleus model which is at fault; the discrepancy has to be blamed on the statistical assumptions which were so very plausible but which have to be modified so that the average cross section be at least in rough accord with the independent particle picture. While these statements appear to imply some mystical correspondence principle role of the independent particle model, this implication is incorrect and Scott, Thomas, Lane, and others have shown very concretely how the results of Weisskopf's model can be obtained as vestigial traces of the independent particle model.[17] Whether this interpretation of the Barschall maxima, as made more precise by these authors, will stand the test of time is as yet uncertain.

Since this model is not yet very generally known, let me spend a few minutes outlining it. If we assume, in the sense of the independent particle model, that the effect of the target nucleus on the incident particle can be accounted for by a suitable potential, one can describe any state of the compound nucleus by specifying a state of the target nucleus and giving also the state of the incident particle in the potential created by the target nucleus. Figure 1a shows a set of levels of the compound nucleus at about 8 Mev excitation. Most of the levels correspond to an *excited* state of the target nucleus plus a suitable state of the incident particle. It is assumed, however, that the particular state marked by crosses corresponds to the *normal* state of the target nucleus and a state of about 8 Mev energy of the incident particle. This state of the compound nucleus—if it is worthy of that name—will disintegrate very fast into the initial target nucleus and the incident particle with its original energy. In fact, the compound state will last only as long as it takes the incident particle to cross the potential generated by the target nucleus. The disintegration of this particular compound state will always pro-

---

[16] H. Feshbach, C. E. Porter, and V. F. Weisskopf, *Phys. Rev.*, 90, 166 (1953); 96, 448 (1954).

[17] J. M. C. Scott, *Phil. Mag.*, 45, 1332 (1954); E. P. Wigner, *Science*, 120, 790 (1954); A. M. Lane, R. G. Thomas, and E. P. Wigner, *Phys. Rev.*, 98, 693 (1955).

ceed by reemission of the incident particle with its original energy; it is a property of the extreme independent particle model that it gives no reaction, only scattering. The other states of the compound nucleus will have a short life-time also; each of them will disintegrate only into one state of the target nucleus, and this will be an excited state for all of the not-crossed states. Conversely, only the crossed state will form if the incident particle strikes the target nucleus in its *normal* state. The probability of disintegration of the various compound states, resulting in the target nucleus in its normal state, is illustrated on the second line

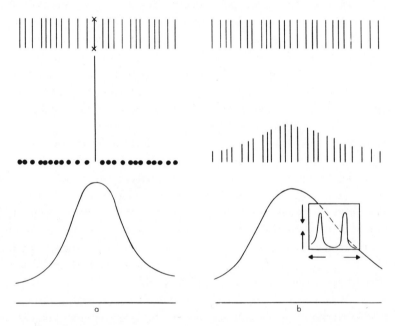

Fig. 1a refers to the independent particle model in which the effect of the target nucleus on the incident particle can be described by a potential. This potential depends, naturally, on the state of excitation of the target nucleus. The top of the figure gives the energy levels of the compound nucleus; the level with crosses corresponds to the normal state of the target nucleus plus a suitable state of the incident particle. The other levels correspond to excited states of the target nucleus. The heights of the lines in the middle of the figure give the transition probabilities from the state of the compound nucleus above them, to the normal state of the target nucleus (plus the incident particle). This probability vanishes for all states of the compound nucleus except the crossed one. The bottom part of the figure gives the cross section as function of energy; the width of the line is due to the large disintegration probability of the crossed state.

of the graph. These probabilities also give the partial widths for the formation of the compound state from the incident particle and the target nucleus in its normal state. Hence, the bottom graph represents the scattering cross section of the target nucleus according to the independent particle model; it is the cross section curve of Bohm and Ford.

If we admit that the independent particle picture is inaccurate, it will not be possible to label the states of the compound nucleus by the states of the target nucleus from which they can be obtained. Rather, every state in the neighborhood of the crossed state will acquire some of the characteristics of that state. The probability of disintegration into the normal state of the target nucleus will be, therefore, much smaller for the originally crossed state but it will be, on the other hand, finite for many compound states for which it vanished in the independent particle model. The same holds for the partial widths of these states, so that the cross section will have resonance character. The situation in this model, as contrasted with the extreme independent particle model, is given in Figure 1b. The average cross section of this model, given in the bottom diagram, will be the cross section of the Feshbach–Porter–Weisskopf clouded crystal ball model.

At the same time, our model indicates a possible reason for systematic deviations from the statistical theory in the sense indicated by the ex-

---

Fig. 1b represents the conditions in the model considered in the text. Chosen a state of the compound nucleus, the state of excitation of the target nucleus is not uniquely given but can be, with various probabilities, one of several states. As a result, there is no definite crossed state of the compound nucleus. Conversely, many states of the compound nucleus can disintegrate into the normal state of the target nucleus (plus the incident particle), the probabilities for such a disintegration of the compound nucleus states are given by the ordinates in the middle of the figure. They are largest for those levels of the compound nucleus which are close, on the energy scale, to the crossed level of the independent particle picture of Figure 1a. The bottom of the figure gives the average cross section of the model; a portion magnified in energy scale but contracted on the cross section scale is given by the insert. The width of the maximum in the average cross section is due, principally, to the fact that the levels of the compound nucleus which can disintegrate into the normal state of the target nucleus are spread out on the energy scale. Nevertheless, the *average* cross section of Figure 1b shows a similarity to the *actual* cross section of the independent particle model, given in Figure 1a.

perimental data. Under certain conditions, the transition probabilities into the various states of the product nucleus are not equal. Rather, the transition probability into all states which lie within unit energy interval is independent of the position of that interval. Under these conditions, the high energy region, although it contains a large number of energy levels, does not any more receive the lion's share of the transitions. The very few levels in a unit range at low energy receive as many transitions as the much more numerous energy levels in a high energy unit interval. This is the preference for the formation of the low energy levels which was mentioned before as explaining the systematic deviations from the statistical model.

The above summary, though far from complete, may give some idea of the variety of the problems to which the compound nucleus model has been applied. Let me proceed, therefore, to the last subject on which I wish to speak, the foundation of the compound model and the basic problems on which it sheds some light.

Basic Aspects of the Compound Nucleus Model

The story of the gradual extension of the compound particle model, always guided by the experimental results, appears to me a story worth telling. The story of the theoretical considerations behind it seems to me even more interesting.

A very restricted problem, the anomalous behavior of the slow neutron absorption of Cd, was the principal problem that Breit and I wanted to explain originally.[18] We made two rather far-reaching assumptions. The first of these is the existence of a somewhat mysterious "compound state," the second the absence of a direct coupling between the states of the continuum. Our formula contained three adjustable parameters, and we now know that the agreement between formula and observation is remarkable even if one considers that three adjustable constants are at one's disposal.

The rest of the story is similar in its main lines, and on a small scale, to the story of almost every physical theory. First, the ephemeral and the general elements of the theory were separated. Second, the general elements were formulated in such a general way that they could serve

[18] G. Breit and E. P. Wigner, *Phys. Rev.,* 49, 519, 642 (1936).

as a framework for the description of a wide variety of phenomena. This, unfortunately, also means that the physical content of the framework is so small that almost any experimental result could be fitted into it. The interest, therefore, shifted away from the framework to the body of information which could be described in the language given by the framework. Third, an attempt was made to deduce from very general principles the physical content which remained in the framework. The story of almost every physical theory goes along this way; some run through it fast, the more important ones less rapidly.

It may be worthwhile to illustrate this by means of an example. Galileo's discovery of the laws of free fall led to a concrete and definite equation. What was ephemeral in this equation was the constancy of the acceleration. The general part of it was formulated as Newton's second law, the proportionality between acceleration and force. This is the first phase mentioned above. However, Newton's second law is so general that it permits almost any type of motion; it provides a language to describe motions rather than determining the motion by itself. Hence, the problem after the establishment of the second law shifted from the description of the motion to the determination of the forces between bodies. This shift of the problem is what was called the second phase of the theory. The last phase of the theory is the search for the fundamental reason for those elements of the general physical law which give it whatever physical content it does have. This is, actually, Newton's first law. Its fundamental basis, the equivalence of moving observers, was embodied eventually in the Galilei and Lorentz transformations.

The most important ephemeral part of the compound nucleus theory was soon recognized as the assumption of a single compound state which entailed the existence of a single resonance level. However, when the theory was extended to assume many compound states, to describe many resonance levels, the number of adjustable parameters also became arbitrary and it became apparent that almost any experimental result on nuclear transformation might be consistent with the theory. As the generality of the resonance formula increased, its specificity decreased and so did the specificity of the assumptions entering the theory. The possibility of carrying out this development ad extremum, and of deriving a framework from practically no specific assumption, was first recognized by Kapur and Peierls.[19] Their theory was little understood

[19] P. L. Kapur and R. Peierls, *Proc. Roy. Soc.* (London), A166, 277 (1938).

at first. It contains, however, many ideas which reappear in practically all subsequent work.

It may be of some interest to describe why and how I returned to the subject. About a year before the end of the last war, Fermi commented to me on the anomaly that the compound nucleus theory had become widely accepted without having a good foundation in basic theory. I considered this as a challenge and made an attempt to formulate assumptions from which the one level formula could be derived. The assumption of the somewhat mysterious "compound state" was replaced by the assumption that the wave function is energy independent in the part of the configuration space in which the incident particle is inside the nucleus or very close to it. Instead of the assumption that there is no interaction between the states of the continuum, it was assumed that, outside of the immediate neighborhood of the target nucleus, the incident particle behaves like a free particle. From these assumptions, the one level formula with its three parameters, a rather specific formula, could be rederived. This corresponds to the first stage of the development which I sketched before.

It was tempting, however, to eliminate the first assumption and to replace it with the more general one that the wave function in the interior part of the configuration space, that is, where target nucleus and incident particle are close together, is a linear combination of several wave functions, with energy dependent coefficients, rather than an energy independent function. This virtually abolished the first of the earlier assumptions because any function can be written as a linear combination of a sufficiently large number of given functions. The only relevant assumption which then remained was that of the finite range of interaction. It should not have surprised me that the development could be carried out with the more general assumption concerning the wave function in the interior part of configuration space: the considerations of Kapur and Peierls and other considerations of Breit clearly foreshadowed this. The simplicity of the final formula was surprising, though. It suggested a simplified approach which was given, almost simultaneously by Eisenbud and by Schwinger and Weisskopf.[20] Similar ideas were formulated even before in radioengineering.

Let me remark, only parenthetically, that the assumption of a finite

[20] L. Eisenbud and E. P. Wigner, *Phys. Rev.*, 72, 29 (1947); T. Teichmann and E. P. Wigner, *ibid.*, 87, 123 (1952).

range of interaction was also eliminated subsequently, by Thomas.[21]
The model, as described for instance in the book of Blatt and Weisskopf,
or in that of Sachs,[22] retains the division of the configuration space into
two parts. All of the typically nuclear interaction takes place in the
internal region; the waves spread essentially freely in the external domain. The nuclear interaction is replaced by a formal connection between the normal derivative and the value of the wave function on the
boundary of these two regions,

$$v_s = \sum_t R_{st}\, d_t. \tag{1}$$

It may be well to repeat that (1) expresses the properties of the internal
part of configuration space, depends on the interaction in the internal
region, and is in fact a substitute for the usual description of this interaction by means of potentials, etc. It does not depend on any interaction
which may take place outside the internal region. The v_s are expansion
coefficients of the value of the wave function on the boundary of the
internal region, the d_t are the expansion coefficients of the normal
derivative. The R_{st} form a matrix, the R matrix, the dependence of which
on the energy is given by

$$R_{st} = \sum_\lambda \frac{\gamma_{\lambda s}\, \gamma_{\lambda t}}{E_\lambda - E}. \tag{2}$$

The E_λ are the energy values of the compound states; they are not to be
confused with the total energy E of the system. The $\gamma_{\lambda s}, \gamma_{\lambda t}$ determine the
probabilities that the compound state λ disintegrate in the mode s or t.
The R becomes very large if E approaches one of the E_λ; this corresponds to a large cross section at the coincidence of the energy E of
the system with an energy level E_λ of the compound nucleus. The one
level formula will be valid if one term in the sum (2) predominates. In
this case the fact that the numerator is a product of two factors, one
depending only on s, the other only on t, assures that the probabilities
of the various modes of disintegration of the compound nucleus are
independent of the mode of formation of the compound nucleus. Thus,
many of the properties of the simple compound nucleus theory remain

[21] R. G. Thomas, *Phys. Rev.*, 100, 25 (1955).
[22] J. Blatt and V. F. Weisskopf, *Theoretical Nuclear Physics* (New York: John
Wiley and Sons, 1952), Chapters VIII and X; R. G. Sachs, *Nuclear Theory* (Cambridge: Addison-Wesley Publishing Co., 1953), pp. 290-304.

apparent in (2). At the same time, (2) contains in general so many parameters—actually an infinite number of them—that it has hardly any direct physical content. In spite of this, (2) is not useless: it gives a framework, that is a language, for the description of nuclear transmutation processes. The reduced widths $\gamma_{\lambda s}^2$ and the resonance energies E_λ constitute a simpler description of the reaction process than all the cross section versus energy curves. These quantities can be compared, interpreted, and even calculated more easily than the cross sections themselves. In fact, a theory has been put forward, and a wealth of data is being accumulated on the magnitude of the $\gamma_{\lambda s}^2$ and E_λ. The validity of (2) has ceased to be an interesting question and has been replaced by the problem of the magnitudes of the $\gamma_{\lambda s}$ and E_λ.

This, it seems to me, answers the question which was posed at the beginning of this talk, concerning the generality of the compound nucleus model as a description of nuclear reactions. The generality is almost complete if we consider the model as a framework for describing nuclear reactions, as a language in which the results can be formulated.[23] The physical content which we originally associated with the model is not general but can be expressed in the language of the model in a particularly simple way. Other, equally simple and important physical pictures are much more difficult to express in that language. Though Thomas formulated the assumptions of the statistical model within the framework of equations (1) and (2), the equally simple picture of direct interaction between incident and target particles, proposed by Courant,[24] has not been formulated in that language. It still appears to me that the language is really useful only when the energy levels of the compound nucleus are well separated, when at least some of the features of the original compound nucleus picture apply. If this is not the case, the language becomes clumsy and often gave me the impression that an equation such as $(\sqrt{(1-x^2)})^2 = 1 - x^2$ is being proved by means of the power series expansion for $\sqrt{(1-x^2)}$.

Here ends the description of the second phase of the theory. If it is permissible to recognize similarities between an elephant and an ant, I would point to the fact that Newton's second law is similarly a frame-

---

[23] It has been shown, in particular, that the process of spontaneous disintegration can also be described by means of Eqs. (1) and (2). See L. Eisenbud and E. P. Wigner, *Nuclear Structure* (Princeton, N.J.: Princeton University Press, 1958), Sec. 9.5.

[24] See footnote 10.

work. Once it was established, the problem became the determination of the forces, their dependence on the material, and distance separating the bodies between which they act. In the case of the compound nucleus theory, the corresponding problems were discussed in the preceding section.

What remains, then, is the third phase in the development, a deeper understanding of the rather meager information that is contained in (2). Because even though (2) represents a very general function of the energy E, it is not an entirely arbitrary function. One can see, for instance, that R_{ss} always increases with increasing energy wherever it is finite.

The basic reason for this and other properties of R has puzzled many of us. It was suggested, finally, by Schultzer and Tiomno.[25] Their work, inspired by earlier investigations of Kronig and of Kramers, indicated that unless R has the form (2), one may have the paradoxical situation that the outgoing wave begins to leave the internal region before the incoming wave has reached it. The principle that such a thing cannot happen has come to be called the "causality condition." Its emergence has contributed a great deal to our understanding of equation (2).

The Causality Condition

The surmise of Tiomno and Schutzer was proved for a wide variety of phenomena by Van Kampen[26] and by Gell-Mann, Goldberger, and Thirring,[27] whose work also contributed greatly to our understanding of the connection between the operator R and the collision matrix.

The following lines appear to me a rather general derivation of the result of Tiomno, Schutzer, Van Kampen, Gell-Mann, Goldberger, Thirring, at least for the non-relativistic case. The basic equation which will be used postulates that the time derivative of the probability of finding the system in the internal region of configuration space is equal to the probability current across the surface of the internal region. If one wishes to use no concepts which refer to the internal region, one

[25] W. Schutzer and J. Tiomno, *Phys. Rev.*, 83, 249 (1951). R. de L. Kronig, *J. Opt. Soc. Am.*, 12, 547 (1926); H. A. Kramers, *Atti. congr. intern. fisici Como 2*, p. 545 (1927).

[26] N. G. Van Kampen, *Phys. Rev.*, 89, 1072 (1953); 91, 1267 (1953). Also J. S. Toll, Princeton University Dissertation, 1952.

[27] M. Gell-Mann, M. L. Goldberger, and W. E. Thirring, *Phys. Rev.*, 95, 1612 (1954).

can postulate instead that the negative derivative of finding the system in the external region is equal to the current across the boundary separating internal and external regions. In order to make use of this postulate, one evidently cannot restrict oneself to stationary wave functions but must consider a superposition of states with different energy values. For the sake of simplicity, the normal derivatives of all the states which will be superposed will depend in the same way on the position on the boundary, i.e., the normal derivative of the total wave function on the boundary shall have the form

$$\mathrm{grad}_n\ \varphi = \sum_k a(E_k)f(x)e^{-iE_k t/\hbar}\ \text{(on the boundary)}, \tag{3}$$

the summation to be extended over several energy values E_k; the variable x describes the points of configuration space. The value of the wave function on the surface will then be given by the R operator

$$\varphi(x) = \sum_k a(E_k)R(E_k)f(x)e^{-iE_k t/\hbar}\ \text{(on the boundary)}. \tag{3a}$$

The current into the internal region is the integral of $-i\,(\varphi\,\mathrm{grad}_n\,\varphi^* - \varphi^*\,\mathrm{grad}_n\,\varphi)$,

$$\text{current} = -i\sum_{lk} a(E_l)^* a(E_k)\, e^{i(E_l - E_k)t/\hbar}$$

$$\times \left(\int f^* R(E_k)\, f\, dS - \int (R(E_l)f)^*\, f dS\right). \tag{4}$$

dS indicates integration over the boundary between internal and external regions.

Although the formulae which were used above do not give an explicit expression therefore, the wave function in the internal region must be completely determined once the normal derivative of a monoenergetic wave is given on the boundary. It then follows from the principle of superposition and from the quadratic nature of all expressions for probabilities in quantum mechanics that the probability of finding the system in the internal region is given by an expression of the form

$$\sum_{kl} P_{lk}\, a(E_l)^*\, a(E_k)\, e^{i(E_l - E_k)t/\hbar}. \tag{5}$$

The P can depend on the function f, which underlies our considerations, but not on time. Furthermore, since the last expression is a probability, the P matrix must be positive definite. Equating the time derivative of this last expression with the expression for the current gives

$$(E_l - E_k)P_{lk} = (R(E_l)f,f) - (f, R(E_k)\, f). \tag{6}$$

The scalar product here indicates integration over the boundary. It can be shown by rather elementary arguments that all R as operators on functions on the boundary S are real and symmetric. Hence, the matrix with the general element

$$P_{lk} = (f, \frac{R(E_l) - R(E_k)}{E_l - E_k} f) \tag{7}$$

is positive definite, no matter how the energy values E_l, E_k are chosen and no matter how many such energy values were chosen, i.e., what the order of the matrix is. This is, however, the condition that

$$(f, R(E) f) = \sum_\lambda \frac{\gamma_\lambda{}^2}{E_\lambda - E} \tag{8}$$

have an expansion as given above, with positive $\gamma_\lambda{}^2$ and the fact that such an expansion exists for all f establishes our basic formula.[28]

The only point at which essential use was made of the non-relativistic nature of the underlying theory is where the expression for the current was given. However, a very similar derivation applies for much more general expressions for the current, such as are compatible with the theory of relativity. The only point at which the derivation treads on doubtful ground is where it assumes that the E_k are arbitrary, e.g., that they can be also negative. If negative E_k are excluded, the result becomes less specific and an integral over negative energy values may have to be added to the sum in the expression for R. This again duplicates Van Kampen's result. It follows that if one wishes to consider (2) to be a consequence of the "causality principle," it is necessary to make another physical assumption.

The assumption which appears most natural to me is that it is permissible to consider any constant potential to prevail in the external region and that the R_{st} in (1) remain the same, no matter what the values of these potentials are. Similar assumptions, involving semipermeable walls, etc., are familiar to us from thermodynamics but these assumptions can now be shown, by the general methods of statistical mechanics, never to lead to contradictions. Whether this will be true of the assumption of arbitrary constant potentials for the various possible reaction products remains to be seen.

[28] K. Loewner, *Math. Z.*, 38, 177 (1953). The considerations of this article have been simplified by E. P. Wigner and J. v. Neumann, *Ann. Math.*, 59, 418 (1954).

II
NUCLEAR ENERGY

8

Theoretical Physics in the
Metallurgical Laboratory of Chicago

Dr. Darrow has suggested that a short introduction may enhance the usefulness of the more specialized papers to be presented to the Society by members of the old Theoretical Physics group of the Metallurgical Laboratory (Plutonium Project). Because the presentation of these papers will have to be very brief and because some of our collaborators could not present abstracts in time for the meetings, I was most happy to follow our Secretary's invitation to summarize our work in general terms.

There were, during the period extending from about the middle of 1942 until about the middle of 1945, that is, for about three years, approximately twenty theoretical physicists assembled on the fourth floor of Eckart Hall who worked on those problems of chain reacting units which could be solved or at least attacked with the methods of theoretical physics. The membership of the group varied somewhat but I am happy to say, and do say it with a great deal of pride, that we formed a happy family and that I hardly remember a disagreement on nontechnical points.

Most of our work was on very urgent problems and only a small fraction of it will bear publication in scientific periodicals. Our group had to do a great deal of engineering work, so much so that the cal-

An address presented to the American Physical Society at the Chicago Meeting, June 22, 1946. Reprinted by permission from the *Journal of Applied Physics,* Vol. 17, No. 11 (November, 1946). Copyright 1946 by the American Institute of Physics.

culation of liquid flow rates became to be considered to be part of our responsibilities. We calculated more than one I-beam dimension, among similar matters, although we felt somewhat out of place when we did that. In addition, we had to maintain numerous contacts with the experimental groups and to take a lively interest in matters ranging from the fabrication and corrosion of aluminum tubes to the radioactivity induced in oxygen by neutron absorption. All this work was necessary and I do not hesitate to say in retrospect that our policy of assuming some of the functions which are usually reserved for engineers proved most useful. In the first place the Plutonium Project was not well provided with engineers in its early days—it had only two or three design engineers at the time when our plan for the W unit (which was later erected at Hanford) was virtually ready*; in the second place it was important, as in any new field such as that of chain reacting units was in 1942, that there be at least a few people who are sufficiently familiar with the whole picture to know about every difficulty and how it may be overcome. This second point will be very important in connection with Dr. Daniels' pile which is to be erected at Clinton. I fear that the present arrangement, which gives those who are mainly interested in this pile even less responsibility than we had with respect to the W pile, will not help in meeting the time schedule which we read about in the newspapers. That time schedule was quite optimistic in the first place and I do not believe that the pile will be in operation before 1948.

As I said, knowing all details of the W plan was our main function and it took up most of our time. Practically all senior members of the group participated in it in one form or another although most of the burden was carried by Messrs. Friedman, Ohlinger, Weinberg, and Young and Miss Way. In addition, in the second year, Mr. J. A. Wheeler was transferred to Wilmington to give direct help to the DuPont Company. While work on the W plans was our most important function in the first two years, at the same time it was the one which is least suitable for being reported in public. In later years, work on the power production occupied most of our interest. However, this subject, to which

---

* It may be interesting to remark that the date on the W report is January 9, 1943, and that it was issued just 42 days after the first nuclear chain reaction was experimentally established by E. Fermi and his collaborators (December 2, 1942). Of course, the relevant dimensions and sizes, etc., of the W pile had to be fixed much prior to that date, although, of course, they had to be verified experimentally later.

Mr. G. Young has contributed so decisively, is still restricted from public discussion, so that my report will deal, essentially, only with incidental studies which we have made. I shall deal with these under four headings:

1. Elementary theory of nuclear chain reactions.
2. More detailed theory of chain reactions.
3. Effect of radiation on matter.
4. Studies in theoretical physics.

I shall give an outline of our work in these fields in the above order.

Elementary Theory of Nuclear Chain Reactions

The great surprise about nuclear chain reactions was the ease with which they could be established. Szilard's paper of January 1940 already described a workable arrangement. Our own early work in this field was not based on Szilard's paper but on Fermi's work, the concepts of which are less intricate than Szilard's. Ideas similar to Fermi's were developed also by others, notably by v. Halban; moreover, the whole work was duplicated, apparently without any major deviation, by the German nuclear physicists.

In a chain reaction of the kind considered by us, uranium nuclei undergo fission and liberate neutrons. These neutrons are first fast but soon slowed down by the moderator which is carbon (graphite) in our case. After being slowed down, the neutrons still diffuse around for a period of time before being absorbed. Most of them are absorbed by uranium, which then undergoes fission and emits the neutrons of the next generation. The ratio of the number of neutrons in one generation to the number of neutrons of the preceding generation is called multiplication constant and was usually denoted by k. Fermi's theory divides the problem of multiplication constants and critical sizes into two parts. The first problem is the calculation of the multiplication constant in an infinite medium k_∞, which is usually referred to briefly as the multiplication constant. It depends only on the geometry and the materials of the chain reacting system and gives the ratio of the numbers of neutrons in successive neutron generations under the assumption that the same materials, arranged in the same geometry, extend all over infinite space.

The second problem is the calculation of a critical length which does not depend on the inner structure of the chain reacting unit but only on its size and shape. This critical length, or its reciprocal κ, permits one to calculate, from k_∞, the second kind of multiplication constant, k_{eff}. This gives the ratio of the numbers of neutrons in successive generations in a finite pile. This second kind of multiplication constant is, of course, the relevant one from a practical point of view. It depends not only on the materials and their arrangement into a lattice which determine k_∞, but depends also on the actual extension of the lattice, i.e., the size and shape of the pile. In a steadily running pile k_{eff} is always 1 and it exceeds 1 only when the power of the pile is increased, e.g., during startup, and then only very little. The k_{eff} is always smaller than k_∞ because in an actual, finite pile some of the neutrons of every generation diffuse out of the pile and do not contribute to the next generation. No such "leakage" exists in an infinite pile.

It would seem that only the effective multiplication constant has real significance but it turns out that the calculation of k_∞ is an almost necessary preliminary for the calculation of k_{eff}.

I will only sketch the calculation of k_∞ which is already given, in principle, in the Smyth report. In order to calculate the number of neutrons of the next generation produced by one neutron of the present generation, one may start at the birth of one neutron. This occurs in the uranium lumps and the neutron has, originally, considerable velocity. As a result, it will be able to induce fission not only in the U[235] nuclei but, what is more important because of their larger numbers, also in the U[238] atoms. Competing with this process are the process of inelastic scattering by U atoms by which the original neutrons may be slowed to a velocity below the fission threshold[1] of U[238], and the process of escape of the neutrons from the U lump into the moderator.

The importance of fast fission was recognized by Szilard and his collaborators. The rest of the factors making up k_∞ were all recognized before, and are contained also in Fermi's considerations.

Let us assume that the original neutron generates $\epsilon - 1$ further neutrons by fast fission. As Fermi has mentioned in his address to this meeting, $\epsilon - 1 \approx .03$, so that for every fission neutron there will be $\epsilon \approx 1.03$ neutrons just below the fission threshold. Most of these neutrons diffuse out into the moderator and are slowed down to thermal energies. Some

---

[1] Haxby, Shoupp, Stephens, and Wells, *Phys. Rev.*, 57, 1088A (1940); 58, 199A (1940).

of them occasionally enter the uranium and are absorbed there by one of the numerous resonance levels of the U^{238}. These absorptions do not lead to fission and constitute an actual loss of neutrons. The importance of this process had already been recognized by N. Bohr in 1940, and others. Only when the neutron has lost sufficient energy to be below the lowest resonance level of U^{238}—which is, according to data in the literature[2] at about 5 ev—is it safe from this fate. The probability that a neutron will escape resonance capture is usually denoted by p. It is a number smaller than 1. As a result of the resonance absorption, ϵp neutrons with an energy smaller than 5 ev will result from every original neutron.

The full description of the actual calculation of p would be too lengthy. Among all the processes which contribute to the chain reaction, the resonance absorption is the only one which was not really understood when we started our work. S. M. Dancoff and I were the ones who were most interested in the physical principles which determine the resonance absorption of macroscopic bodies, but ideas similar to ours were developed also by others. The actual calculation of p was described by R. F. Christy, A. M. Weinberg, and myself, although many others, including H. L. Anderson, contributed to it. The material constants necessary for the calculation were measured by Creutz, Jupnik, Snyder, and R. R. Wilson* in Princeton, and later by Mitchell's group at Indiana University.

We now have ϵp neutrons with an energy below the resonance levels of uranium. According to theory, they will be slowed down to thermal energies by the moderator. After that, they will be absorbed, some of them by the moderator and the impurities present in the pile, some of them by the uranium. Fermi denotes this last fraction by f so that, altogether, ϵpf thermal neutrons are absorbed by the uranium, giving

$$k_\infty = \epsilon pf\eta \tag{1}$$

secondary neutrons, η being the number of fission (fast) neutrons produced in the uranium per thermal neutron absorbed. The principles for the calculation of the "thermal utilization" f were established inde-

[2] H. L. Anderson, *Phys. Rev.*, 57, 566 (1940).
* See several articles in Volume 26 (1955) of *J. Appl. Phys.* (Note added with the proofs of this book.)

pendently by Fermi, Placzek, and our group. The formulae which we used were derived by Christy, Mrs. Monk, Plass, and myself in a way which is similar to the calculation of wave functions in metals by the cellular method.[3]

On the whole, the calculation of the multiplication constant for an infinite lattice is quite "straightforward" and one of the great surprises of the Plutonium Project was how easy it was. Mr. G. N. Plass and myself happened to be the ones who attempted to calculate the "optimal lattice" (i.e., the lattice with the highest k_∞) early in 1942. Although the physical constants were not known at that time too accurately, the dimensions we obtained (later incorporated in the first chain reacting unit) are now believed to give a k_∞ just $\frac{1}{2}$ percent short of the k_∞ of the real optimal lattice. We are quite convinced that any reasonably competent people would have arrived at the same results. In later years, computations of k_∞ were much facilitated by diagrams prepared for this purpose by Mrs. Monk and Mrs. Uchiyamada, under Professor Wheeler's direction. The calculation of k_∞ was extended to all sorts of lattices, containing heavy and ordinary water, etc. Most of this work was done by A. M. Weinberg and his collaborators, Mrs. Monk, Mr. Plass, Mrs. Uchiyamada, Mr. Stephenson, and others. Qualitatively, the results were quite similar for all systems considered.

In spite of this, the properties which make a lattice optimal are not very simple. One may note that it is good if the high energy neutrons remain in the uranium to give a high ϵ. On the other hand, it is best if the lower energy (resonance) neutrons keep out of the uranium as much as possible so that p may remain reasonably close to 1. Again, the thermal neutrons should return to the uranium to give a high f—as close to 1 as possible. These conflicting requirements determine the geometry of the optimal lattice, i.e., give the ratio of the amounts of moderator and uranium as well as the lattice constant. However, even relatively large deviations from the optimal dimensions do not decrease k_∞ to a very great extent.

The foregoing describes the calculation of k_∞. Although Fermi has given a method for calculating k_{eff} from k_∞, I will not give his method here but will turn to the more advanced theory which permits a direct calculation of k_{eff}.

[3] Cf., e.g., F. Seitz, *The Modern Theory of Solids* (New York: McGraw-Hill Book Company, Inc., 1940), Chap. IX.

More Detailed Theory of Chain Reactions

The more detailed theory of chain reactions should provide more accurate methods both for the calculation of k_∞ and for the calculation of k_{eff}. However, as far as k_∞ is concerned, only a few improvements were made. None of these improvements occurred in the calculation of ϵ and p; only one occurred in the calculation of f.

The behavior of "thermal" neutrons in a moderator-uranium lattice is far from simple. Evidently, it would take infinitely many collisions to establish real thermal equilibrium between the neutrons and the moderator, and in a well-designed lattice the neutrons will be absorbed by the uranium after a relatively small number of collisions. As a result, the energy spectrum of the neutrons will remain quite complex and their average energy will stay considerably above $\frac{3}{2}kT$. This average energy will be different even at different points of the lattice. The actual energy distribution will be influenced by the absorbing power of the material as well as by its moderating power. The latter is influenced in turn by the atomic weight of the moderator, by Fermi's chemical binding effect, and by the crystalline nature of the moderator, which gives a considerable anisotropy to the scattered (refracted) neutrons.

The only serious attempt to take these factors (excepting the crystal effect) into account is due to E. Teller and his collaborators, mainly N. Metropolis and P. Morrison. A more rigorous but much more formal attempt later by E. J. Wilkins and myself did not contribute much to the qualitative picture. Wick reported on Thursday about some work which he did on this problem. Teller's work gave, at least, an approximate measure for the difference in the effective temperature of the neutrons and the moderator. In spite of this we are far from having an adequate knowledge of the energy spectrum of the neutrons in a chain reacting unit.

Moreover, the problem of calculating f remains far from being simple even if the energy spectrum of the neutrons is known. It is, in fact, quite complicated even if one assumes that all the neutrons have the same energy. The reason for this is that the ordinary diffusion theory proves to be quite inadequate. G. Placzek carried out the most accurate calculations for the diffusion of monoenergetic neutrons. Some of his results were obtained also by German and Italian theorists[4] and pub-

[4] G. C. Wick, Z. *Physik*, 121, 702 (1943).

lished. Our work along this line was not pushed with much vigor because we were, perhaps, too well aware of the inadequacy of the model
which uses monoenergetic neutrons. Actually, there is evidence that the
errors in our primitive diffusion equations are quite substantial and in
the direction indicated by Placzek's work.

There is no relevant difference between the fast effect in a finite and
infinite lattice. However, the probability p that a neutron with an energy
just below fission threshold should become a thermal neutron is smaller
in a finite lattice than in an infinite one because, in addition to being captured by the uranium, some neutrons will be lost from a finite lattice
by "leaking" (diffusing) out of it. This leakage was calculated by Fermi
and his co-workers[5] even before fission was discovered. For a finite
lattice, their work gives

$$p_{\text{eff}} = p \exp(-\tau\kappa^2), \tag{2}$$

where τ is one-sixth the mean square distance, in an infinite lattice, between the point where the neutron originated and the point where it
becomes thermal. The quantity κ^2 is the ratio $-\Delta n/n$, where n is the
average of the neutron density over a lattice cell and will be discussed
presently.

According to (2) the effective p is smaller than it would be for the
constant n of an infinite lattice, i.e., for $\kappa = 0$. The leakage depends on
the "age" τ, which in its turn increases with increasing mean free path
of the neutrons in the moderator and with the number of collisions which
are necessary to slow down the neutrons to thermal energies. The quantity τ, and hence the leakage, is smallest in a water moderated pile and
much greater in a graphite moderated pile.

Just as the fraction of neutrons which are slowed down to thermal
energies in the pile is, because of the leakage, smaller in a finite than in
an infinite pile, so is the fraction of thermal neutrons absorbed by the
uranium decreased by the escape of some of the thermal neutrons from
the pile. The equation analogous to (2) is

$$f_{\text{eff}} = f(1 + L_p^2\kappa^2)^{-1}. \tag{3}$$

The significance of κ in (3) is the same as in (2), that of L_p^2 similar to
that of τ in (2): L_p^2 is one-sixth of the mean square distance in an infinite

[5] E. Fermi and F. Rasetti, *Ricerca Sci.*, 9, 472 (1938); G. Placzek, *Phys. Rev.*, 69, 423 (1946).

lattice between the point where the neutron becomes thermal and the point to which it has diffused when it gets absorbed. L_p is also called the diffusion length of thermal neutrons in the lattice because the n decreases with an exponential relaxation distance L_p,

$$n \sim \exp(-x/L_p), \tag{4}$$

in a region in which no thermal neutrons are produced. G. N. Plass showed, by means of a calculation which is similar to Bardeen's work[6] on metallic wave functions that

$$L_p{}^2 = L_m{}^2(1 - f) \tag{5}$$

is a very good approximation for L_p if L_m is the diffusion length in the pure moderator, without uranium lumps.

The condition that a lattice can maintain a chain reaction at a steady rate is that $k_{\text{eff}} = 1$, i.e., that

$$k_{\text{eff}} = \epsilon p_{\text{eff}} f_{\text{eff}} \eta = 1. \tag{6}$$

Using the expressions (2) and (3), this becomes

$$\epsilon p f \eta \exp(-\tau \kappa^2)(1 + L_p{}^2 \kappa^2)^{-1} = 1$$

or, by (1),

$$k_\infty = (1 + L_p{}^2 \kappa^2) \exp(\tau \kappa^2), \tag{7}$$

an equation essentially identical to one already obtained by Fermi.

This last equation can be considered to be an equation for κ which, in its turn, will be seen to depend only on the size and shape of the pile. Hence (7) gives us the size of a pile if its shape and internal structure, in particular its infinite multiplication constant k_∞, are given.

The connection between the quantity κ and the size and shape of the pile is established by the classical equation

$$\Delta n + \kappa^2 n = 0, \tag{8}$$

in which the average neutron density n is subject to the boundary condition that it vanish at the outer boundaries of the pile. It is well known that (8) allows a solution only for definite, discrete values of κ^2 which depend on the size and shape of the region on the boundary of which n has to vanish, i.e., on the size and shape of the pile. Only for the smallest of these κ^2 is n positive throughout, and this smallest κ^2 is the

---

[6] J. Bardeen, *Phys. Rev.*, 49, 653 (1936). Cf. also reference 3.

one which occurs in (7). Equation (8), so to say, gives an effective dimension κ^{-1} to every size and shape and (6) shows how this effective dimension affects the effective multiplication constant. If the κ of the pile, as defined by (8), is larger than the solution of (7), the pile is under critical, its effective multiplication constant smaller than 1. If the solution of (7) is larger than the κ satisfying (8), the pile is above critical.

The quantity n to which (8) applies is the average neutron density, the average to be taken over a cell. Evidently, an equation, applying to such an average as (8) does, can be accurate only if this average does not change too rapidly from cell to cell. The relation of the n of (8) to the actual neutron density is similar to the relation of the macroscopic density of bodies to their rapidly fluctuating density as given by their atomistic structure. The theory of Eq. (8) is therefore called the macroscopic pile theory while the quantities of Eqs. (1) to (7) are concepts of the microscopic pile theory. Actually, (8) is only the simplest equation of macroscopic pile theory; it applies if the spatial variation of the neutron density is independent of energy. This is an important particular case but does not hold in general. For instance, most control rods absorb only low energy, thermal neutrons. The surface of a control rod is, therefore, a boundary where the density of thermal neutrons vanishes. However, the density of fast neutrons does not vanish at the surface of the control rod and the densities of fast and of slow neutrons are not proportional any more. Problems of this nature call for more complicated equations than (8). The most important results toward the solutions of these problems are due to Messrs. F. L. Friedman, A. M. Weinberg, and J. A. Wheeler.

Even the simple Eq. (8) raises a number of interesting problems. If the shape of the pile is at all complicated—which is almost invariably the case if the chain reacting material is liquid—the solution of (8) could be obtained only by perturbation methods. Some of these show a remarkable similarity to the Rayleigh-Schrödinger method with which we are familiar from its application to quantum-mechanical problems. We owe many interesting results on (8) to Messrs. F. Murray, L. W. Nordheim, and H. Soodak.

A good part of the work in this connection is too special to be taken up in detail. Another part will be dealt with by the speakers following my address, so that I may close the subject of the calculation of multiplication constants and critical sizes. I would not like to do this before emphasizing that, in my opinion, a good deal of work remains to be done in this field. In particular, the behavior of "thermal" neutrons in the pile and the transition from fast to thermal energies require further clarification both from the experimental and from the theoretical side. But there remain interesting details to be worked out in almost any part of the theory. There are, also, some problems which have already commanded considerable attention but which I have not even touched. Chief among these is the change in the neutron densities with time if Eqs. (6), (7) are not exactly fulfilled and the pile is either below or above critical. Messrs. R. F. Christy, L. W. Nordheim, and J. E. Wilkins were particularly active in this field.

Effect of Radiation on Matter

The radiation densities, both γ and neutron, are higher in a plutonium producing pile than can be maintained outside the pile for extended periods. The effect of these radiations on the structure of materials was one of our early concerns from the theoretical point of view. The experimental work was carried out in the Chemistry Division. Dr. M. Burton reported at the Atlantic City meeting of the American Chemical Society about his, his collaborators', and Dr. J. Franck's work on the subject. On the theoretical side, M. Goldberger, R. S. Mulliken, and F. Seitz shared my interest in the subject, which still has some aspects about which we cannot talk freely.

Clearly, the collision of neutrons with the atoms of any substance placed into the pile will cause displacements of these atoms. If the substance is a chemical compound, the displacement will result in chemical changes which were, of course, investigated even before chain reacting units came into being and are summarized, e.g., in the booklet of Lind.[7] All these changes are much more intense in the pile, owing to the more intense radiation. But substantial effects can be expected in elementary substances also. The matter has great scientific interest because pile irradiation should permit the artificial formation of displacements in definite numbers and a study of the effect of these on thermal and electrical conductivity, tensile strength, ductility, etc., as demanded by theory. One may expect that studies of the solid state, particularly of

[7] Cf., e.g., S. C. Lind, *Chemical Effects of α Particles and Electrons* (New York: Chemical Catalogue Company, 1928).

the structure sensitive properties, will be greatly stimulated by the additional experimental facility given by the pile.

Before a final interpretation of the experimental results can be made, our knowledge of the ranges of low energy ions will have to be extended. It is on this subject that most of Messrs. Goldberger's and Seitz's work was concentrated and you will hear from them presently. A good deal of the rest of our work was speculation which will either be confirmed or refuted by future experiments.

Theoretical Physics

As I emphasized before, real theoretical physics was always somewhat of a stepchild. This situation hardly could be remedied in view of our many pressing obligations. We tried to free Mr. S. M. Dancoff as much as possible from the pressure of urgent work and he carried out several investigations which are of considerable general interest. There is only one other function which we did not permit to be pushed into the background and this was the problem of keeping tables of nuclear constants up to date. Mrs. Uchiyamada was in charge of these tables but she received a good deal of help from the Project Information Department, in particular from Mr. Goldsmith, who made a really brilliant contribution. We were happy to learn that these tables may be at least partially published soon.

The theoretical work of the group fell into two categories; help with the evaluation and planning of experimental work, and real theoretical work. Into the first category falls the work of Messrs. Cahn, Schweinler, Weinberg, and others on the so-called pile oscillator. This is an instrument which permits an absorber of known or unknown neutron absorbing characteristics to be put into periodic motion in the pile. The oscillation of the neutron absorber causes intensity waves to spread all over the pile. These waves are similar to the temperature waves in the earth, generated by the daily and yearly heat fluctuations of the heat input on the earth's surface. The amplitude and wave-length of the waves permits one to evaluate the characteristics of the neutron absorbing oscillators and of properties of the pile.

The work on neutron diffraction received considerable attention on the part of Goldberger and Seitz. They interpreted and extended Wein-

stock's results[8] considerably and took into account phenomena not previously considered. Their work is being continued by Mr. M. Moshinsky
in Princeton. There is little need for my going into details on this question since Seitz and Goldberger will tell you about them presently.

As a last example, I would like to mention Dancoff's work on short
range α-particles. This work actually started because of some acute
problem which was practically forgotten by the time Dancoff took over.
He noticed that the intensity of short range α's is often anomalous in
the light of Gamow's theory,[9] which stipulates that the α-particle
leaves behind an excited residual nucleus. Dancoff investigated several
other mechanisms, among which the excitation of the residual nucleus
by the α-particle after it has already penetrated the potential barrier
seems to be the most important. These theoretical investigations have
now received added interest in view of Chang's[10] experimental results.
Chang has discovered Dancoff's mechanism independently. Dancoff will
tell you about this phase of his work in the afternoon.

I would not like to close my review of the work of our group without
expressing my sincere thanks to all members of the group for their most
unselfish and loyal cooperation. I have to extend my apologies to those
whose work I may have slighted. As I said before, we had a very concrete objective in mind during the course of the work and the most
important problems solved were not always the ones which now appear
most worth remembering. We have, however, encountered a good many
interesting problems, several of which will bear a great deal of further
study. A glimpse at these problems, together with the knowledge of the
importance of our aims, contributed a great deal to making the relations
within our group cordial.

[8] R. Weinstock, *Phys. Rev.*, 65, 1 (1944).

[9] Cf. G. Gamow, *Structure of Atomic Nuclei* (Oxford: Clarendon Press, 1937),
pp. 104 ff.

[10] W. Y. Chang, *Phys. Rev.*, 69, 60 (1946).

9

The Effects of Radiation on Solids

In the anxious days when atomic scientists were building the first chain-reacting pile in the "Metallurgical Laboratory" at the University of Chicago, one of the questions which worried us greatly was how the pile would be affected by its own radiation after it became active. On most of the other problems—the critical requirements for the chain reaction, controls, shielding, cooling—the physicists felt fairly confident of their calculations. But the radiation question was full of uncertainties. It was known that exposure even to weak natural radioactivity could change the structure and properties of materials. What would happen to the uranium rods in the reactor under the disruptive forces of intense neutron radiation, nuclear fissions, and so on? More serious still, what would happen to the graphite moderator? Graphite was a part of the actual structure of the pile; unlike the uranium, it was not to be removed or replaced from time to time; and it was known to be subject to damage by radiation.

The group concerned with the future health of the new atomic "child" was so uncertain and pessimistic about the reactor's ability to survive radiation and other "diseases" that it reported: "It would be unscientific to claim a useful life longer than about 100 days." More than 50 times that period has now passed and nearly all the original reactors are still alive and operating. What we did not realize at the time was that graphite, as well as metal, has some ability to recover from radiation damage

Reprinted by permission from the *Scientific American*, Vol. 195, No. 2 (August, 1956). *Article written jointly with Frederick Seitz*.

—to heal its wounds, so to speak. Nevertheless, the effect of radiation on solids remains an important and absorbing study. It is still a major practical problem in the construction of reactors; besides this, it has become a valuable tool for fundamental research into the properties of solids. Research on radiation damage is now being carried on not only in the national laboratories of the Atomic Energy Commission but also at a number of universities and industrial laboratories. The AEC recently announced eight such research contracts totaling well over $250,000 a year. The program of study of radiation effects on solids has steadily grown both in magnitude and in scope.

Let us try to describe some of the facts we have learned about radiation damage. Metals and nonmetals react differently; we shall consider first the effects on a nonmetal—the graphite (crystalline carbon) commonly used as the moderator in a reactor. The neutrons released by uranium fission in a reactor have a kinetic energy of about one million electron volts. When a fast neutron strikes the nucleus of a carbon atom in the moderator, it transfers a substantial fraction of its kinetic energy to the atom, and the latter recoils from the impact. Since the carbon atom's recoil energy is much greater than the binding energy holding it in the crystal lattice (which is less than 10 electron volts), the atom is thrown out of its normal position. This results in two defects in the lattice: the dislodged atom occupies an interstitial space in the lattice (like a marcher out of his row in a parade), and it leaves behind a vacant site in the regular order.

The foregoing describes the direct effect of collisions between fast neutrons and atoms in the lattice. These collisions in themselves account for only a small part of the damage actually produced. A fast neutron dislodges about 60 carbon atoms, at most, before it is slowed to a harmless speed. It is the recoiling carbon atoms that produce most of the damage in the lattice. They have bulk as well as speed. The first carbon atom hit by a million-volt neutron, for example, recoils with an energy of about 150,000 electron volts. In effect it acts like a strong and husky man who decides to get out of a very crowded subway rather suddenly. It throws the other atoms to right and left until it reaches the end of its range, that is, until its energy is exhausted.

Now it develops that in the atomic world this series of events takes a turn which is the opposite of what one might expect if one thinks in terms of mechanical collisions. The charging atom creates more havoc

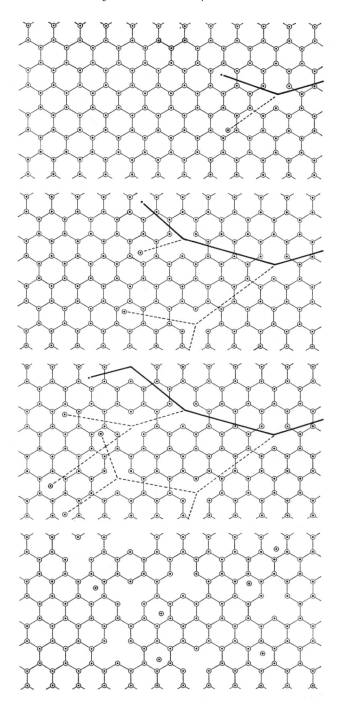

near the end of its rush than it does at the beginning. The reason is that we are dealing here with interatomic forces rather than what we usually think of as physical contact. As the fast-moving atom begins its dash through the crowd of surrounding atoms, its encounter with each one is too fleeting to permit much transfer of its momentum. It therefore dislodges only an occasional atom from its lattice position. But as the traveling atom slows down, the interatomic forces have more time to act, and it displaces more and more atoms. Finally, when it drops to a certain low velocity, it transfers its remaining energy to a local cluster of atoms. As a result the tiny local region suddenly heats up, sometimes to a temperature as high as 10,000 degrees centigrade. This phenomenon, called a "thermal spike" or "displacement spike," lasts only about one hundredth of a billionth of a second, but it may damage or deform the crystal.

Its effects are fairly complicated and not yet well understood. It appears that the minute "spike" region melts. Evidence of this melting has been found in radiation experiments on a carefully prepared alloy of copper and zinc. The atoms were arranged in a regular lattice in which each copper atom was surrounded by eight zinc atoms and *vice versa*. Bombardment of this crystal with neutrons was done at very low temperatures, near the temperature of liquid helium, in order to "freeze in" any changes in the crystal. Analyses afterward showed that the atoms had become mixed in a disordered way, and that most of the disordering must have taken place in regions of thermal spikes.

Besides melting, the heated regions expand. Such swelling causes deformations of the crystal, some of which presumably remain after the hot regions cool, so that the material around them is permanently distorted.

In a crystal damaged by radiation it is very difficult to distinguish how much of the damage is due to these spikes and how much to simple displacement of atoms. We can assume that spikes are a more impor-

---

Fig. 1 Lattice defects are produced when a neutron strikes a graphite crystal. The hexagonal crystal structure is represented diagrammatically in two dimensions. At top the neutron (black dot) has struck and dislodged a single atom. The next two drawings show how the process builds up, with both neutron and recoiling atoms acting to dislodge further atoms (neutron path is connected line; atom paths are broken lines). At bottom is the final result: a lattice with a number of vacant sites and "interstitial" atoms.

tant source of damage in metals than in graphite, because in the heavier elements recoiling atoms produce spikes at a higher energy level and therefore have a larger fraction of their energy left for producing them. In the case of graphite, the moving carbon atoms have used up most of their energy dislodging atoms before they drop to the low velocity at which they generate spikes. We can estimate that the most damaging part of the flight of recoil atoms in graphite is in the velocity range from 100,000 down to 10,000 electron volts.

It has become clear that radiation can produce a great variety of defects in the lattice, resulting in varying damage to the material.

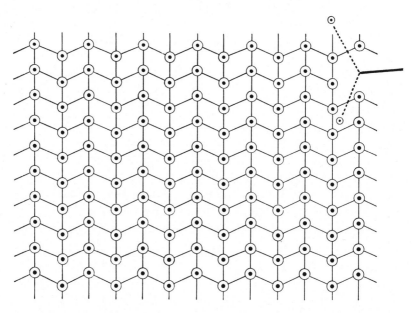

Fig. 2   Uranium lattice, also shown in two dimensions, suffers the same kind of damage as the carbon lattice, with an added complication. Sometimes the neutron is absorbed by the uranium nucleus, causing fission. The fission products may do more damage than neutrons.

In this account of the process that produces radiation damage in solids we have given most attention to graphite, but much of what we have said applies to the metal fuel in a reactor as well. The agent of damage is essentially the same: namely, flying particles. The principal difference is that in uranium the important bombarding particles are not neutrons but fission products. The heavy fission fragments hit atoms in the crystal lattice far harder than neutrons, and the atoms receive, on the average, about 1,000 times more energy. The damage is therefore much greater. In addition, the fission conversion of part of the uranium into other elements also weakens the metal. Fortunately metals are tough and can stand a lot, particularly if they do not have to stand it too long!

Let us consider now the recuperating powers of materials damaged by radiation. Usually, dislodged atoms attempt to return to something resembling their original positions in the lattice and to restore their original properties. We can investigate the recovery process best at low temperatures. If the damaged material is held at a temperature where the atoms can move around a bit, the interstitial atoms and vacancies will begin to recombine and the lattice distortion will heal. The crystal's properties then tend to return to normal. This is well illustrated by a study of the recovery of copper after it was irradiated near the temperature of liquid helium. The property measured was its conduction of electricity. Copper, which is a nearly ideal metal, recovers very rapidly if it is irradiated near room temperature; to "freeze in" all the damage and prevent recovery during irradiation it must be kept not far above absolute zero. Now when the temperature of the irradiated specimen is raised to about 35 degrees Kelvin, its electrical conductivity increases sharply. It is not yet known whether this abrupt and irreversible change, common to copper and many other metals, is a result of the reunion of vacancies and interstitial atoms which are very close to one another or whether it is due to healing of some of the distortion produced by thermal spikes. This is one of the critical questions being investigated at several laboratories.

It is interesting to note that each increase in temperature permits a little more of the damage to heal. This shows that there is a spectrum of different types of defects, some of which are more resistant to correction than others. We know that small traces of impurity atoms can have a significant influence on the rate of recovery. Some of the defects produced are so stable that one must heat the metals to temperatures nearly halfway to the melting point in order to remove them.

On the whole, pure metals are the most resistant of all materials to radiation damage and recover most easily, presumably because the atoms in metals are most mobile. But reactions like those in metals have

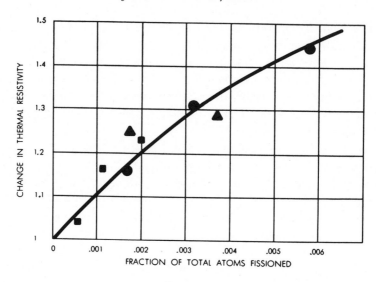

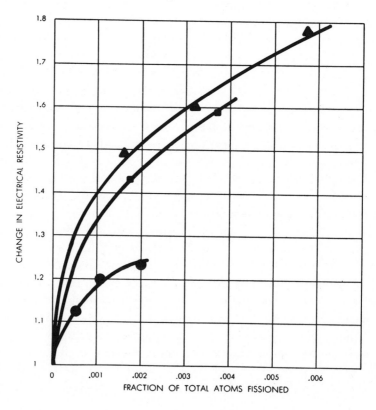

been found in valence compounds such as diamond, silicon, and germanium, and in simple salts and oxides such as sodium chloride and beryllium oxide. On the other hand, organic materials, particularly polymers such as plastics, are exceedingly sensitive to radiation and suffer permanent and irreparable changes. In these cases the damage is associated with the breaking of chemical bonds which are difficult to rejoin in the original way. Most polymers lose their ductility when given even moderate exposures. In brief, they behave in a way almost opposite to that of the metals.

From the practical standpoint, what are the types of damage—and the possible benefits—produced by radiation? As we have seen, the microscopic result of irradiation is the formation of lattice defects. How do these defects alter the properties of the material? There are four important kinds of predictable changes.

First, we know that properties such as conduction of electricity and heat depend on a regular and undistorted lattice. We are not surprised to find, then, that the conductivity of materials for both electricity and heat falls sharply with increasing irradiation [see Figs. 3 and 4]. Losses of conductivity up to 30-fold have been measured. Fortunately reactors do not rely too heavily on the heat conductivity of the moderator, and that of metals is less severely affected by radiation. Hence the decreases in conductivity do not cause real concern from the point of view of reactor operation. We must quickly add, however, that these changes do affect the instruments stuck into the reactor and must be taken into account in problems concerned with instrumentation.

The second type of radiation damage is represented by a loss of ductility. The lattice defects have the effect of blocking the glide planes of the crystals. Thus the materials behave as if work-hardened, and in fact may become brittle. This damage affects the handling of uranium

---

Fig. 3 Change in properties of uranium-aluminum alloys caused by fission of some of the uranium atoms was measured by D. S. Billington of Oak Ridge National Laboratory. The upper graph shows the increase in resistance to the flow of heat; the lower graph, the increase in resistance to electricity. Squares, circles, and triangles represent observations on alloys containing, respectively, 5.7, 15, and 17.2 per cent uranium by weight. The vertical scales give the ratio of final to initial value. Thus the upper graph shows that when two thousandths of the atoms have split, the thermal resistivity is 1.2 times its normal value.

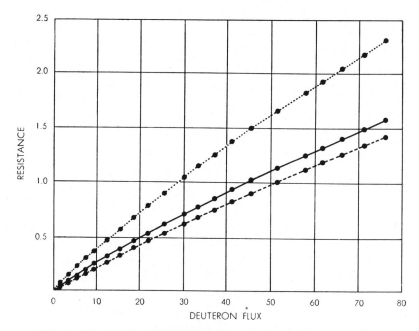

Fig. 4 Deuteron bombardment of copper (*broken curve*), silver (*solid curve*), and gold (*dotted curve*) increases the electrical resistance of these metals. The horizontal scale gives the number of particles, which have crossed each 10^{-15} square centimeters of cross section of the beam. The vertical scale shows the increase in resistance, measured in ten millionths of an ohm, of a one-centimeter cube. Measurements were made at 10 degrees above absolute zero.

fuel elements and is a major cause for concern. The changes in ductility can be spectacular. The effect was demonstrated in a U. S. atomic energy display at Geneva. Every few seconds a light ball was thrown alternately at two copper cylinders, which looked identical but differed in the fact that one had been exposed to the neutrons of the Oak Ridge reactor. The normal cylinder, when hit by the light ball, gave no sound. But the irradiated one sang like a tuning fork. We understand that no amount of normal cold-working could endow copper with as much rigidity as this irradiated specimen possessed.

These first two types of effects—on conductivity and ductility—are the most striking but not necessarily the most harmful changes caused by irradiation. From the point of view of reactor operation there are two others which have caused more anxiety.

One is a swelling of the material. The displacement of atoms to irregular positions in the lattice expands the crystals. Hence the volume of a block of material increases as the dosage of radiation increases. When the Materials Testing Reactor of the AEC in Idaho went into operation with its new beryllium oxide moderator, the moderator expanded about 1 per cent the first day. Fortunately this expansion did not proceed linearly with time: after 10 days it was much less than 10 per cent. Nevertheless, it can be very disconcerting to have to use as structural elements materials which change their dimensions after they are installed.

The other disquieting effect of radiation is an unstable energy situation. The interstitial atoms represent a considerable amount of stored energy. When they move back into vacancies in the lattice, they release this energy. The amount of sword-of-Damocles energy stored in this way can reach values up to hundreds of calories per mole (one gram multiplied by the molecular weight of the material). Obviously a sudden release of it could lead to unpleasant complications. On the other hand, this property also has constructive possibilities: some have suggested using irradiated graphite as a kind of storage battery.

We call the various effects mentioned "damage" because they change critical properties of materials that have been placed in reactors to perform definite functions based in part on these properties. The changes in properties are regarded as harmful not because they would not be useful under certain circumstances, but because they impair the behavior for which the material was selected. To minimize the effects of these changes in a reactor, it has been suggested that materials might be deliberately irradiated before they go into the reactor. This stratagem might yield materials with desired properties and stability against further irradiation.

Indeed, we can expect that irradiated materials will be put to more and more uses as understanding of their properties and potentialities grows. Graphite storage batteries and the superhardening of copper are only a beginning of the list of possibilities. We have scarcely scratched the surface of knowledge of the radiation-induced properties of materials.

Speaking as individuals who have been interested in radiation effects on solids since the conception of the first large reactors, we find it gratifying that a phenomenon which originated as a pure nuisance promises to provide us with useful information about the solid state in general and about many of the materials we use every day.

10

Atomic Energy

The years that have passed since the discovery of the nuclear chain reaction have not damped our high expectations in the future usefulness of atomic energy for peaceful pursuits. They have, furthermore, helped us to recognize, in addition to the size of this giant, its special skills. However, they have also helped us to realize, perhaps more clearly than we first did, that much hard and persevering work will be necessary before any of the benefits of atomic energy will be really ours.

During the period of abundance of the sources of energy which are now in use there will be two ways in which atomic energy can prove its significance. It may compete with our current sources of fossil energy and, second, it may open up new fields. As to the former, our industrial and even our everyday life has adapted itself to the possibilities of chemical fuels to a degree of which we are rarely conscious. The transition to a new source of energy would involve a reorientation of many methods of manufacturing and also cause a shift in the character of many of the commodities and services which industry can make available. It will not be easy, therefore, for atomic energy to woo away very much territory from the chemical fuels in the near future. Even if it did, its success along this line would be quite comparable with the success of the turbine—which is great, but not decisive for the over-all economic or social life.

Real success will therefore come to atomic energy in the near future only on the second path—by the discovery of new needs which atomic energy is able to satisfy better than existing sources can, by opening up

Reprinted by permission from *Science*, Vol. 108, No. 2811 (November 12, 1948).

new possibilities which it would be difficult or even impossible to realize with the sources of energy which are now in use. This task atomic energy has not yet achieved or even tackled. In fact, research on nuclear energy has to be so sheltered and separated from other industrial and economic problems that it will require extraordinarily keen vision to discover those needs which it is particularly suited to satisfy.

TABLE 1

Source	Coal	Oil	Atomic energy	Solar energy
Energy available in U.S.A., in units of 10^{15} kcal	18,000	25 high-grade 300 low-grade	100 high-grade ores, 3×10^{10} very low-grade ores and rocks	20,000 per year
Consumption per year	3.6	2.5 high-grade 0.5 low-grade	?	
Investment per/kw power plant	$110		A total of $250 for both purposes	
Investment for producing 1 kjoule fuel/sec		$110 from high-grade $150 from low-grade sources		

Some time hence, when the currently used sources of energy will near exhaustion, the situation will be different. Then nuclear energy may become the savior of our abundant life. But even then, nuclear energy will not be the only one in the field; it will have to compete at least with solar energy, of which there is an immense abundance.

Table 1,[1] which I am sure you have seen before in this or another form but the contents of which are well kept in mind, illustrates this situation.

[1] The following publications were used to obtain the figures of Table 1: (a) V. M. Goldschmidt, "Geochemische Verteilungsgesetze der Elemente," *Norske Videnskaps Akademi i Oslo, Mat. Naturv. Klasse,* 1937; (b) Gale Young, "Power and Fuel Data," December, 1945 (unpublished); (c) C. A. Thomas et al., "Nuclear Power," Scientific Information Transmitted to the United Nations Atomic Energy Commission by the United States Representative, Vol. IV, September, 1946. Also, C. A. Thomas, "Non-Military Uses of Atomic Energy," *Chem. Eng. News,* 24, 2480 (1946), and J. B. Condliffe et al., "Atomic Energy: Its Future in Power Production," *Chem. Eng.,* 53, 125 (1946); (d) Gale Young, "The New Power," Chap. 4 in *One World or None* (New York: McGraw-Hill, 1946); (e) E. V. Murphree, "Natural Gas, Coal, Oil Shale as Sources of Liquid Fuels," *Oil and Gas J.,* April, 1948.

It gives, for the different energy resources—coal, oil, atomic energy, and sunshine—the magnitude of the reserves and the yearly consumption. With respect to coal we have enough for 5,000 years at the present consumption. The situation with respect to oil is more precarious. As to atomic energy, you see that there is not too much of it in the form of high-grade ores. The supply in low-grade ores is practically inexhaustible. The magnitude of the solar energy is obviously great.

There are three points in Table 1 which I want to emphasize particularly. First, the total amount of coal under the ground in the United States has somewhat less heat content than the United States receives as sunshine during a single year. The over-all situation for the whole earth is even worse. Paradoxical as it may sound, the sunshine which falls on an acre of land during a single year would have, in the form of coal, a value of about $5,000. Second, if we look a little further ahead than a few hundred years, the chemical sources of energy are surely insufficient, and some of the new sources of energy will have to be utilized. Only two such sources are now known: nuclear energy from low-grade ores and solar energy. The question to which of these belongs the future will probably be decided by the relative convenience with which these two sources of power can be utilized and by the magnitude of the effort needed to exploit low-grade ores, on the one hand, and to concentrate solar energy, on the other. The last point which I wish to make is that oil or gasoline consumption is, in spite of the higher price of this fuel, almost as great as that of coal. This shows that the price of fuel is not always the decisive consideration; its adaptability and concentration are often more important.

The figures of our table clearly show that coal and oil cannot remain very long the predominant fuels. Nuclear energy may eventually replace them, but the above figures do not do more than to leave this possibility open. As for the present, a number of independent studies show, first, that nuclear energy is on the verge of competing with coal and, second, that a cheapening of power may have a stimulating influence on our economy, which could go far beyond the direct benefits calculable on a dollar-and-cent basis. The stimulating influence on more backward countries may be even greater.[2]

[2] Cf. in particular John R. Menke, "Nuclear Fission as a Source of Power," and Jacob Marschak, Sam H. Schurr, and Philip Sporn, "Economic Aspects of Atomic Power," *The Special Papers of the Cowles Commission* (Chicago: University of Chicago Press, 1947). Also, Walter Isard, "Some Economic Implications of Atomic Energy," *Quart. J. Econ.*, 72, 202 (1948). I am also personally indebted to Prof.

My personal impression would be that the emphasis on the stimulation of economic life is perhaps somewhat exaggerated. A similar and even more intense stimulation could be expected from the easier availability of many other types of goods—for instance, ingredients of housing. On the other hand, it seems to me that most price estimates disregard the ability of a stationary power plant, to use the raw materials uranium and thorium not only to furnish heat and electricity but also to manufacture a pure fissionable material which is bound to occupy the role of a high-grade fuel (such as gasoline). The investment cost for nuclear energy, given in the last row, which militates so strongly against the economic attractiveness of nuclear energy, should be compared, therefore, not with the investment cost of a stationary power plant but with the joint investment costs of a power plant plus an oil refinery. This would improve considerably the economic attractiveness of atomic energy, while the first point I made would tend to decrease the importance of energy sources in general for our present economy. Perhaps even more important than these factors, which can be reduced to a dollar-and-cent basis, will be the relative convenience and safety with which the different types of plants can be operated. The full impact of the enormously dangerous radioactivity accompanying all nuclear energy operations is being felt increasingly, and the need of training a large number of people in new techniques involves an additional investment, the magnitude of which is difficult to estimate.

Let me now go over somewhat to the technical side, and, although this has been done on many occasions before, describe once more the broad features of the arrangements in which uranium can be used for the generation of energy.

Just as a single log cannot burn in our fireplace, in a similar way there is a minimum amount of uranium which is necessary to produce power. This minimum amount is called the critical amount. Once this critical amount is assembled in the so-called reactor space, it undergoes fission, and the energy of the fission fragments is converted into heat. This heat can be transferred by means of a heat transfer medium, which circulates through the reactor space, to a conventional heat engine.

Nothing could be simpler in principle than this, and there are only two problems which are not encountered in conventional engineering. These are the limitations of the heat transfer medium to substances

Marschak, Dr. Schurr, and their collaborators for communicating to me a vast amount of unpublished material.

which do not stop the chain reaction and the need to surround most of the equipment with a tight and thick shield. This shield has to protect the environment from the deadly radiation of the reactor and of the heat transfer medium which becomes radioactive within it.

The energy which can be liberated from uranium is about 3,000,000 times greater than that contained in the same mass of coal. The ratio is 10,000,000 if we add to the weight of coal the weight of oxygen which it needs for burning. This establishes the most important characteristic of uranium as a fuel: it is practically weightless. This is, of course, not true of the whole power-generating equipment. In particular, the weight of the shield in many, if not most, cases overbalances the saving in fuel weight. This is particularly true in small engines and when refueling is easy. A serious disadvantage of the nuclear fuel is, furthermore, that any accident which breaks the shield is likely to liberate a vast amount of radioactivity and thus develop into a calamity much beyond the calamity which may result from an accident in the operation of the conventional sources of power.

Primarily, nuclear energy appears as the kinetic energy of fission fragments. The velocity of these corresponds to a temperature of about 600,000,000,000° C, and one feels that it is a pity to degrade this high temperature to a pittance of a couple of thousand degrees. For this reason, a good deal of thought has been spent on methods for a direct utilization of the energy of fission. Electric, electromagnetic, thermoelectric, and chemical methods have been discussed in some detail.[3] To date, none of these methods has proved attractive, and it is at least temporarily conceded that the fission energy will have to be converted into heat at a tractable temperature before it is further utilized. For land-based power plants, in which the rejected heat can be easily discarded at a few hundred degrees, this is not a major disadvantage, since the efficiency in this case is already close to its optimal value if the prime heat is delivered above 1,000°. However, the need for converting the energy of the fission fragments into heat becomes more of a drawback if one tries to exploit the most outstanding feature of nuclear energy— its enormous concentration.

Figs. 1 and 2 show the by now conventional arrangements to generate power and thus illustrate what I have previously called the competitive uses of nuclear energy. In the arrangement of Fig. 1 the heat transfer

[3] Much of the material referred to remains unpublished. Cf., however, Marschak, Schurr, and Sporn, footnote 2.

medium first traverses the fissionable material through a number of channels, gathering up the heat generated, and then flows to a heat exchanger. In this heat exchanger the heat of the primary coolant is transferred to another medium which, in its turn, drives a turbine or a reciprocating engine. In the arrangement of Fig. 2 the primary coolant drives the turbine directly. This arrangement has fewer parts, but a larger shield than the former, and a turbine which is, because of the radioactivity of the primary coolant, inaccessible. It is not yet possible to say with certainty which of the two arrangements is more advantageous and under what conditions.

The time scale for the development of nuclear energy on a substantial scale naturally comes up at this point, but it is a question most difficult to answer. Our uncertainty concerning this point has its origin not only in our inability to answer several technical and scientific questions, but is caused, to an equal degree, by the circumstance that the answer is bound to depend on the strength of our desire to see nuclear energy prove itself soon, on our courage, and on our confidence in our technical judgment and foresight. In other words, the human element strongly enters the picture.

Disregarding this human element, M. H. L. Pryce gave a tentative

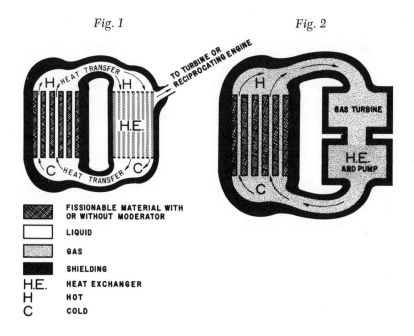

Fig. 1   *Fig. 2*

FISSIONABLE MATERIAL WITH OR WITHOUT MODERATOR

LIQUID

GAS

SHIELDING

H.E.   HEAT EXCHANGER
H   HOT
C   COLD

answer in a most thoughtful article in a recent issue of the *Bulletin of Atomic Scientists* (1948, 4, 245). He estimates that nuclear energy may begin to replace coal in about 30 years. The number 30 is uncertain,* but it is not likely to be less than 5 or more than a few hundred.

Let me now go over to the more speculative uses of nuclear energy. The high concentration of nuclear energy would seem to make it the ideal fuel for providing power for transportation. As long as one considers the most conventional types of transportation—land and sea routes—the rejection of part of the energy still remains a subordinate difficulty, and it is, in fact, in powering ships, in which the problem of radioactivity can be mastered more easily, that the first application of nuclear energy may come. In long-range aircraft, flying at high altitudes, the rejection of the waste heat is already much more difficult, unless one is willing to take higher temperatures of rejection into the bargain and thus reduce thermodynamic efficiency. If one considers, finally, travel outside the gravitational sphere of the earth, the problem of the rejection of waste heat becomes dominant.

In order to escape the gravitational field of the earth, one needs about 15,000 kcal/kg of escaping material. Since the energy content of a fissionable material is more than 1,000,000 times greater than this, the energy requirement is not, in itself, prohibitive even if one assumes a relatively low efficiency, η, for the process which furnishes the needed energy. However, for an efficiency, η, the waste heat amounts to $15,000 (1 - \eta) / \eta$ kcal/kg, and unless one can dispose of this, it will surely vaporize the body of the ship. As we discussed it before, the problem of elimination of the waste heat can easily be solved on the sea; it can also be solved in the air, but if the ship is to have power also outside the atmosphere, it can keep cool only either by throwing off hot parts or by radiation. The first alternative is the one discussed most commonly,[4] but it has definite limitations. Current opinion is that it may be barely sufficient to achieve the purpose: to raise a rocket off our planet. What runs out first is, characteristically, not the energy of the uranium but the hydrogen.

The second alternative, discarding the waste heat by radiation, also has clear limitations. The efficiency decreases very strongly if the time of ascent is much more than 1,000 sec. Taking this into account, one

---

* It now seems quite accurate. (Note added with the proofs of this book.)

[4] Cf., e.g., "Atomic Power for Airplanes and Rockets," article in the March, 1947, issue of *Atomic Information* based on L. Alvarez's address.

finds that, for a radiating temperature of 200° C, a radiating area of about 20 $(1 - \eta)/\eta$ m²/kg of the vessel is needed—a practical impossibility. For a radiating temperature of 1,000° C the radiating area becomes more manageable: about $0.4(1 - \eta)/\eta$m²/kg. At this temperature of the radiator, however, the thermodynamic efficiency is necessarily rather low in any conventional heat engine. This example shows again how problems of an apparently secondary nature can push themselves in a most disappointing fashion into the center of the picture.

Breaking the gravitational prison of the earth is so challenging a problem that I wanted to say a few words about it, even though it would be clearly premature to discuss it in detail. Furthermore, it is not the direction in which nuclear energy has so far proved itself most decisively. That field is indeed an application of nuclear energy in which a new need has been discovered. It is the procurement of research facilities for biology, chemistry, and physics by radioactive tracers, by new and more intense types of radiation. Even though this subject is the last one on my list, it is at present the most important one, and it is quite possible that it will maintain this position for a long time. The subject, which has received adequate treatment on several occasions,[5] lies outside the scope of our symposium. If we could divest ourselves from our admiration of the spectacular, we might easily find that the nuclear research facilities are for the present more important than nuclear energy. The success of the research they support is a more real and truly human need than is the need for additional energy and power.

However, there is good reason to look forward with confidence also to the more direct applications of nuclear energy. In order to be fully successful, these applications will require more of the undeviating interest which is so necessary for technical success but not enough of which they have received so far. They will surely receive this interest in the future, and we may hope that they will receive it from us—not only from our neighbors and children. And we may even dare to hope that the success may be so overwhelming that the first application of nuclear energy will appear just as insignificant, in comparison, as the first and still most efficient heat engine, the cannon, is in comparison with our generators of electricity and industrial power.

[5] See, for example, (a) M. D. Kamen, *Radioactive Tracers in Biology* (New York: Academic Press, 1947); (b) *The Use of Isotopes in Medicine and Biology* (Symposium Report) (Madison: University of Wisconsin Press, 1948); (c) various articles in *Nucleonics,* 1948.

11

Longer Range View of Nuclear Energy

It may be startling to realize that only about 3 per cent of the U.S.
national income is spent to furnish the energy we use. From this, it is
evident that no golden age can be created by reducing this expenditure
—not even by reducing it to nothing.

On the other hand, a substantial increase in the effort now necessary
to provide our energy requirements might be a serious calamity. Thus,
the true objective of reactor research may well be the preservation of
our present iron age. This point underlies the following discussion[1] of
whether reactor research ought to have as its primary aim the development of "burners" or of "breeders."

Breeders and Burners

Natural uranium contains only 0.7 per cent of the fissionable isotope
U-235. In "burners" (burner reactors) only this 0.7 per cent of the total
energy content of the uranium is utilized, and even this fraction cannot
be utilized completely. "Converter" reactors are somewhat more efficient; in their present-day embodiments, they produce enough plutonium to permit, in principle, the doubling of the energy content of the
U-235.

Breeder reactors, on the other hand, can convert virtually all of U-238

Reprinted by permission from the *Bulletin of the Atomic Scientists*, Vol. XVI, No.
10 (December, 1960). Copyright 1960 by the Educational Foundation for Nuclear
Science, Inc. *Article written jointly with Alvin M. Weinberg.*
[1] See also E. P. Wigner, *Acta Physica Austriaca*, 11, 410 (1958).

into fissionable plutonium, producing about 140 times more energy than burners, and 70 times more than low-conversion ratio reactors.

The breeder vs. burner argument, therefore, revolves around the question: How necessary is it to utilize the bulk of the energy content of uranium and thorium, and to what extent can we be satisfied with the utilization of a small fraction of this energy content. Throughout this article we will assume that the future energy economy will be based on fission, i.e., on the energy content of uranium and/or thorium. The discussion will also be based on the supply and consumption as they can be expected to develop in the United States. The conditions in most other parts of the world will probably become quite comparable to those in this country. Hence, it appears justifiable to base our conclusions on the conditions which we know best.

On the basis of these assumptions, the problem of breeder vs. burner reduces to the question of the supply of uranium (and thorium) available, vs. future energy requirements.

Supply and Demand of Uranium

The amount of uranium available, in the form of uranium oxide (U_3O_8), depends on the price one is willing to pay to obtain it. Thus, the cost of the energy obtained, whether from a burner, a converter, or a breeder, may depend on the cost of the uranium. This is shown in Table 1. The figures of this table are, of course, only estimates. This applies particularly to the magnitude of the supplies of more highly priced material, which should actually be tripled if breeders come into general use, because of the increased usability of thorium.

It may be mentioned at this point that the total coal reserves of the United States[2] amount to about 2×10^{12} tons, with an energy content of 50×10^{18} BTU. At present, about one-third of all the energy produced in the United States is derived from coal. The price of bituminous coal is about $4.50 per ton, giving a price of about 17¢ per 10^6 BTU. Even though used at present to a similar extent, the total energy content of the oil and gas supplies is much lower than that of coal. Furthermore,

---

[2] See, for instance, *Statistical Abstract of the U.S.*, 1957, Government Printing Office, Washington, D.C., pages 733 and 730; also Sam H. Schurr's statement before congressional subcommittee, *Reprint 14*, Resources for the Future, Inc., Washington, 1959.

about one-half of the total coal reserves can be obtained only at more than twice the present cost. Hence, if only fuel costing less than twice the present price is considered to be available, the total fossil fuel of the U.S. amounts to 25×10^{18} BTU (4 BTU are 1 kcal).

TABLE 1

Cost in $/lb.	10^6 tons U_3O_8	Cost in cents/10^6 BTU			Energy content in 10^{18} BTU		
		only U^{235}	low conv.	breeding	only U^{235}	low conv.	breeding
10	0.9	5.5	2.7	0.039	0.39	0.78	56
20	3.5	11	5.5	0.077	1.35	2.7	190
30	8	16.5	8.2	0.12	3.5	7	500
50	30	27	13.5	0.19	13	26	1850
100	80	55	27	0.39	35	70	5000

The second column gives the amount of U_3O_8 that is available at the price given in the first column. The data are based on *An Analysis of the Current and Long-Term Availability of Uranium and Thorium Raw Materials,* TID-8201, Technical Information Service, Atomic Energy Commission, and on Sornein's estimate (article in *The Industrial Challenge of Nuclear Energy,* Office of European Economic Cooperation, June, 1957) according to which the available amounts of uranium are roughly proportional to the square of the price one is willing to pay. This assumption is consistent with the data of the Technical Information Service. Furthermore, the numbers of Table 1 are very nearly equal to those given in a recent study by C. S. Starr and R. A. Laubenstein (*The Availability of Uranium for a Nuclear Power Industry,* Report AI-4945, Atomics International, 1960).

The cost of the fuel per unit amount of energy depends on the fraction of the fuel that is used. Hence, the price of the fuel in cents per million BTU, given in columns three, four, and five, is different for the three types of reactors considered. Column three refers to a pure burner, column four to a reactor with conversion ratio 0.5, column five to a breeder. The figures are somewhat optimistic because no fuel can be used completely. The last three columns give the total energy obtainable in the types of reactors just enumerated. The unit of energy is 10^{18} BTU (1 BTU = 0.252 kcal = 1,055 joules).

On the basis of Table 1, breeding appears to have an enormous advantage over burning. It must be remembered, however, that the price of the fuel is only one of the cost items of a reactor (around 20 per cent) and it is believed that, as a rule, the capital cost of a breeder may be higher than that of a burner. The present tendency to build burners clearly shows that it is at least *easier* to build a burner than a breeder. Finally, beyond a certain point, the reduction of the price of the fuel influences the cost of power very little.

Similarly, the need for energy has its limits and the availability of further energy in the form of fuel is, beyond a certain point, more of academic than of real interest.[3] On the other hand, the fact that the energy content of low-price uranium, used in a low-conversion reactor, is only a small fraction of the energy content of fossil fuels, appears most significant. This will become evident when the power requirements are discussed.

Future Power Requirements

The magnitude of the energy requirements will not be based on the production of electrical power for two reasons. First, the electrical power produced in the U.S. is less than 6 per cent of our total energy consumption. Even after making generous allowance for the relatively low thermal efficiency of the production of electrical power, it is clear that it accounts for only a fraction of our energy requirements. Second, the energy requirements increase only slowly, whereas the increase in the production of electrical energy is relatively fast. The former slow increase can be expected to remain more nearly steady over extended periods of time. It may be worth noting, however, that the conclusions to be arrived at would be modified only little if the calculation were based on the electrical power production. In fact, at least for the more distant future, the calculation used here gives lower energy requirements.

The total energy consumption in the United States was 40×10^{15} BTU in 1955, and the consumption appears to double in a little less than 25 years.[4] Table 2 gives the total consumption in 10^{18} BTU estimated, on the basis of the permanence of this increase, up to the year 2080, when it will be about thirty times the 1955 level.

TABLE 2

Year	1980	2005	2030	2055	2080	
Cumulative consumption	1.6	4.7	11	23	48	$\times 10^{18}$ BTU

The objection may be raised that it is very dangerous to make any forecast for the distant future, and this objection is quite justified. Nevertheless, the figures of Table 2 seem to be the most reasonable ones—one

---

[3] See, however, Alvin M. Weinberg, *Physics Today*, 12, 18 (1959).
[4] Reference 2, page 526; also Sam. H. Schurr, *loc. cit.*

may even expect them to be underestimates.[5] They show, first, that the supply of fossil fuels (around 25×10^{18} BTU) should last for not more than 100 years. Serious local shortages are bound to develop much before. Second, they show that by the time there will be a real need for a substitute for the fossil fuels, low-conversion reactors would consume all the uranium supply of the country in about 25 years, as long as one does not wish to pay a higher price for the energy contained in uranium than one now pays for the energy contained in coal (line before last of Table 1). Hence, low-conversion-ratio reactors would provide only a stopgap for a short period when an urgent need for a new energy source will arise.[6]

On the contrary, the energy supply can be expected to be ample for many hundreds of years if uranium and thorium are used in a breeding cycle. The reason for this is not only that a pound of these materials gives about 70 times more energy if used in the breeding cycle; even more important is the fact that the exploitation of the ample supply of low concentration ores becomes possible without an increase in the price of the energy content of the fuel above the present price. As Table 1 shows, the cost of a certain amount of energy in the form of uranium remains about 140 times lower if this uranium is used in a breeding cycle, that is, completely, than if only the skim of it—the U-235— is used. The ratio is 70 against a low-conversion reactor. As a result, according to Sornein's rule, the amount obtainable at a given price is $140^2 = 20,000$ times greater than for burners, and $70^2 = 5,000$ times greater than for low-conversion-ratio converters. It is this disparity between both price and availability of energy, through the use of burners and of low-conversion reactors on the one hand, and breeders on the other, which induces so many students of these questions to emphasize the advantages of the breeders over the burners.

Why Develop Nuclear Power?

In view of the sufficiency of the fossil fuels for about 100 more years, one may doubt the present need for the development of any new source of energy. It should be pointed out, however, that the situation may be

[5] The picture presented in Palmer C. Putnam's book, *Energy in the Future* (Princeton, N.J.: Van Nostrand & Co., 1953), is much more pessimistic.

[6] This conclusion remains valid under the assumptions made in Palmer C. Putnam's book (reference 5).

rather worse than indicated, principally because fossil fuels are needed for many purposes other than energy production—for instance, for the reduction of iron ores. Hence, it would be irresponsible to exhaust the supply of fossil fuels to a very large extent. We must not forget that what we are after is the preservation of our iron age. This point has been brought out with particular clarity by G. Young; he even proposes the name "fossil organics" for coal, oil, and perhaps also for natural gas. As a result of these circumstances, the need for new energy sources may appear earlier than in a hundred years, even if the relatively low estimates of the energy requirements given in Table 2 should prove to be valid.

Second, the rapidity of our progress in science should not blind us to the fact that far-reaching changes in our methods of production continue to take a long time. Power plants, in particular, have a useful life of about 50 years, so that the conversion to nuclear economy will surely extend over a long period of time. It should not be forgotten, either, that all present thinking is directed toward replacing fossil fuels by fission energy in the electrical power industry; the problem of the replacement of fossil fuels for other purposes is still essentially untouched. As mentioned before, at present only a relatively small, though increasing, fraction of our energy is used for the generation of electricity.

Third, the transition to nuclear economy will be possible only if vast amounts of fissionable material will be available when needed. Some such fissionable material will come from isotope separation plants. However, the large inventories necessary for the huge nuclear fueled power industry of the future can be conveniently obtained only from breeders which produce fissionable material well ahead of the time when these materials will be needed for power production. In fact, several generations of breeders fueled by materials produced by earlier breeders will be necessary to produce the inventories for the critical period.

Need for Burners

There is, finally, a fourth and perhaps most important factor which renders a deliberate approach toward the use of fission energy imperative: the attendant production of vast amounts of radioactive materials. The storage and disposal of these materials will present many problems, the solution of which will have to be based on protracted practical experience. Not many mistakes can be allowed while the proposed solutions are tried out. If there were no other reasons for developing some nuclear power fast, the difficulty and urgency of the problem of the disposal of radioactive wastes would be an adequate reason.

There are, however, several other important reasons for producing nuclear power on a reasonable scale in the near future, and it is hoped that the present analysis will not be interpreted as a blanket rejection of the development and use of burners. Three of these reasons are most cogent from our point of view:

(*a*) As has been emphasized, it is quite uncertain whether the problems of the breeder will be solved by a frontal assault, or by successive improvements on burners.

(*b*) Nuclear power, even before it becomes economical on a large scale, will have many specialized applications in which it may be not only economical but almost irreplaceable. The Army Package Power Reactor may not fall into this latter category, but the nuclear batteries for rockets may. Once low-weight high-capacity batteries are easily available, many uses will be found for them.

(*c*) Burners will make it possible to tackle the waste disposal problem at an early date.

Conclusions

The preceding analysis suggests first, more emphasis on the search for a practical breeder; second, more emphasis on the improvement of the conversion ratio of burners; and third, more emphasis on solving the long-term waste disposal problem. As of today, nuclear energy for large power stations is uneconomical. Hence, it makes little difference whether it is very uneconomical. The large-scale use of money and of scientific manpower for the development of nuclear energy cannot be justified on the basis that it leads only to a small economical disadvantage. It can be justified only if it is directed toward the use of nuclear energy when it will be needed, and if the use of nuclear energy will indeed satisfy the need which will arise. This will be true only if breeders will be available. Short-term economic advantages, or rather, diminution of the disadvantages, are, in this connection, largely irrelevant.

III

EPISTEMOLOGY AND QUANTUM MECHANICS

12

The Problem of Measurement

Introduction

The last few years have seen a revival of interest in the conceptual foundations of quantum mechanics.[1] This revival was stimulated by the attempts to alter the probabilistic interpretation of quantum mechanics. However, even when these attempts turned out to be less fruitful than its protagonists had hoped,[2] the interest continued. Hence, after the subject had been dormant for more than two decades, we again hear discussions on the basic principles of quantum theory and the epistemologies that are compatible with it. As is often the case under similar

Reprinted by permission from the *American Journal of Physics,* Vol. 31, No. 1 (January, 1963).
[1] Some of the more recent papers on the subject are: Y. Aharonov and D. Bohm, *Phys. Rev.,* 122, 1649 (1961); *Nuovo Cimento,* 17, 964 (1960); B. Bertotti, *Nuovo Cimento Suppl.,* 17, 1 (1960); L. de Broglie, *J. Phys. Radium,* 20, 963 (1959); J. A. de Silva, *Ann. Inst. Henri Poincaré,* 16, 289 (1960); A. Datzeff, *Compt. Rend.,* 251, 1462 (1960); *J. Phys. Radium,* 21, 201 (1960); 22, 101 (1961); J. M. Jauch, *Helv. Phys. Acta,* 33, 711 (1960); A. Landé, *Z. Physik,* 162, 410 (1961); 164, 558 (1961); *Am. J. Phys.,* 29, 503 (1961); H. Margenau and R. N. Hill, *Progr. Theoret. Phys.,* 26, 727 (1961); A. Peres and P. Singer, *Nuovo Cimento,* 15, 907 (1960); H. Putnam, *Phil. Sci.,* 28, 234 (1961); M. Renninger, *Z. Physik,* 158, 417 (1960); L. Rosenfeld, *Nature,* 190, 384 (1961); F. Schlögl, *Z. Physik,* 159, 411 (1960); J. Schwinger, *Proc. Natl. Acad. Sci. U.S.,* 46, 570 (1960); J. Tharrats, *Compt. Rend.,* 250, 3786 (1960); H. Wakita, *Progr. Theoret. Phys.,* 23, 32 (1960); 27, 139 (1962); W. Weidlich, *Z. Naturforsch.,* 15a, 651 (1960); J. P. Wesley, *Phys. Rev.,* 122, 1932 (1961). See also the articles of E. Teller, M. Born, A. Landé, F. Bopp, and G. Ludwig in *Werner Heisenberg und die Physik unserer Zeit* (Braunschweig: Friedrich Vieweg und Sohn, 1961).
[2] See the comments of V. Fock in the *Max Planck Festschrift* (Berlin: Deutscher Verlag der Wissenschaften, 1958), p. 177, particularly Sec. II.

circumstances, some of the early thinking had been forgotten; in fact, a small fraction of it remains as yet unrediscovered in the modern literature. Equally naturally, some of the language has changed but, above all, new ideas and new attempts have been introduced. Having spoken to many friends on the subject which will be discussed here, it became clear to me that it is useful to review the standard view of the late "Twenties," and this will be the first task of this article. The standard view is an outgrowth of Heisenberg's paper in which the uncertainty relation was first formulated.[3] The far-reaching implications of the consequences of Heisenberg's ideas were first fully appreciated, I believe, by von Neumann,[4] but many others arrived independently at conclusions similar to his. There is a very nice little book, by London and Bauer,[5] which summarizes quite completely what I shall call the orthodox view.

The orthodox view is very specific in its epistemological implications. This makes it desirable to scrutinize the orthodox view very carefully and to look for loopholes which would make it possible to avoid the conclusions to which the orthodox view leads. A large group of physicists finds it difficult to accept these conclusions and, even though this does not apply to the present writer, he admits that the far-reaching nature of the epistemological conclusions makes one uneasy. The misgivings, which are surely shared by many others who adhere to the orthodox view, stem from a suspicion that one cannot arrive at valid epistemological conclusions without a careful analysis of the *process of the acquisition of knowledge*. What will be analyzed, instead, is only the type of information which we can acquire and possess concerning the external inanimate world, according to quantum-mechanical theory.

We are facing here the perennial question whether we physicists do not go beyond our competence when searching for philosophical truth.

[3] W. Heisenberg, *Z. Physik*, 43, 172 (1927); also his article in *Niels Bohr and the Development of Physics* (London: Pergamon Press, 1955); N. Bohr, *Nature*, 121, 580 (1928); *Naturwissen.*, 17, 483 (1929) and particularly *Atomic Physics and Human Knowledge* (New York: John Wiley & Sons, Inc., 1958).

[4] See J. von Neumann, *Mathematische Grundlagen der Quantenmechanik* (Berlin: Verlag Julius Springer, 1932), English translation (Princeton, N.J.: Princeton University Press, 1955). See also P. Jordan, *Anschauliche Quantentheorie* (Berlin: Julius Springer, 1936), Chapter V.

[5] F. London and E. Bauer, *La Théorie de l'observation en mécanique quantique* (Paris: Hermann et Cie., 1939); or E. Schrödinger, *Naturwissen.*, 23, 807 ff. (1935); *Proc. Cambridge Phil. Soc.*, 31, 555 (1935).

I believe that we probably do.[6] Nevertheless, the ultimate implications of quantum theory's formulation of the laws of physics appear interesting even if one admits that the conclusions to be arrived at may not be the ultimate truth.

The Orthodox View

The possible states of a system can be characterized, according to quantum-mechanical theory, by state vectors. These state vectors—and this is an almost verbatim quotation of von Neumann—change in two ways. As a result of the passage of time, they change continuously, according to Schrödinger's time-dependent equation—this equation will be called the equation of motion of quantum mechanics. The state vector also changes discontinuously, according to probability laws, if a measurement is carried out on the system. This second type of change is often called the reduction of the wavefunction. It is this reduction of the state vector which is unacceptable to many of our colleagues.

The assumption of two types of changes of the state vector is a strange dualism. It is good to emphasize at this point that the dualism in question has little to do with the oft-discussed wave-versus-particle dualism. This latter dualism is only part of a more general pluralism or even "infinitesilism" which refers to the infinity of noncommuting measurable quantities. One can measure the position of the particles, or one can measure their velocity, or, in fact, an infinity of other observables. The dualism here discussed is a true dualism and refers to the *two* ways in which the state vector changes. It is also worth noting, though only parenthetically, that the probabilistic aspect of the theory is almost diametrically opposite to what ordinary experience would lead one to expect. The place where one expects probability laws to prevail is the change of the system with time. The interaction of the particles, their collisions, are the events which are ordinarily expected to be governed by statistical laws. This is not at all the case here: the uncertainty in the behavior of a system does not increase in time if the system is left alone, that is, if it is not subjected to measurements. In this case, the properties of the system, as described by its state vector,

---

[6] This point is particularly well expressed by H. Margenau, in the first two sections of the article in *Phil. Sci.*, 25, 23 (1958).

change causally, no matter what the period of time is during which it is left alone. On the contrary, the phenomenon of chance enters when a measurement is carried out on the system, when we try to check whether its properties did change in the way our causal equations told us they would change. However, the extent to which the results of all possible measurements on the system can be predicted does not decrease, according to quantum-mechanical theory, with the time during which the system was left alone; it is as great right after an observation as it is a long time thereafter. The uncertainty of the result, so to say, increases with time for some measurements just as much as it decreases for others. The Liouville theorem is the analog for this in classical mechanics. It tells us that, if the point which represents the system in phase space is known to be in a finite volume element at one given time, an equally large volume element can be specified for a given later time which will then contain the point representing the state of the system. Similarly, the uncertainty in the result of the measurement of Q, at time 0, is exactly equal to the uncertainty of the measurement of $Q_t = \exp(-iHt/\hbar)Q_0 \exp(iHt/\hbar)$ at time t. The information which is available at a later time may be less valuable than the information which was available on an earlier state of the system (this is the cause of the increase of the entropy); in principle, the amount of information does not change in time.

Consistency of the Orthodox View

The simplest way that one may try to reduce the two kinds of changes of the state vector to a single kind is to describe the whole process of measurement as an event in time, governed by the quantum-mechanical equations of motion. One might think that, if such a description is possible, there is no need to assume a second kind of change of the state vector; if it is impossible, one might conclude, the postulate of the measurement is incompatible with the rest of quantum mechanics. Unfortunately, the situation will turn out not to be this simple.

If one wants to describe the process of measurement by the equations of quantum mechanics, one will have to analyze the interaction between object and measuring apparatus. Let us consider a measurement from the point of view of which the "sharp" states are $\sigma^{(1)}, \sigma^{(2)}, \cdots$. For these states of the object the measurement will surely yield the values $\lambda_1, \lambda_2,$

···, respectively. Let us further denote the initial state of the apparatus by a; then, if the initial state of the system was $\sigma^{(\nu)}$, the total system—apparatus plus object—will be characterized, before they come into interaction, by $a \times \sigma^{(\nu)}$. The interaction should not change the state of the object in this case and hence will lead to

$$a \times \sigma^{(\nu)} \rightarrow a^{(\nu)} \times \sigma^{(\nu)}. \tag{1}$$

The state of the object has not changed, but the state of the apparatus has and will depend on the original state of the object. The different states $a^{(\nu)}$ may correspond to states of the apparatus in which the pointer has different positions, which indicate the state of the object. The state $a^{(\nu)}$ of the apparatus will therefore be called also "pointer position ν." The state vectors $a^{(1)}, a^{(2)}, \cdots$ are orthogonal to each other —usually the corresponding states can be distinguished even macroscopically. Since we have considered, so far, only "sharp" states, for each of which the measurement in question surely yields one definite value, no statistical element has yet entered into our considerations.[7]

Let us now see what happens if the initial state of the object is not sharp, but an arbitrary linear combination $\alpha_1\sigma^{(1)} + \alpha_2\sigma^{(2)} + \cdots$. It then *follows* from the linear character of the quantum-mechanical equation of motion (as a result of the so-called superposition principle) that the state vector of object-plus-apparatus after the measurement becomes the right side of

$$a \times [\textstyle\sum \alpha_\nu\sigma^{(\nu)}] \rightarrow \textstyle\sum \alpha_\nu[a^{(\nu)} \times \sigma^{(\nu)}]. \tag{2}$$

Naturally, there is no statistical element in this result, as there cannot be. However, in the state (2), obtained by the measurement, there is a statistical correlation between the state of the object and that of the apparatus: the simultaneous measurement on the system—object-plus-apparatus—of the two quantities, one of which is the originally measured quantity of the object and the second the position of the pointer of the apparatus, always leads to concordant results. As a result, one of these measurements is unnecessary: The state of the object can be ascertained by an observation on the apparatus. This is a consequence of the special form of the state vector (2), of not containing any $a^{(\nu)} \times \sigma^{(\mu)}$ term with $\nu \neq \mu$.

---

[7] The self-adjoint (Hermitean) character of every observable can be derived from Eq. (1) and the unitary nature of the transformation indicated by the arrow. Cf. E. Wigner, *Z. Physik*, 133, 101 (1952), footnote 2 on p. 102.

It is well known that statistical correlations of the nature just described play a most important role in the structure of quantum mechanics. One of the earliest observations in this direction is Mott's explanation of the straight track left by the spherical wave of outgoing α particles.[8] In fact, the principal conceptual difference between quantum mechanics and the earlier Bohr-Kramers-Slater theory is that the former, by its use of configuration space rather than ordinary space for its waves, allows for such statistical correlations.

Returning to the problem of measurement, we see that we have not arrived either at a conflict between the theory of measurement and the equations of motion, nor have we obtained an explanation of that theory in terms of the equations of motion. The equations of motion permit the description of the process whereby the state of the object is mirrored by the state of an apparatus. The problem of a measurement on the object is thereby transformed into the problem of an observation on the apparatus. Clearly, further transfers can be made by introducing a second apparatus to ascertain the state of the first, and so on. However, the fundamental point remains unchanged and a full description of an observation must remain impossible since the quantum-mechanical equations of motion are causal and contain no statistical element, whereas the measurement does.

It should be admitted that when the quantum theorist discusses measurements, he makes many idealizations. He assumes, for instance, that the measuring apparatus will yield some result, no matter what the initial state of the object was. This is clearly unrealistic since the object may move away from the apparatus and never come into contact with it. More importantly, he has appropriated the word "measurement" and used it to characterize a special type of interaction by means of which information can be obtained on the state of a definite object. Thus, the measurement of a physical constant, such as cross section, does not fall into the category called "measurement" by the theorist. His measurements answer only questions relating to the ephemeral state of a physical system, such as, "What is the x component of the momentum of this atom?" On the other hand, since he is unable to follow the path of the information until it enters his, or the observer's, mind, he considers the measurement completed as soon as a statistical relation has been established between the quantity to be measured and the state of some

8 N. F. Mott, *Proc. Roy. Soc.* (London), 126, 79 (1929).

idealized apparatus. He would do well to emphasize his rather special-ized use of the word "measurement."

This will conclude the review of the orthodox theory of measurement. As was mentioned before, practically all the foregoing is contained, for instance, in the book of London and Bauer.

Critiques of the Orthodox Theory

There are attempts to modify the orthodox theory of measurement by a complete departure from the picture epitomized by Eqs. (1) and (2). The only attempts of this nature which will be discussed here presuppose that the result of the measurement is not a state vector, such as (2), but a so-called mixture, namely, *one* of the state vectors

$$a^{(\mu)} \times \sigma^{(\mu)}, \tag{3}$$

and that this particular state will emerge from the interaction between object and apparatus with the probability $|\alpha_\mu|^2$. If this were so, the state of the system would not be changed when one ascertains—in some unspecified way—which of the state vectors (3) corresponds to the actual state of the system; one would merely "ascertain which of various pos-sibilities has occurred." In other words, the final observation only in-creases our knowledge of the system; it does not change anything. This is not true if the state vector, after the interaction between object and apparatus, is given by (2) because *the state represented by the vector (2) has properties which neither of the states (3) has.* It may be worth-while to illustrate this point, which is fundamental though often dis-regarded, by an example.

The example is the Stern-Gerlach experiment,[9] in which the projection of the spin of an incident beam of particles, into the direction which is perpendicular to the plane of the drawing, is measured. (See Fig. 1.) The index ν has two values in this case; they correspond to the two possible orientations of the spin. The "apparatus" is that positional co-ordinate of the particle which is also perpendicular to the plane of the drawing. If this coordinate becomes, in the experiment illustrated, positive, the spin is directed toward us; if it is negative, the spin is directed away from us. The experiment illustrates the statistical correla-

[9] The same experiment was discussed recently from another point of view by H. Wakita, *Progr. Theoret. Phys.*, 27, 139 (1962).

tion between the state of the "apparatus" (the position coordinate) and the state of the object (the spin) which we have discussed. The ordinary use of the experiment is to obtain the spin direction, by observing the position, i.e., the location of the beam. The measurement is, therefore, as far as the establishment of a statistical correlation is concerned, complete when the particle reaches the place where the horizontal spin arrows are located.

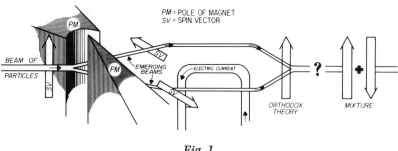

PM = POLE OF MAGNET
SV = SPIN VECTOR

BEAM OF PARTICLES

EMERGING BEAMS

ELECTRIC CURRENT

ORTHODOX THEORY

MIXTURE

Fig. 1

What is important for us, however, is the right side of the drawing. This shows that the state of the system—object-plus-apparatus (spin and positional coordinates of the particle, i.e., the whole state of the particle)— shows characteristics which neither of the separated beams alone would have. If the two beams are brought together by the magnetic field due to the current in the cable indicated, the two beams will interfere and the spin will be vertical again. This could be verified by letting the united beam pass through a second magnet which is, however, not shown on the figure. If the state of the system corresponded to the beam toward us, its passage through the second magnet would show that it has equal probabilities to assume its initial and the opposite directions. The same is true of the second beam which was deflected away from us. Even though the experiment indicated would be difficult to perform, there is little doubt that the behavior of particles and of their spins conforms to the equations of motion of quantum mechanics under the conditions considered. Hence, the properties of the system, object-plus-apparatus, are surely correctly represented by an expression of the form (2) which gives, *in this case*, properties which are different from those of *either* alternative (3).

In the case of the Stern-Gerlach experiment, one can thus point to a specific and probably experimentally realizable way to distinguish between the state vector (2), furnished by the orthodox theory, and the more easily visualizable mixture of the states (3) which one would offhand expect. There is little doubt that in this case the orthodox theory is correct. It remains remarkable how difficult it is, even in this very simple case, to distinguish between the two, and this raises two questions. The first of these is whether there is, in more complicated cases, a principle which makes the distinction between the state vector (2), and the mixture of the states (3), impossible. As far as is known to the present writer, this question has not ever been posed seriously heretofore, and it will be considered in the present discussion also only obliquely. The second question is whether there is a continuous transition between (2) and the mixture of states (3) so that in simpler cases (2) is the result of the interaction between object and measuring apparatus, but in more complicated and more realistic cases the actual state of object-plus-apparatus more nearly resembles a mixture of the states (3). Again, this question can be investigated within the framework of quantum mechanics, or one can postulate deviations from the quantum-mechanical equations of motion, in particular from the superposition principle.

"More complicated" and "more realistic" mean in the present context that the measuring apparatus, the state of which is to be correlated with the quantity to be measured, is of such a nature that it is easy to measure *its* states, i.e., correlate it with the state of another "apparatus." If this is done, the state of that second "apparatus" will be correlated also to the state of the object. The case of establishing correlations between the state of the apparatus which came into direct contact with the object and another "apparatus" is usually greatest if the first one is of macroscopic nature, i.e., complicated from the quantum-mechanical point of view. The ease with which the secondary correlations can be established is a direct measure of how realistically one can say that the measurement has been completed. Clearly, if the state of the apparatus which carried out the primary measurement is just as difficult to ascertain as the state of the object, it is not very realistic to say that the establishment of a correlation between its and the object's state is a fully completed measurement. Nevertheless, it is so regarded by the orthodox theory. The question which we pose is, therefore, whether it is consistent with the principles of quantum mechanics to assume that at the end of a realistic measurement the state of object-plus-apparatus is not a wavefunction, as given by (2), but a mixture of the states (3). We shall see that the answer is negative. Hence, the modification of the orthodox theory of measurement mentioned at the beginning of this section is not consistent with the principles of quantum mechanics.

Let us now proceed with the calculation. Even though this point is not usually emphasized, it is clear that, in order to obtain a mixture of states as a result of the interaction, the initial state must have been a mixture already.[10] This follows from the general theorem that the characteristic values of the density matrix are constants of motion. The assumption that the initial state of the system, object-plus-apparatus, is a mixture, is indeed a very natural one because the state vector of the apparatus, which is under the conditions now considered usually a macroscopic object, is hardly ever known. Let us assume, therefore, that the initial state of the apparatus is a mixture of the states $A^{(1)}$, $A^{(2)}$, $\cdots$, the probability of $A^{(\rho)}$ being p_ρ. The vectors $A^{(\rho)}$ can be assumed to be mutually orthogonal. The equations of motion will yield, for the state $A^{(\rho)}$ of the apparatus and the state $\sigma^{(\nu)}$ of the object, a final state

$$A^{(\rho)} \times \sigma^{(\nu)} \to A^{(\rho\nu)} \times \sigma^{(\nu)}. \tag{4}$$

Every state $A^{(1\nu)}$, $A^{(2\nu)}$, $\cdots$ will indicate the same state $\sigma^{(\nu)}$ of the object; the position of the pointer is ν for all of these. For different ν, however, the position of the pointer is also different. It follows that the $A^{(\rho\nu)}$, for different ν, are orthogonal, even if the ρ are also different. On the other hand, $A^{(\rho\nu)}$ and $A^{(\sigma\nu)}$, for $\rho \neq \sigma$, are also orthogonal because

---

[10] This point is disregarded by several authors who have rediscovered von Neumann's description of the measurement, as given by (1) and (2). These authors assume that it follows from the macroscopic nature of the measuring apparatus that if several values of the "pointer position" have finite probabilities [as is the case if the state vector is (2)], the state is necessarily a *mixture* (rather than a linear combination) of the states (3)—that is, of states in each of which the pointer position is definite (sharp). The argument given is that classical mechanics applies to macroscopic objects, and states such as (2) have no counterpart in classical theory. *This argument is contrary to present quantum-mechanical theory.* It is true that the motion of a macroscopic body can be adequately described by the classical equations of motion if its state has a classical description. That this last premise is, according to present theory, not always fulfilled, is clearly, though in an extreme fashion, demonstrated by Schrödinger's cat-paradox (cf. reference 5). Further, the discussion of the Stern-Gerlach experiment, given in the text, illustrates the fact that there are, in principle, observable differences between the state vector given by the right side of (2), and the *mixture* of the states (3), each of which has a definite position. Proposals to modify the quantum-mechanical equations of motion so as to permit a mixture of the states (3) to be the result of the measurement even though the initial state was a state vector, will be touched upon later.

$A^{(\rho\nu)} \times \sigma^{(\nu)}$ and $A^{(\sigma\nu)} \times \sigma^{(\nu)}$ are obtained by a unitary transformation from two orthogonal states, $A^{(\rho)} \times \sigma^{(\nu)}$ and $A^{(\sigma)} \times \sigma^{(\nu)}$ and the scalar product of $A^{(\rho\nu)} \times \sigma^{(\nu)}$ with $A^{(\sigma\nu)} \times \sigma^{(\nu)}$ is $(A^{(\rho\nu)}, A^{(\sigma\nu)})$. Hence, the $A^{(\rho\nu)}$ form an orthonormal (though probably not complete) system

$$(A^{(\rho\nu)}, A^{(\sigma\mu)}) = \delta_{\rho\sigma}\delta_{\nu\mu}. \tag{5}$$

It again follows from the linear character of the equation of motion that, if the initial state of the object is the linear combination $\sum \alpha_\nu \sigma^{(\nu)}$, the state of object-plus-apparatus will be, after the measurement, a mixture of the states

$$A^{(\rho)} \times \sum \alpha_\nu \sigma^{(\nu)} \to \sum_\nu \alpha_\nu [A^{(\rho\nu)} \times \sigma^{(\nu)}] = \Phi^{(\rho)}, \tag{6}$$

with probabilities p_ρ. This same mixture should then be, according to the postulate in question, equivalent to a mixture of orthogonal states

$$\Psi^{(\mu k)} = \sum_\rho x_\rho^{(\mu k)} [A^{(\rho\mu)} \times \sigma^{(\mu)}]. \tag{7}$$

These are the most general states for which the originally measured quantity has a definite value, namely λ_μ, and in which this state is coupled with some state (one of the states $\sum_\rho x_\rho^{(\mu\kappa)} A^{(\rho\mu)}$) with a pointer position μ. Further, if the probability of the state $\Psi^{(\mu k)}$ is denoted by $P_{\mu k}$, we must have

$$\sum_k P_{\mu k} = |\alpha_\mu|^2. \tag{7a}$$

The $x_\rho^{(\mu k)}$ will naturally depend on the α.

It turns out, however, that a mixture of the states $\Phi^{(\rho)}$ cannot be, at the same time, a mixture of the states $\Psi^{(\mu k)}$ (unless only one of the α is different from zero). A necessary condition for this would be that the $\Psi^{(\mu k)}$ are linear combinations of the $\Phi^{(\rho)}$, so that one should be able to find coefficients u so that

$$\sum_\rho x_\rho^{(\mu k)} [A^{(\rho\mu)} \times \sigma^{(\mu)}] = \Psi^{(\mu k)} = \sum_\rho u_\rho \Phi^{(\rho)}$$
$$= \sum_{\rho\nu} u_\rho \alpha_\nu [A^{(\rho\nu)} \times \sigma^{(\nu)}]. \tag{8}$$

From the linear independence of the $A^{(\rho\nu)}$ it then follows that

$$u_\rho \alpha_\nu = \delta_{\nu\mu} x_\rho^{(\mu k)}, \tag{8a}$$

which cannot be fulfilled if more than one α is finite. It follows that it is not compatible with the equations of motion of quantum mechanics to assume that the state of object-plus-apparatus is, after a measurement, a mixture of states each with one definite position of the pointer.

It must be concluded that *measurements which leave the system object-plus-apparatus in one of the states with a definite position of the pointer cannot be described by the linear laws of quantum mechanics.* Hence, if there are such measurements, quantum mechanics has only limited validity. This conclusion must have been familiar to many even though the detailed argument just given was not put forward before. Ludwig, in Germany, and the present writer have independently suggested that the equations of motion of quantum mechanics must be modified so as to permit measurements of the aforementioned type.[11] These suggestions will not be discussed in detail because they are suggestions and do not have convincing power at present. Even though either may well be valid, one must conclude that the only known theory of measurement which has a solid foundation is the orthodox one and that this implies the dualistic theory concerning the changes of the state vector. It implies, in particular, the so-called reduction of the state vector. However, to answer the question posed earlier: yes, there is a continuous transition between the state vector (2), furnished by orthodox theory, and the requisite mixture of the states (3), postulated by a more visualizable theory of measurement.[11]

What Is the State Vector?

The state vector concept plays such an important part in the formulation of quantum-mechanical theory that it is desirable to discuss its role and the ways to determine it. Since, according to quantum mechanics, all information is obtained in the form of the results of measurements, the standard way to obtain the state vector is also by carrying out measurements on the system.[12]

In order to answer the question proposed, we shall first obtain a for-

[11] See G. Ludwig's article "Solved and Unsolved Problems in the Quantum Mechanics of Measurement" (reference 1) and the present author's article "Remarks on the Mind-Body Question" in *The Scientist Speculates*, edited by I. J. Good (London: William Heinemann, 1962), p. 284, reprinted in this volume.

[12] There are, nevertheless, other procedures to bring a system into a definite state. These are based on the fact that a small system, if it interacts with a large system in a definite and well-known state, may assume itself a definite state with almost absolute certainty. Thus, a hydrogen atom, in some state of excitation, if placed into a large container with no radiation in it, will almost surely transfer all its energy to the radiation field of the container and go over into its normal state. This method of preparing a state has been particularly stressed by H. Margenau.

mula for the probability that successive measurements carried out on a system will give certain specified results. This formula will be given both in the Schrödinger and in the Heisenberg picture. Let us assume that n successive measurements are carried out on the system, at times $t_1, t_2, \cdots, t_n$. The operators of the quantities which are measured are, in the Schrödinger picture, $Q_1, Q_2, \cdots, Q_n$. The characteristic vectors of these will all be denoted by ψ with suitable upper indices. Similarly, the characteristic values will be denoted by q so that

$$Q_j \psi_\kappa{}^{(j)} = q_\kappa{}^{(j)} \psi_\kappa{}^{(j)} \tag{9}$$

The Heisenberg operators which correspond to these quantities, if measured at the corresponding times, are

$$Q_j{}^H = e^{iHt_j} Q_j e^{-iHt_j} \tag{10}$$

and the characteristic vectors of these will be denoted by $\varphi_\kappa{}^{(j)}$, where

$$\varphi_\kappa{}^{(j)} = e^{iHt_j} \psi_\kappa{}^{(j)} \qquad Q_j{}^H \varphi_\kappa{}^{(j)} = q_\kappa{}^{(j)} \varphi_\kappa{}^{(j)}. \tag{10a}$$

If the state vector is originally Φ, the probability for the sequence $q_\alpha{}^{(1)}$, $q_\beta{}^{(2)}, \ldots, q_\mu{}^{(n)}$ of measurement-results is the absolute square of

$$\left(e^{-iHt_1}\Phi, \psi_\alpha{}^{(1)}\right) \left(e^{-iH(t_2-t_1)} \psi_\alpha{}^{(1)}, \psi_\beta{}^{(2)}\right) \cdots$$
$$\left(e^{-iH(t_n-t_{n-1})} \psi_\lambda{}^{(n-1)}, \psi_\mu{}^{(n)}\right). \tag{11}$$

The same expression in terms of the characteristic vectors of the Heisenberg operators is simpler,

$$(\Phi, \varphi_\alpha{}^{(1)})(\varphi_a{}^{(1)}, \varphi_\beta{}^{(2)}) \cdots (\varphi_\lambda{}^{(n-1)}, \varphi_\mu{}^{(n)}). \tag{11a}$$

It should be noted that the probability is not determined by the n Heisenberg operators $Q_j{}^H$ and their characteristic vectors: the *time order* in which the measurements are carried out enters into the result essentially. Von Neumann already derived these expressions as well as their generalizations for the case in which the characteristic values $q_\alpha{}^{(1)}$, $q_\beta{}^{(2)}, \cdots$ have several characteristic vectors. In this case, it is more appropriate to introduce projection operators for every characteristic value $q^{(j)}$ of every Heisenberg operator $Q_j{}^H$. If the projection operator in question is denoted by $P_{j\kappa}$, the probability for the sequence $q_\alpha{}^{(1)}, q_\beta{}^{(2)}, \cdots,$ $q_\mu{}^{(n)}$ of measurement-results is

$$(P_{n\mu} \cdots P_{2\beta} P_{1\alpha} \Phi, P_{n\mu} \cdots P_{2\beta} P_{1\alpha} \Phi). \tag{12}$$

The expressions (11) or (11a) can be obtained also by postulating that the state vector became $\psi_\kappa^{(j)}$ when the measurement of $Q^{(j)}$ gave the result $q_\kappa^{(j)}$. Indeed, the statement that the state vector is $\psi_\kappa^{(j)}$ is only a short expression for the fact that the last measurement on the system, of the quantity $Q^{(j)}$, just carried out, gave the result $q_\kappa^{(j)}$. In the case of simple characteristic values the state vector depends only on the result of the last measurement and the future behavior of the system is independent of the more distant past history thereof. This is not the case if the characteristic value $q^{(j)}$ is multiple.

The most simple expression for the Heisenberg state vector, when the jth measurement gave the value $q_\kappa^{(j)}$, is, in this case,

$$P_{j\kappa} \cdots P_{2\beta} P_{1\alpha} \Phi, \tag{12a}$$

properly normalized. If, after normalization, the expression (12a) is independent of the original state vector Φ, the number of measurements has sufficed to determine the state of the system completely and a pure state has been produced. If the vector (12a) still depends on the original state vector Φ, and if this was not known to begin with, the state of the system is a mixture, a mixture of all the states (12a), with all possible Φ. Evidently, the measurement of a single quantity Q, the characteristic values of which are all nondegenerate, suffices to bring the system into a pure state though it is not in general foreseeable which pure state will result.

We recognize, from the preceding discussion, that the state vector is only a shorthand expression of that part of our information concerning the past of the system which is relevant for predicting (as far as possible) the future behavior thereof. The density matrix, incidentally, plays a similar role except that it does not predict the future behavior as completely as does the state vector. We also recognize that *the laws of quantum mechanics only furnish probability connections between results of subsequent observations carried out on a system.* It is true, of course, that the laws of classical mechanics can also be formulated in terms of such probability connections. However, they can be formulated also in terms of objective reality. The important point is that the laws of quantum mechanics can be expressed only in terms of probability connections.

Problems of the Orthodox View

The incompatibility of a more visualizable interpretation of the laws of quantum mechanics with the equations of motion, in particular the superposition principle, may mean that the orthodox interpretation is here to stay; it may also mean that the superposition principle will have to be abandoned. This may be done in the sense indicated by Ludwig, in the sense proposed by me, or in some third, as yet unfathomed sense. The dilemma which we are facing in this regard makes it desirable to review any possible conceptual weaknesses of the orthodox interpretation and the present, last, section will be devoted to such a review.

The principal conceptual weakness of the orthodox view is, in my opinion, that it merely abstractly postulates interactions which have the effect of the arrows in (1) or (4). For some observables, in fact for the majority of them (such as xyp_z), nobody seriously believes that a measuring apparatus exists. It can even be shown that no observable which does not commute with the additive conserved quantities (such as linear or angular momentum or electric charge) can be measured precisely, and in order to increase the accuracy of the measurement one has to use a very large measuring apparatus. The simplest form of the proof heretofore was given by Araki and Yanase.[13] On the other hand, most quantities which we believe to be able to measure, and surely all the very important quantities such as position, momentum, fail to commute with all the conserved quantities, so that their measurement cannot be possible with a microscopic apparatus. This raises the suspicion that the macroscopic nature of the apparatus is necessary in principle and reminds us that our doubts concerning the validity of the superposition principle for the measurement process were connected with the macroscopic nature of the apparatus. The oint state vector (2), resulting from a measurement with a very large apparatus, surely *cannot be distinguished* as *simply from a mixture* as was the state vector obtained in the Stern-Gerlach experiment which we discussed.[14]

A second, though probably less serious, difficulty arises if one tries to

[13] H. Araki and M. Yanase, *Phys. Rev.*, 120, 666 (1961); cf. also E. P. Wigner, *Z. Physik*, 131, 101 (1952).
[14] This point was recognized already by D. Bohm. See Section 22.11 of his *Quantum Theory* (Englewood Cliffs, New Jersey: Prentice-Hall, Inc., 1951).

calculate the probability that the interaction between object and apparatus be of such nature that there exist states $\sigma^{(\nu)}$ for which (1) is valid. We recall that an interaction leading to this equation was simply postulated as the type of interaction which leads to a measurement. When I talk about the probability of a certain interaction, I mean this in the sense specified by Rosenzweig or by Dyson, who have considered ensembles of possible interactions and defined probabilities for definite interactions.[15] If one adopts their definition (or any similar definition) the probability becomes zero for the interaction to be such that there are states $\sigma^{(\nu)}$ satisfying (1). The proof for this is very similar to that[16] which shows that the probability is zero for finding reproducing systems—in fact, according to (1), each $\sigma^{(\nu)}$ is a reproducing system. The resolution of this difficulty is presumably that if the system with the state vector a—that is, the apparatus—is very large, (1) can be satisfied with a very small error. Again, the large size of the apparatus appears to be essential for the possibility of a measurement.

The simplest and least technical summary of the conclusions which we arrived at when discussing the orthodox interpretation of the quantum laws is that these laws merely provide probability connections between the results of several consecutive observations on a system. This is not at all unreasonable and, in fact, this is what one would naturally strive for once it is established that there remains some inescapable element of chance in our measurements. However, there is a certain weakness in the word "consecutive," as this is not a relativistic concept. Most observations are not local and one will assume, similarly, that they have an irreducible extension in time, that is, duration. However, the "observables" of the present theory are instantaneous, and hence unrelativistic, quantities. The only exceptions from this are the local field operators and we know, from the discussion of Bohr and Rosenfeld, how many extreme abstractions have to be made in order to describe their measurement.[17] This is not a reassuring state of affairs.

---

[15] C. E. Porter and N. Rosenzweig, *Suomalaisen Tiedeakatemian Toimotuksia*, VI, No. 44 (1960); *Phys. Rev.*, 120, 1698 (1960); F. Dyson, *J. Math. Phys.*, 3, 140, 157, 166 (1962). See also E. P. Wigner, *Proceedings of the Fourth Canadian Mathematics Congress* (Toronto: University of Toronto Press, 1959), p. 174, reprinted in this volume.

[16] Cf. the writer's article in *The Logic of Personal Knowledge* (London: Routledge and Kegan Paul, 1961), p. 231, reprinted in this volume.

[17] N. Bohr and L. Rosenfeld, *Kgl. Danske Videnskab. Selskab, Mat.-fys. Medd.*, 12, No. 8 (1933); *Phys. Rev.*, 78, 194 (1950); E. Corinaldesi, *Nuovo Cimento*, 8, 494 (1951); B. Ferretti, *ibid.*, 12, 558 (1954).

The three problems just discussed—or at least two of them—are real. It may be useful, therefore, to re-emphasize that they are problems of the formal mathematical theory of measurement, and of the description of measurements by macroscopic apparatus. They do not affect the conclusion that a "reduction of the wave packet" (however bad this terminology may be) takes place in some cases. Let us consider, for instance, the collision of a proton and a neutron and let us imagine that we view this phenomenon from the coordinate system in which the center of mass of the colliding pair is at rest. The state vector is then, if we disregard the unscattered beam, in very good approximation (since there is only S-scattering present),

$$\psi(r_p, r_n) = r^{-1} e^{ikr} w(r), \tag{13}$$

where $r = |r_p - r_n|$ is the distance of the two particles and $w(r)$ some very slowly varying damping function which vanishes for $r < r_0 - \tfrac{1}{2}c$ and $r > r_0 + \tfrac{1}{2}c$, where r_0 is the mean distance of the two particles at the time in question and c the coherence length of the beam. If a measurement of the momentum of one of the particles is carried out—the possibility of this is never questioned—and gives the result p, the state vector of the other particle suddenly becomes a (slightly damped) plane wave with the momentum $-p$. This statement is synonymous with the statement that a measurement of the momentum of the second particle would give the result $-p$, as follows from the conservation law for linear momentum. The same conclusion can be arrived at also by a formal calculation of the possible results of a joint measurement of the momenta of the two particles.

One can go even further[18]: instead of measuring the linear momentum of one particle, one can measure its angular momentum about a fixed axis. If this measurement yields the value $m\hbar$, the state vector of the other particle suddenly becomes a cylindrical wave for which the same component of the angular momentum is $-m\hbar$. This statement is again synonymous with the statement that a measurement of the said component of the angular momentum of the second particle certainly would give the value $-m\hbar$. This can be inferred again from the conservation law of the angular momentum (which is zero for the two

---

[18] See, in this connection, the rather similar situation discussed by A. Einstein, B. Podolsky, and N. Rosen, *Phys. Rev.*, 47, 777 (1935).

particles together) or by means of a formal analysis. Hence, a "contraction of the wave packet" took place again.

It is also clear that it would be wrong, in the preceding example, to say that even before any measurement, the state was a mixture of plane waves of the two particles, traveling in opposite directions. For no such pair of plane waves would one expect the angular momenta to show the correlation just described. This is natural since plane waves are not cylindrical waves, or since (13) is a state vector with properties different from those of any mixture. The statistical correlations which are clearly postulated by quantum mechanics (and which can be shown also experimentally, for instance in the Bothe-Geiger experiment) demand in certain cases a "reduction of the state vector." The only possible question which can yet be asked is whether such a reduction must be postulated also when a measurement with a macroscopic apparatus is carried out. The considerations around Eq. (8) show that even this is true *if* the validity of quantum mechanics is admitted for all systems.

13

Remarks on the Mind-Body Question

Introductory Comments

F. Dyson, in a very thoughtful article,[1] points to the everbroadening scope of scientific inquiry. Whether or not the relation of mind to body will enter the realm of scientific inquiry in the near future—and the present writer is prepared to admit that this is an open question—it seems worthwhile to summarize the views to which a dispassionate contemplation of the most obvious facts leads. The present writer has no other qualification to offer his views than has any other physicist and he believes that most of his colleagues would present similar opinions on the subject, if pressed.

Until not many years ago, the "existence" of a mind or soul would have been passionately denied by most physical scientists. The brilliant successes of mechanistic and, more generally, macroscopic physics and of chemistry overshadowed the obvious fact that thoughts, desires, and emotions are not made of matter, and it was nearly universally accepted among physical scientists that there is nothing besides matter. The epitome of this belief was the conviction that, if we knew the positions and velocities of all atoms at one instant of time, we could compute the fate of the universe for all future. Even today, there are adherents to this

Reprinted by permission from *The Scientist Speculates*, I. J. Good, ed. (London: William Heinemann, Ltd., 1961; New York: Basic Books, Inc., 1962).

[1] F. J. Dyson, *Scientific American*, 199, 74 (1958). Several cases are related in this article in which regions of inquiry, which were long considered to be outside the province of science, were drawn into this province and, in fact, became focuses of attention. The best-known example is the interior of the atom, which was considered to be a metaphysical subject before Rutherford's proposal of his nuclear model, in 1911.

view[2] though fewer among the physicists than — ironically enough — among biochemists.

There are several reasons for the return, on the part of most physical scientists, to the spirit of Descartes's *"Cogito ergo sum,"* which recognizes the thought, that is, the mind, as primary. First, the brilliant successes of mechanics not only faded into the past; they were also recognised as partial successes, relating to a narrow range of phenomena, all in the macroscopic domain. When the province of physical theory was extended to encompass microscopic phenomena, through the creation of quantum mechanics, the concept of consciousness came to the fore again: it was not possible to formulate the laws of quantum mechanics in a fully consistent way without reference to the consciousness.[3] All that quantum mechanics purports to provide are probability connections between subsequent impressions (also called "apperceptions") of the consciousness, and even though the dividing line between the observer, whose consciousness is being affected, and the observed physical object can be shifted towards the one or the other to a considerable degree,[4] it cannot be eliminated. It may be premature to believe that the present philosophy of quantum mechanics will remain a permanent feature of future physical theories; it will remain remarkable, in whatever way our future concepts may develop, that the very study of the external world led to the conclusion that the content of the consciousness is an ultimate reality.

It is perhaps important to point out at this juncture that the question concerning the existence of almost anything (even the whole external world) is not a very relevant question. All of us recognize at once how meaningless the query concerning the existence of the electric field in vacuum would be. All that is relevant is that the concept of the electric

---

[2] The book most commonly blamed for this view is E. F. Haeckel's *Welträtsel* (1899). However, the views propounded in this book are less extreme (though more confused) than those of the usual materialistic philosophy.

[3] W. Heisenberg expressed this most poignantly [*Daedalus,* 87, 99 (1958)]: "The laws of nature which we formulate mathematically in quantum theory deal no longer with the particles themselves but with our knowledge of the elementary particles." And later: "The conception of objective reality . . . evaporated into the . . . mathematics that represents no longer the behavior of elementary particles but rather our knowledge of this behavior." The "our" in this sentence refers to the observer who plays a singular role in the epistemology of quantum mechanics. He will be referred to in the first person and statements made in the first person will always refer to the observer.

[4] J. von Neumann, *Mathematische Grundlagen der Quantenmechanik* (Berlin: Julius Springer, 1932), Chapter VI; English translation (Princeton, N.J.: Princeton University Press, 1955).

field is useful for communicating our ideas and for our own thinking. The statement that it "exists" means only that: (*a*) it can be measured, hence uniquely defined, and (*b*) that its knowledge is useful for understanding past phenomena and in helping to foresee further events. It can be made part of the *Weltbild*. This observation may well be kept in mind during the ensuing discussion of the quantum mechanical description of the external world.

The Language of Quantum Mechanics

The present and the next sections try to describe the concepts in terms of which quantum mechanics teaches us to store and communicate information, to describe the regularities found in nature. These concepts may be called the language of quantum mechanics. We shall not be interested in the regularities themselves, that is, the contents of the book of quantum mechanics, only in the language. It may be that the following description of the language will prove too brief and too abstract for those who are unfamiliar with the subject, and too tedious for those who are familiar with it.[5] It should, nevertheless, be helpful. However, the knowledge of the present and of the succeeding section is not necessary for following the later ones, except for parts of the section on the Simplest Answer to the Mind-Body Question.

Given any object, all the possible knowledge concerning that object can be given as its wave function. This is a mathematical concept the exact nature of which need not concern us here—it is composed of a (countable) infinity of numbers. If one knows these numbers, one can foresee the behavior of the object as far as it *can* be foreseen. More precisely, the wave function permits one to foretell with what probabilities the object will make one or another impression on us if we let it interact with us either directly, or indirectly. The object may be a radiation field, and its wave function will tell us with what probability we shall see a

[5] The contents of this section should be part of the standard material in courses on quantum mechanics. They are given here because it may be helpful to recall them even on the part of those who were at one time already familiar with them, because it is not expected that every reader of these lines had the benefit of a course in quantum mechanics, and because the writer is well aware of the fact that most courses in quantum mechanics do not take up the subject here discussed. See also, in addition to references 3 and 4, W. Pauli, *Handbuch der Physik*, Section 2.9, particularly page 148 (Berlin: Julius Springer, 1933). Also F. London and E. Bauer, *La Théorie de l'observation en mécanique quantique* (Paris: Hermann and Co., 1939). The last authors observe (page 41), "Remarquons le rôle essential que joue la conscience de l'observateur. . . ."

flash if we put our eyes at certain points, with what probability it will leave a dark spot on a photographic plate if this is placed at certain positions. In many cases the probability for one definite sensation will be so high that it amounts to a certainty—this is always so if classical mechanics provides a close enough approximation to the quantum laws.

The information given by the wave function is communicable. If someone else somehow determines the wave function of a system, he can tell me about it and, according to the theory, the probabilities for the possible different impressions (or "sensations") will be equally large, no matter whether he or I interact with the system in a given fashion. In this sense, the wave function "exists."

It has been mentioned before that even the complete knowledge of the wave function does not permit one always to foresee with certainty the sensations one may receive by interacting with a system. In some cases, one event (seeing a flash) is just as likely as another (not seeing a flash). However, in most cases the impression (e.g., the knowledge of having or not having seen a flash) obtained in this way permits one to foresee later impressions with an increased certainty. Thus, one may be sure that, if one does not see a flash if one looks in one direction, one surely does see a flash if one subsequently looks in another direction. The property of observations to increase our ability for foreseeing the future follows from the fact that all knowledge of wave functions is based, in the last analysis, on the "impressions" we receive. In fact, the wave function is only a suitable language for describing the body of knowledge—gained by observations—which is relevant for predicting the future behaviour of the system. For this reason, the interactions which may create one or another sensation in us are also called observations, or measurements. One realises that *all* the information which the laws of physics provide consists of probability connections between subsequent impressions that a system makes on one if one interacts with it repeatedly, i.e., if one makes repeated measurements on it. The wave function is a convenient summary of that part of the past impressions which remains relevant for the probabilities of receiving the different possible impressions when interacting with the system at later times.

An Example

It may be worthwhile to illustrate the point of the preceding section on a schematic example. Suppose that all our interactions with the system consist in looking at a certain point in a certain direction at times

$t_0, t_0 + 1, t_0 + 2, \cdot \cdot \cdot$, and our possible sensations are seeing or not seeing a flash. The relevant law of nature could then be of the form: "If you see a flash at time t, you will see a flash at time $t + 1$ with a probability $\frac{1}{4}$, no flash with a probability $\frac{3}{4}$; if you see no flash, then the next observation will give a flash with the probability $\frac{3}{4}$, no flash with a probability $\frac{1}{4}$; there are no further probability connections." Clearly, this law can be verified or refuted with arbitrary accuracy by a sufficiently long series of observations. The wave function in such a case depends only on the last observation and may be ψ_1 if a flash has been seen at the last interaction, ψ_2 if no flash was noted. In the former case, that is for ψ_1, a calculation of the probabilities of flash and no flash after unit time interval gives the values $\frac{1}{4}$ and $\frac{3}{4}$; for ψ_2 these probabilities must turn out to be $\frac{3}{4}$ and $\frac{1}{4}$. This agreement of the predictions of the law in quotation marks with the law obtained through the use of the wave function is not surprising. One can either say that the wave function was invented to yield the proper probabilities, or that the law given in quotation marks has been obtained by having carried out a calculation with the wave functions, the use of which we have learned from Schrödinger.

The communicability of the information means, in the present example, that if someone else looks at time t, and tells us whether he saw a flash, we can look at time $t + 1$ and observe a flash with the same probabilities as if we had seen or not seen the flash at time t ourselves. In other words, he can tell us what the wave function is: ψ_1 if he did, ψ_2 if he did not see a flash.

The preceding example is a very simple one. In general, there are many types of interactions into which one can enter with the system, leading to different types of observations or measurements. Also, the probabilities of the various possible impressions gained at the next interaction may depend not only on the last, but on the results of many prior observations. The important point is that the impression which one gains at an interaction may, and in general does, modify the probabilities with which one gains the various possible impressions at later interactions. In other words, the impression which one gains at an interaction, called also *the result of an observation*, modifies the wave function of the system. The modified wave function is, furthermore, in general unpredictable before the impression gained at the interaction has entered our consciousness: it is the entering of an impression into our consciousness which alters the wave function because it modifies our

appraisal of the probabilities for different impressions which we expect
to receive in the future. It is at this point that the consciousness enters
the theory unavoidably and unalterably. If one speaks in terms of the
wave function, its changes are coupled with the entering of impressions
into our consciousness. If one formulates the laws of quantum mechanics
in terms of probabilities of impressions, these are *ipso facto* the primary
concepts with which one deals.

It is natural to inquire about the situation if one does not make the
observation oneself but lets someone else carry it out. What is the wave
function if my friend looked at the place where the flash might show
at time t? The answer is that the information available about the *object*
cannot be described by a wave function. One could attribute a wave
function to the joint system: friend plus object, and this joint system
would have a wave function also after the interaction, that is, after my
friend has looked. I can then enter into interaction with this joint system
by asking my friend whether he saw a flash. If his answer gives me
the impression that he did, the joint wave function of friend + object
will change into one in which they even have separate wave functions
(the total wave function is a product) and the wave function of the
object is ψ_1. If he says no, the wave function of the object is ψ_2, i.e., the
object behaves from then on as if I had observed it and had seen no
flash. However, even in this case, in which the observation was carried
out by someone else, the typical change in the wave function occurred
only when some information (the *yes* or *no* of my friend) entered *my*
consciousness. It follows that the quantum description of objects is
influenced by impressions entering my consciousness.[6] Solipsism may
be logically consistent with present quantum mechanics, monism in
the sense of materialism is not. The case against solipsism was given at
the end of the first section.

The Reasons for Materialism

The principal argument against materialism is not that illustrated in
the last two sections: that it is incompatible with quantum theory. The

[6] The essential point is not that the states of objects cannot be described by means
of position and momentum co-ordinates (because of the uncertainty principle).
The point is, rather, that the valid description, by means of the wave function, is
influenced by impressions entering our consciousness. See in this connection the remark of London and Bauer, quoted above, and S. Watanabe's article in *Louis de
Broglie, Physicien et Penseur* (Paris: Albin Michel, 1952), p. 385.

principal argument is that thought processes and consciousness are the primary concepts, that our knowledge of the external world is the content of our consciousness and that the consciousness, therefore, cannot be denied. On the contrary, logically, the external world could be denied—though it is not very practical to do so. In the words of Niels Bohr,[7] "The word consciousness, applied to ourselves as well as to others, is indispensable when dealing with the human situation." In view of all this, one may well wonder how materialism, the doctrine[8] that "life could be explained by sophisticated combinations of physical and chemical laws," could so long be accepted by the majority of scientists.

The reason is probably that it is an emotional necessity to exalt the problem to which one wants to devote a lifetime. If one admitted anything like the statement that the laws we study in physics and chemistry are limiting laws, similar to the laws of mechanics which exclude the consideration of electric phenomena, or the laws of macroscopic physics which exclude the consideration of "atoms," we could not devote ourselves to our study as wholeheartedly as we have to in order to recognise any new regularity in nature. The regularity which we are trying to track down must appear as the all-important regularity—if we are to pursue it with sufficient devotion to be successful. Atoms were also considered to be an unnecessary figment before macroscopic physics was essentially complete—and one can well imagine a master, even a great master, of mechanics to say: "Light may exist but I do not need it in order to explain the phenomena in which I am interested." The present biologist uses the same words about mind and consciousness; he uses them as an expression of his disbelief in these concepts. Philosophers do not need these illusions and show much more clarity on the subject. The same is true of most truly great natural scientists, at least in their years of maturity. It is now true of almost all physicists—possibly, but not surely, because of the lesson we learned from quantum mechanics. It is also possible that we learned that the principal problem is no longer the fight with the adversities of nature but the difficulty of understanding ourselves if we want to survive.

[7] N. Bohr, *Atomic Physics and Human Knowledge*, section on "Atoms and Human Knowledge," in particular p. 92 (New York: John Wiley & Sons, 1960).

[8] The quotation is from William S. Beck, *The Riddle of Life, Essay in Adventures of the Mind* (New York: Alfred A. Knopf, 1960), p. 35. This article is an eloquent statement of the attitude of the open-minded biologists toward the questions discussed in the present note.

Simplest Answer to the Mind-Body Question

Let us first specify the question which is outside the province of physics and chemistry but is an obviously meaningful (because operationally defined) question: Given the most complete description of my body (admitting that the concepts used in this description change as physics develops), what are my sensations? Or, perhaps, with what probability will I have one of the several possible sensations? This is clearly a valid and important question which refers to a concept—sensations—which does not exist in present-day physics or chemistry. Whether the question will eventually become a problem of physics or psychology, or another science, will depend on the development of these disciplines.

Naturally, I have direct knowledge only of my own sensations and there is no strict logical reason to believe that others have similar experiences. However, everybody believes that the phenomenon of sensations is widely shared by organisms which we consider to be living. It is very likely that, if certain physico-chemical conditions are satisfied, a consciousness, that is, the property of having sensations, arises. This statement will be referred to as our first thesis. The sensations will be simple and undifferentiated if the physico-chemical substrate is simple; it will have the miraculous variety and colour which the poets try to describe if the substrate is as complex and well organized as a human body.

The physico-chemical conditions and properties of the substrate not only create the consciousness, they also influence its sensations most profoundly. Does, conversely, the consciousness influence the physico-chemical conditions? In other words, does the human body deviate from the laws of physics, as gleaned from the study of inanimate nature? The traditional answer to this question is, "No": the body influences the mind but the mind does not influence the body.[9] Yet at least two reasons can be given to support the opposite thesis, which will be referred to as the second thesis.

The first and, to this writer, less cogent reason is founded on the

[9] This writer does not profess to a knowledge of all, or even of the majority of all, metaphysical theories. It may be significant, nevertheless, that he never found an affirmative answer to the query of the text—not even after having perused the relevant articles in the earlier (more thorough) editions of the *Encyclopaedia Britannica*.

quantum theory of measurements, described earlier in sections 2 and 3. In order to present this argument, it is necessary to follow my description of the observation of a "friend" in somewhat more detail than was done in the example discussed before. Let us assume again that the object has only two states, ψ_1 and ψ_2. If the state is, originally, ψ_1, the state of object plus observer will be, after the interaction, $\psi_1 \times \chi_1$; if the state of the object is ψ_2, the state of object plus observer will be $\psi_2 \times \chi_2$ after the interaction. The wave functions χ_1 and χ_2 give the state of the observer; in the first case he is in a state which responds to the question "Have you seen a flash?" with "Yes"; in the second state, with "No." There is nothing absurd in this so far.

Let us consider now an initial state of the object which is a linear combination $\alpha \psi_1 + \beta \psi_2$ of the two states ψ_1 and ψ_2. It then *follows* from the linear nature of the quantum mechanical equations of motion that the state of object plus observer is, after the interaction, $\alpha (\psi_1 \times \chi_1) + \beta (\psi_2 \times \chi_2)$. If I now ask the observer whether he saw a flash, he will with a probability $|\alpha|^2$ say that he did, and in this case the object will also give to me the responses as if it were in the state ψ_1. If the observer answers "No"—the probability for this is $|\beta|^2$—the object's responses from then on will correspond to a wave function ψ_2. The probability is zero that the observer will say "Yes," but the object gives the response which ψ_2 would give because the wave function $\alpha (\psi_1 \times \chi_1) + \beta (\psi_2 \times \chi_2)$ of the joint system has no $(\psi_2 \times \chi_1)$ component. Similarly, if the observer denies having seen a flash, the behavior of the object cannot correspond to χ_1 because the joint wave function has no $(\psi_1 \times \chi_2)$ component. All this is quite satisfactory: the theory of measurement, direct or indirect, is logically consistent so long as I maintain my privileged position as ultimate observer.

However, if after having completed the whole experiment I ask my friend, "What did you feel about the flash before I asked you?" he will answer, "I told you already, I did [did not] see a flash," as the case may be. In other words, the question whether he did or did not see the flash was already decided in his mind, before I asked him.[10] If we accept this, we are driven to the conclusion that the proper wave func-

---

[10] F. London and E. Bauer (*op. cit.*, reference 5) on page 42 say, "Il [l'observateur] dispose d'une faculté caractéristique et bien familière, que nous pouvons appeler la 'faculté d'introspection': il peut se rendre compte de manière immédiate de son propre état."

tion immediately after the interaction of friend and object was already either $\psi_1 \times \chi_1$ or $\psi_1 \times \chi_2$ and not the linear combination $\alpha (\psi_1 \times \chi_1) + \beta (\psi_2 \times \chi_2)$. This is a contradiction, because the state described by the wave function $\alpha (\psi_1 \times \chi_1) + \beta (\psi_2 \times \chi_2)$ describes a state that has properties which neither $\psi_1 \times \chi_1$ nor $\psi_2 \times \chi_2$ has. If we substitute for "friend" some simple physical apparatus, such as an atom which may or may not be excited by the light-flash, this difference has observable effects and *there is no doubt that* $\alpha (\psi_1 \times \chi_1) + \beta \cdot (\psi_2 \times \chi_2)$ *describes the properties of the joint system correctly, the assumption that the wave function is either* $\psi_1 \times \chi_1$ *or* $\psi_2 \times \chi_2$ *does not.* If the atom is replaced by a conscious being, the wave function $\alpha (\psi_1 \times \chi_1) + \beta (\psi_2 \times \chi_2)$ (which also follows from the linearity of the equations) appears absurd because it implies that my friend was in a state of suspended animation before he answered my question.[11]

It follows that the being with a consciousness must have a different role in quantum mechanics than the inanimate measuring device: the atom considered above. In particular, the quantum mechanical equations of motion cannot be linear if the preceding argument is accepted. This argument implies that "my friend" has the same types of impressions and sensations as I—in particular, that, after interacting with the object, he is not in that state of suspended animation which corresponds to the wave function $\alpha (\psi_1 \times \chi_1) + \beta (\psi_2 \times \chi_2)$. It is not necessary to see a contradiction here from the point of view of orthodox quantum mechanics, and there is none if we believe that the alternative is meaningless, whether my friend's consciousness contains either the impression of having seen a flash or of not having seen a flash. However, to deny the existence of the consciousness of a friend to this extent is surely an

---

[11] In an article which will appear soon [*Werner Heisenberg und die Physik unserer Zeit* (Braunschweig: Friedr. Vieweg, 1961)] G. Ludwig discusses the theory of measurements and arrives at the conclusion that quantum mechanical theory cannot have unlimited validity (see, in particular, Section IIIa, also Ve). This conclusion is in agreement with the point of view here represented. However, Ludwig believes that quantum mechanics is valid only in the limiting case of microscopic systems, whereas the view here represented assumes it to be valid for all inanimate objects. At present, there is no clear evidence that quantum mechanics becomes increasingly inaccurate as the size of the system increases, and the dividing line between microscopic and macroscopic systems is surely not very sharp. Thus, the human eye can perceive as few as three quanta, and the properties of macroscopic crystals are grossly affected by a single dislocation. For these reasons, the present writer prefers the point of view represented in the text even though he does not wish to deny the possibility that Ludwig's more narrow limitation of quantum mechanics may be justified ultimately.

unnatural attitude, approaching solipsism, and few people, in their hearts, will go along with it.

The preceding argument for the difference in the roles of inanimate observation tools and observers with a consciousness—hence for a violation of physical laws where consciousness plays a role—is entirely cogent so long as one accepts the tenets of orthodox quantum mechanics in all their consequences. Its weakness for providing a specific effect of the consciousness on matter lies in its total reliance on these tenets—a reliance which would be, on the basis of our experiences with the ephemeral nature of physical theories, difficult to justify fully.

The second argument to support the existence of an influence of the consciousness on the physical world is based on the observation that we do not know of any phenomenon in which one subject is influenced by another without exerting an influence thereupon. This appears convincing to this writer. It is true that under the usual conditions of experimental physics or biology, the influence of any consciousness is certainly very small. "We do not need the assumption that there is such an effect." It is good to recall, however, that the same may be said of the relation of light to mechanical objects. Mechanical objects influence light—otherwise we could not see them—but experiments to demonstrate the effect of light on the motion of mechanical bodies are difficult. It is unlikely that the effect would have been detected had theoretical considerations not suggested its existence, and its manifestation in the phenomenon of light pressure.

More Difficult Questions

Even if the two theses of the preceding section are accepted, very little is gained for science as we understand science: as a correlation of a body of phenomena. Actually, the two theses in question are more similar to existence theorems of mathematics than to methods of construction of solutions and we cannot help but feel somewhat helpless as we ask the much more difficult question: how could the two theses be verified experimentally? i.e., how could a body of phenomena be built around them. It seems that there is no solid guide to help in answering this question and one either has to admit to full ignorance or to engage in speculations.

Before turning to the question of the preceding paragraph, let us note in which way the consciousnesses are related to each other and to the physical world. The relations in question again show a remarkable similarity to the relation of light quanta to each other and to the material bodies with which mechanics deals. Light quanta do not influence each other directly[12] but only by influencing material bodies which then influence other light quanta. Even in this indirect way, their interaction is appreciable only under exceptional circumstances. Similarly, consciousnesses never seem to interact with each other directly but only via the physical world. Hence, any knowledge about the consciousness of another being must be mediated by the physical world.

At this point, however, the analogy stops. Light quanta can interact directly with virtually any material object but each consciousness is uniquely related to some physico-chemical structure through which alone it receives impressions. There is, apparently, a correlation between each consciousness and the physico-chemical structure of which it is a captive, which has no analogue in the inanimate world. Evidently, there are enormous gradations between consciousnesses, depending on the elaborate or primitive nature of the structure on which they can lean: the sets of impressions which an ant or a microscopic animal or a plant receives surely show much less variety than the sets of impressions which man can receive. However, we can, at present, at best, guess at these impressions. Even our knowledge of the consciousness of other men is derived only through analogy and some innate knowledge which is hardly extended to other species.

It follows that there are only two avenues through which experimentation can proceed to obtain information about our first thesis: observation of infants where we may be able to sense the progress of the awakening of consciousness, and by discovering phenomena postulated by the second thesis, in which the consciousness modifies the usual laws of physics. The first type of observation is constantly carried out by millions of families, but perhaps with too little purposefulness. Only very crude observations of the second type have been undertaken in the past, and all these antedate modern experimental methods. So far as it is known, all of them have been unsuccessful. However, every phenomenon is unexpected and most unlikely until it has been discovered—and some of them remain unreasonable for a long time after they have been discovered. Hence, lack of success in the past need not discourage.

[12] This statement is certainly true in an approximation which is much better than is necessary for our purposes.

Non-linearity of Equations as Indication of Life

The preceding section gave two proofs—they might better be called indications—for the second thesis, the effect of consciousness on physical phenomena. The first of these was directly connected with an actual process, the quantum mechanical observation, and indicated that the usual description of an indirect observation is probably incorrect if the primary observation is made by a being with consciousness. It may be worthwhile to show a way out of the difficulty which we encountered.

The simplest way out of the difficulty is to accept the conclusion which forced itself on us: to assume that the joint system of friend plus object cannot be described by a wave function after the interaction—the proper description of their state is a mixture.[13] The wave function is $(\psi_1 \times \chi_1)$ with a probability $|\alpha|^2$; it is $(\psi_2 \times \chi_2)$ with a probability $|\beta|^2$. It was pointed out already by Bohm[14] that, if the system is sufficiently complicated, it may be in practice impossible to ascertain a difference between certain mixtures, and some pure states (states which *can* be described by a wave function). In order to exhibit the difference, one would have to subject the system (friend plus object) to very complicated observations which cannot be carried out in practice. This is in contrast to the case in which the flash or the absence of a flash is registered by an atom, the state of which I can obtain precisely by much simpler observations. This way out of the difficulty amounts to the postulate that the equations of motion of quantum mechanics cease to be linear, in fact that they are grossly non-linear if conscious beings enter the picture.[15] We saw that the linearity condition led uniquely to the

[13] The concept of the mixture was put forward first by L. Landau, Z. *Physik*, 45, 430 (1927). A more elaborate discussion is found in J. von Neumann's book (footnote 4), Chapter IV. A more concise and elementary discussion of the concept of mixture and its characterisation by a statistical (density) matrix is given in L. Landau and E. Lifshitz, *Quantum Mechanics* (London: Pergamon Press, 1958), pp. 35-38.

[14] The circumstance that the mixture of the states $(\psi_1 \times \chi_1)$ and $(\psi_2 \times \chi_2)$, with weights $|\alpha|^2$ and $|\beta|^2$, respectively, cannot be distinguished in practice from the state $\alpha(\psi_1 \times \chi_1) + \beta(\psi_2 \times \chi_2)$, if the states χ are of great complexity, has been pointed out already in Section 22.11 of D. Bohm's *Quantum Theory* (New York: Prentice Hall, 1951). The reader will also be interested in Sections 8.27, 8.28 of this treatise.

[15] The non-linearity is of a different nature from that postulated by W. Heisenberg in his theory of elementary particles [cf., e.g., H. P. Dürr, W. Heisenberg, H. Mitter, S. Schlieder, K. Yamazaki, Z. *Naturforsch.*, 14, 441 (1954)]. In our case the equations giving the time variation of the state vector (wave function) are postulated to be non-linear.

unacceptable wave function $\alpha\,(\psi_1 \times \chi_1) + \beta\,(\psi_2 \times \chi_2)$ for the joint state. Actually, in the present case, the final state is uncertain even in the sense that it cannot be described by a wave function. The statistical element which, according to the orthodox theory, enters only if I make an observation enters equally if my friend does.

It remains remarkable that there is a continuous transition from the state $\alpha(\psi_1 \times \chi_1) + \beta(\psi_2 \times \chi_2)$ to the mixture of $\psi_1 \times \chi_1$ and $\psi_2 \times \chi_2$, with probabilities $|\alpha|^2$ and $|\beta|^2$, so that every member of the continuous transition has all the statistical properties demanded by the theory of measurements. Each member of the transition, except that which corresponds to orthodox quantum mechanics, is a mixture, and must be described by a statistical matrix. The statistical matrix of the system friend-plus-object is, after their having interacted ($|\alpha|^2 + |\beta|^2 = 1$),

$$\left|\left| \begin{matrix} |\alpha|^2 & \alpha\beta^* \cos\delta \\ \alpha^*\beta \cos\delta & |\beta|^2 \end{matrix} \right|\right|$$

in which the first row and column corresponds to the wave function $\psi_1 \times \chi_1$, the second to $\psi_2 \times \chi_2$. The $\delta = 0$ case corresponds to orthodox quantum mechanics; in this case the statistical matrix is singular and the state of friend-plus-object can be described by a wave function, namely, $\alpha(\psi_1 \times \chi_1) + \beta(\psi_2 \times \chi_2)$. For $\delta = \frac{1}{2}\pi$, we have the simple mixture of $\psi_1 \times \chi_1$ and $\psi_2 \times \chi_2$, with probabilities $|\alpha|^2$ and $|\beta|^2$, respectively. At intermediate δ, we also have mixtures of two states, with probabilities $\frac{1}{2} + (\frac{1}{4} - |\alpha\beta|^2 \sin\delta)^{1/2}$ and $\frac{1}{2} - (\frac{1}{4} - |\alpha\beta|^2 \sin^2\delta)^{1/2}$. The two states are $\alpha(\psi_1 \times \chi_1) + \beta(\psi_2 \times \chi_2)$ and $-\beta^*(\psi_1 \times \chi_1) + \alpha^*(\psi^2 \times \chi^2)$ for $\delta = 0$ and go over continuously into $\psi_1 \times \chi_1$ and $\psi_2 \times \chi_2$ as δ increases to $\frac{1}{2}\pi$.

The present writer is well aware of the fact that he is not the first one to discuss the questions which form the subject of this article and that the surmises of his predecessors were either found to be wrong or unprovable, hence, in the long run, uninteresting. He would not be greatly surprised if the present article shared the fate of those of his predecessors. He feels, however, that many of the earlier speculations on the subject, even if they could not be justified, have stimulated and helped our thinking and emotions and have contributed to re-emphasize the ultimate scientific interest in the question, which is, perhaps, the most fundamental question of all.

14

Two Kinds of Reality

The present discussion arose from the desire to explain, to an audience of non-physicists,[1] the epistemology to which one is forced if one pursues the quantum mechanical theory of observation to its ultimate consequences. However, the conclusions will not be derived from the aforementioned theory but obtained on the basis of a rather general analysis of what we mean by real. Quantum theory will form the background but not the basis for the analysis. The concept of the real to be arrived at shows considerable similarity to that of the idealist. As the title indicates, it is formulated as a dualism. It is quite possible that it will soon be rejected not only by the community of the philosophers but also by that of the scientists. If this should be the case, the attempt to derive an epistemology from physics will prove to have been premature. Naturally, the author hopes that this will not be the case because, quite apart from the quantum theoretical background, the concepts to be presented appear natural also as an outgrowth of common sense considerations. They have been arrived at by many (including Schrödinger) who did not accept the epistemology of quantum mechanics.

Disclaimer of Authority

The problems of the present inquiry have been grappled with by the keenest minds, and for much longer periods than the present writer has

Reprinted by permission from *The Monist,* Vol. 48, No. 2 (April, 1964).
[1] Conference at Marquette University, Summer 1961.

devoted to them. His only qualification for speaking about them is that he believes to represent the view at which most physicists would arrive if they were sufficiently pressed for their opinions on the subject. He realizes the profundity of his ignorance of the thinking of some of the greatest philosophers and is under no illusion that the views to be presented will be very novel. His hope is that they will appear sensible.

The discussion will be divided into two parts. The first part will describe two kinds of realities of very different characters. It is my conviction that the distinction to be made is valid and represents a large measure of consensus among physicists and perhaps even natural scientists. The second part of the discussion will be concerned with the relation of these two "realities" and will touch some of the thorniest problems which have puzzled each of us and which even the greatest philosophers have failed to solve completely. The second part of the discussion will not contain an attempt at the solution of these questions. It will be confined to the statement of some of the problems, and to questions as to what the prospect of their solution is and what such a solution would mean.

Even though it is not strictly relevant, it may be useful to give the reason for the increased interest of the contemporary physicist in problems of epistemology and ontology. The reason is, in a nutshell, that physicists have found it impossible to give a satisfactory description of atomic phenomena without reference to the consciousness. This had little to do with the oft rehashed problem of wave and particle duality and refers, rather, to the process called the "reduction of the wave packet." This takes place whenever the result of an observation enters the consciousness of the observer—or, to be even more painfully precise, my own consciousness, since I am the only observer, all other people being only subjects of my observations. Alternatively, one could say that quantum mechanics provides only probability connections between the results of my observations as I perceive them. Whichever formulation one adopts, the consciousness evidently plays an indispensable role.[2]

---

[2] This is not the proper place to give a detailed proof for this assertion since such a proof would have to be based on the mathematical formulation of quantum mechanics and more particularly on the superposition principle. It should suffice, therefore, to mention that the fact was pointed out with full clarity first by von Neumann (see Chapter VI of his *Mathematical Foundations of Quantum Mechanics*, [Princeton, N.J.: Princeton University Press, 1955], or the German original [Berlin: J. Springer, 1932]). It would not be difficult to mount a battery of authorities affirming the assertion of the text, the clearest being W. Heisenberg's statement: "The laws of

In outline, the situation is as follows. The interaction between the measuring apparatus and the system on which the measurement should take place (the *object* of the measurement) results in a state in which there is a strong statistical correlation between the state of the apparatus and the state of the object. In general, neither apparatus nor object is in a state which has a classical description. However, the state of the united system, apparatus plus object, is after the interaction such that only one state of the object is compatible with any given state of the apparatus. Hence, the state of the object can be ascertained by determining the state of the apparatus after the interaction has taken place between them. It follows that the measurement of the state of the object has been reduced to the measurement of the state of the apparatus. However, since the state of the apparatus has no classical description, the measurement of the state of the apparatus is, from the conceptual point of view, not different from the measurement on the original object. In a similar way, the problem can be transferred from one link of a chain to the next, and so on. However, the measurement is not completed until its result enters our consciousness. This last step occurs when a correlation is established between the state of the last measuring apparatus and something which directly affects our consciousness.[3] This last step is, at the present state of our knowledge, shrouded in mystery and no explanation has been given for it so far in terms of quantum mechanics, or in terms of any other theory.

It would be, in my opinion, not only premature but even foolhardy to draw far-reaching ontological conclusions from our present way of expressing the laws of inanimate nature—in terms of measurements as described above—just as foolhardy, though less absurd, than was the attempt to consider the materialistic philosophy to be established on

---

nature which we formulate mathematically in quantum theory deal no longer with the particles themselves but with our knowledge of the elementary particles" [*Daedalus*, 87, 99 (1958)]. In this writer's opinion, the most readable exposition of the epistemological implications of quantum mechanics is F. London and E. Bauer's *La Théorie de l'observation en mécanique quantique* (Paris: Hermann and Co., 1939). See also the writer's article on "The Problem of Measurement," *Am. J. Phys.*, 31, 6-15 (1963), particularly the section "What Is the State Vector?" (reprinted in this volume), and a forthcoming article by P. A. Moldauer.

[3] London and Bauer (*loc. cit.*, reference 2, page 40) say: "Il [l'observateur] dispose d'une faculté caractéristique et bien familière, que nous pouvons appeler la 'faculté d'introspection': il peut se rendre compte de manière, immédiate de son propre état." They could add that, from the point of view of quantum mechanics, the faculty in question is completely unexplained.

the basis of an earlier set of physical laws. We know far, far too little of the properties and the working of the consciousness to propose a philosophy on a scientific basis. In particular, the "reduction of the wave packet" enters quantum mechanical theory as a *deus ex machina,* without any relation to the other laws of this theory. Nevertheless, the fact that the laws of inanimate nature, at least at one stage of the development, could not be formulated without reference to the consciousness remains significant and provides a proper background for the rest of our discussion.

Two Kinds of Reality

It seems idle to think about the meaning of the existence of a material object which one has in one's hand, or can grasp at any minute. However, as a physicist, one is often confronted with more subtle questions of reality, and my point of departure will be such a question. Does a magnetic field in the vacuum exist? For many years, this was a burning question; it is now a forgotten one. Nevertheless, most of us physicists would answer the question in the affirmative. Then, if we analyze the meaning of the statement that a magnetic field exists in the vacuum, we find that the statement means for us that it is convenient to think of such a field, that it enters our calculations, that we can explain to others our calculations, and the conclusions resulting from these calculations, more easily if we may refer to the magnetic field, as given by Maxwell's equations, everywhere, even in interstellar space. The reality of the magnetic field in vacuum consists of the usefulness of the magnetic field concept everywhere; reality is in this case synonymous with the usefulness of the concept, both for our own thinking, and for communicating with others.[4]

One has to go but one step further to realize that the existence of a book which I am holding in my hand is of the same nature. The existence manifests itself in my inability to bring my fingers together, in my knowledge that I would hear a noise if I failed to press my fingers toward each other, in the possibility that I might open and read it. The book is a convenient expression for describing some of the sensations which I have and which codetermines further sensations which I could

[4] See P. W. Bridgman's article in *The Nature of Physical Knowledge* (Bloomington: Indiana University Press, 1960), page 20.

have myself or cause in others by acting in certain ways—for instance, by throwing the book at them. The only difference between the existence of the book and of the magnetic field in interstellar space is that the usefulness of the concept of the book is much more direct, both for guiding my own actions, and for communicating with other people. It appears that there exists only one concept the reality of which is not only a convenience but absolute: the content of my consciousness, including my sensations.[5]

It also follows from the preceding discussion that there are two kinds of reality or existence: the existence of my consciousness and the reality or existence of everything else. This latter reality is not absolute but only relative. In a gathering of physicists, the existence of the aforementioned magnetic field is an almost absolute one. If I were cast upon an island abounding with poisonous snakes and had to defend my life against them, the reality of the magnetic field in vacuum would fade, at least temporarily, into insignificance. What I am saying is that, excepting immediate sensations and, more generally, the content of my consciousness, everything is a construct, in the sense in which, for instance, Margenau uses this term,[6] but some constructs are closer, some farther, from the direct sensations.

The First Kind of Reality

It is profoundly baffling that the existence of the first kind of reality could ever be forgotten. Yet one finds even now serious articles which completely disregard it or even relegate its existence into the realm of wish-dreams. The only explanation that I can conceive for this is that mankind was, for a long time, engaged in an intense struggle for survival and everyone had to concentrate his attention on the external, inimical

[5] Dr. S. A. Basri made this same point at the conference which is reported on in the book cited in reference 4 (page 131). It appears from the discussion that he was not understood. However, the most eloquent statement of the prime nature of the consciousness with which this writer is familiar and which is of recent date is on page 2 of E. Schrödinger's *Mind and Matter* (Cambridge: Cambridge University Press, 1958): "Would it (the world) otherwise (without consciousness) have remained a play before empty benches, not existing for anybody, thus quite properly not existing?"

[6] H. Margenau, *The Nature of Physical Reality* (New York: McGraw-Hill Book Co., 1950), particularly Chapters 4 and 5. The first sentence of *Mind and Matter* (reference 5) reads: "The world is a construct of our sensations, perceptions, memories." See also page 44.

forces. We learned somehow that our consciousness is extinguished unless we undertake certain actions and these actions, and the preparation for them, claimed all our attention. *Primum vivere, deinde philosophare* is the old adage. The philosopher is also a man and he became a victim of the universal preoccupation with survival.

It is, at first, also surprising that biologists are more prone to succumb to the error of disregarding the obvious than are physicists. The explanation for this may be similar to the one advanced for the more general phenomenon: as a result of the less advanced stage of their discipline, they are so concerned with establishing *some* regularities in their own field that the temptation is great to turn their minds away from the more difficult and profound problems which need, for their solution, techniques not yet available. Yet, it is not difficult to provoke an admission of the reality of the "I" from even a convinced materialist if he is willing to answer a few questions, and I suspect that, if carefully analyzed and followed to its conclusions, his philosophy becomes the most solipsistic of all.

The fact that the first kind of reality is absolute, and the circumstance that we discuss the realities of the second kind much more, may lead to the impression that the first kind of reality is something very simple. We all know that this is not the case. On the contrary, the content of the consciousness is something very complicated and it is my impression that not even the psychologists can give a truly adequate picture of it. There always seems to be some single sensation or thought at the center of my attention, but there are other sensations which cast shadows on this center, as if they were just outside my field of vision. Then, there is my whole store of knowledge and recollections which can enter the center of my attention at any time; there are subconscious processes which can suddenly jump into the center of my attention, such as that I should have reconfirmed my reservation. There is then the truly subconscious, discovered in different contexts by Freud, by the great writers, and by Poincaré.[7] Hence, the nature of the first kind of reality is already quite complex and the inadequacy of our appreciation of its

[7] As to the writers' and poets' instinctive realization of many of Freud's recognitions, the reader may be interested in Freud's letters to A. Schnitzler, *Letters of Sigmund Freud* (New York: Basic Books, 1960), particularly letter 123. Poincaré's realization of the role of the subconscious is the basis of J. Hadamard's *The Psychology of Invention in the Mathematical Field* (Princeton, N.J.: Princeton University Press, 1949).

properties may be one of the most potent barriers against establishing the nature of universal realities at the present time. The writer would like to underline this paragraph three times.

A second point worth keeping in mind is the complexity of our perceptions, the fact that when they enter our upper consciousness they are already sophisticated translations of our primitive sensations. Thus, if we pass a STOP sign, what enters into our consciousness is not an octagonal table, with four small figures on it, the first snake-like, the second consisting of two perpendicular lines, etc., but simply a STOP sign. More strikingly, most people do not know what the face of their watch looks like, even though they "take in" several times a day what the watch tells them. The complexity of the perceptive process was commented upon also by Schrödinger. He observed that the routine operations of the mind are relegated to the subconscious and only the learning process becomes conscious. Whether or not this last observation is accurate, it is clear that the content of the consciousness is difficult to specify precisely, that it depends on the part of the consciousness to which one refers, and that the boundaries of the first kind of reality may not be sharply defined. It is even possible that only a limiting case of the first kinds of realities should be called "absolute."

The Second Kind of Reality

If we deny the absolute reality of objects such as a book or, rather, attribute to them a different type of reality from that of sensations, are we in any way in conflict with the fact that we continue to act as if these objects were real? I do not believe so, if we admit that the usefulness of the concept of objects is so great that it would be virtually suicidal to refuse using it, in one form or another. As far as reality is concerned, there is a sharp division between the reality of my consciousness—which is absolute—and the reality of objects, which ranges over a wide spectrum. In order to doubt the usefulness and hence the validity of thinking in terms of the existence of this book, it would be necessary to consider extravagant improbabilities as, for instance, that I am now asleep. If I were, the book would be only part of my dream, and it could fade away as objects often do in a dream. In order to doubt the existence of—that is, the usefulness of assuming—a magnetic field where there is no matter, no such improbable circumstances need be assumed. One may not be interested in the way in which light from the stars reaches the Earth, or assume that light does not produce magnetic fields along its path. There are other phenomena, connected with Northern Lights and cosmic radiation, which one would have to forget about temporarily. Even less is lost if one denies the existence of a wave function describing the external world, and there are, of course, concepts of much smaller significance. This shows that there is a continuous spectrum of the reality of existence from absolute necessity for life to insignificance. A corollary to this statement is that the existence and validity of spiritual values is hardly different from that of objects or concepts as we have considered them. On the other hand, there are many useful concepts, such as mathematical ones, which one would not call "real."

Not only material objects and mental constructs have a reality of the second type: the sensations of other people also fall into this category. We all have had unpleasant experiences when we, I am sure through a lapse, forgot about this reality. It is, therefore, on the very cogent end of the spectrum. Even those who profess to an extremely materialistic point of view act, as a rule, as if the sensations of others were just as real as any material object. They are, in this regard, just as inconsistent as the absolute idealist, or the positivist, whose acts betray that he does believe in the reality of the material world. From the point of view adopted here, the sensations of others, and the material world, have the same *type* of reality and, I might add, also about the same *degree* of reality.

The recognition that physical objects and spiritual values have a very similar kind of reality has contributed in some measure to my mental peace. Apart from this point, however, there is a good deal of uneasiness in my mind—uneasiness that my point of view is so clearly correct that it is also uninteresting. At any rate, it is the only known point of view which is consistent with quantum mechanics. I will admit, on the other hand, that I do not always think or speak in terms of the picture presented.

Before going on to the discussion of the relation of the two realities to each other—this is the thorny problem mentioned in the introduction—I would like to make two remarks: one on the nature of scientific explanations, the other on the relation of a possible universal reality to the two kinds of realities of the present section. The first remark will be a very brief one.

The Nature of Scientific Explanations

There is an anecdote in the Preface to the second volume of Boltzmann's *Kinetic Theory of Gases* which illustrates the emptiness of the simple, naive concept of explanation better than I could in a number of learned paragraphs.[8] The fact is that what we call scientific explanation of a phenomenon is an exploration of circumstances, properties, and conditions of the phenomenon, a coordination thereof into a larger group of similar phenomena, and the ensuing discovery of a more encompassing point of view. This more encompassing point of view, the "theory," should permit one to describe not only the original phenomenon but also the phenomena related to it, give an account of the relations between these phenomena and their properties and circumstances. The "explanation" tells us why the phenomenon occurs only in terms of new postulates. It should give, on the other hand, a clear and accurate description not only of the phenomenon itself, but also of the circumstances surrounding it, its relation to other phenomena—some of which may not have been known before the explanation of the original phenomenon was discovered. This is, then, what we should expect eventually of the explanation of the relation of the two types of realities.

The Universal Reality

Once it has been admitted that the only absolute reality is a personal one, there is always some embarrassment in trying to develop a concept of any other type of reality. This need not be so. *The universal or impersonal reality as a concept is a reality of the second type* which, as all other concepts with a second-type reality, may be very useful for my own thinking and for communicating my ideas to others. It may have

[8] The story is that he (Boltzmann) was, in his youth, dissatisfied with the looseness of the logic in the books on physics. Finally, he heard about a physics book with an impeccable logic. He rushed to the library to get it but found to his dismay, first, that the book was out on loan (a rather frequent occurrence in Vienna libraries), second, that it was all in English. At that time, Boltzmann spoke no English. He went home, in low spirits, but his brother—much wiser than himself, according to Boltzmann—comforted him. If the book is really all that splendid, he said, it is surely worth waiting for a few weeks (Boltzmann's brother must have been an optimist). Further, if it is truly logical, the language can't really matter because the author will surely explain every term carefully before he uses it. Boltzmann implies that this event cured him from trying to be too deductive in his physics.

some features of a group photograph which includes oneself and which we like to keep even though it distorts us and is not as good as the original which, after all, we cannot possibly lose. The consideration of the universal or impersonal reality as a concept with a second-type reality may strike one as unnatural but it is hard to see from what other point of view the impersonal reality could be considered.

Even if considered from the point of view of usefulness, the validity of the concept of universal reality may not stand the test. It may evaporate just as the concept of every object's localization evaporated with the advent of quantum mechanics and had to be replaced by more subtle concepts. If this should *not* turn out to be the case, one might like to speak about a universal reality. It is clear, however, that it will not be possible to use this concept meaningfully without being able to give an account of the phenomena of the mind, which is much deeper than our present notions admit. This is a consequence of the fact that, clearly, from a non-personal point of view, other people's sensations are just as real as my own. In all our present scientific thinking, either sensations play no role at all—this is the extreme materialistic point of view which is clearly absurd *and,* as mentioned before, is also in conflict with the tenets of quantum mechanics—or my own sensations play an entirely different role from those of others. It follows that before we can usefully speak of universal reality, a much closer integration of our understanding of physical and mental phenomena will be necessary than we can even dream of at present. This writer sees no cogent reason to doubt the possibility of such an integration—with regard to this point he probably differs from many of his colleagues—but he does see that it has not yet taken place. For this reason it appears that the concept of universal reality is not a useful concept at present.

One can and does speak, of course, of physical realities, emotional and mental realities, and even of political realities. The qualifying adjectives show, however, that these are not universal realities and the concepts defined by them, though they are useful in their own domain, are not sufficiently deep to be interesting in the present context.

The Relation Between the Two Kinds of Reality

If my consciousness is the only absolute reality, one would expect it to be independent of the constructs which are the realities of the second type. This is not so. It is true that I can go into a dark and silent room and think—perhaps think better than in my office—but this would all cease if I stayed there without air or food and water for any length of time. The ideal of the Buddha, detached from all material support and worries, is possible only as a non-existent Buddha. Similarly, one would expect that my consciousness, the only absolute reality, should be permanent. It should have existed always and remain in existence forever. Again, this is clearly not so. On the contrary, there are realities of the second kind of which we think as permanent—electric charges, heavy particles. Surely the permanence of these objects after my death is meaningless; but as long as I live, it is useful to think of them as permanent.

One must admit that the absolute realities do not have the properties which one would expect. This is not a logical contradiction: scientific inquiry has shown many other relations to be very different from what the naive mind believed. It only means that our expectations in regard to the first kind of realities are not fulfilled, that it is useful for me to act and think as if my sensations had not existed always and my consciousness would dissolve into nothing some day. Then, there will be no absolute reality—and indeed there will be nothing. Of the two terminations of all reality, that in the future is much more useful to keep in mind, because its possible arrival affects my sensations much more than the one in the past and because I can influence its onset to some degree. In conformity with this, we think much more about our death than about our birth.

Even if the phenomena of birth and death do not invalidate the rather tautological description of the two types of realities, they do not fit into a satisfactory and neat picture with them, either. Neither does the depressing dependence of our sensations on our environment, in particular on the physical and chemical state of our body. Nevertheless, the truth of the two kinds of reality seem irrefutable. Will it ever be possible to resolve and understand this desperately unsatisfactory conflict between known phenomena and our expectations? We do not know. However, if it will be possible to "understand" the awakening of the consciousness at birth, and its extinction at death, it will be possible through a study of these phenomena on a broad scale—similar to the study of the properties of materials or of motion.

In our present scientific thinking, either sensations and the consciousness play no role at all, or they are brought in as a *deus ex machina,* as in quantum mechanics. It would be contrary to all our past experience with science, if we had understood the phenomena most deeply affecting the realities of the first kind with as perfunctory an effort as we have made so far. If such an understanding is ever to be obtained, it will be obtained after a careful and detailed study of the awakening and extinction of the consciousness, not only in humans but also in animals. Of the two processes, the awakening may be the more simple to understand because it is not so greatly affected by accidental circumstances.

The Role of Science

The preceding discussion lumps together a great variety of "realities": material, spiritual, and scientific. There are some aspects of the role of scientific recognitions in our set of "realities" which I would like to consider. The discussion will use, to a certain extent, the methods and language of quantum mechanics, not only because I am familiar with that language and not because I believe that the epistemology of quantum mechanics represents the ultimate truth. I will use it because its concepts are undoubtedly more concrete than those of any other language developed for discussing epistemology.

In his remarks on the Future of Science, C. N. Yang quotes Einstein,[9] according to whom the purpose of physics is to find universal laws of nature "from which the cosmos can be built up by pure deduction." This is probably the most ambitious goal of science, reminiscent of the materialistic philosophy. Actually, the validity of this goal could hardly be justified even on the basis of materialistic philosophy because the laws of nature, even if they had the all-pervading force attributed to them by the materialists, would suffice only to predict the future of the cosmos, assuming that its present condition is known. They would not suffice to "build up" the cosmos—this would imply also the explanation of its present condition, or, more precisely, the selection of one state of motion from all the infinitely many states of motion which obey the laws of mechanics.

The concepts of quantum physics are very different from those which created the great expectations concerning the power of the laws of nature which is epitomized by Einstein's words. Rather than justifying

[9] C. N. Yang, address at the Centennial Celebration of M.I.T., 1961. The passage appears in *Essays in Science* (New York: Philosophical Library, 1964).

these expectations, they raise the question whether physics, as we know it, can exist independent of the interpretation of our most usual sensations which are, apparently, born with us and which have no scientific origin.

According to quantum mechanical theory, all of our information about the external world derives from "measurements." These were discussed and described in a general way at the beginning of this article. The relevant point which is important for us now is that no measurement could be interpreted by us if we had no previous knowledge of the properties and structure of the measuring apparatus. This is not the "reading" of the apparatus which was referred to before as a second measurement; it is the knowledge of the type of correlation that is being established between object and apparatus. To put it more crudely, the question is whether the measuring apparatus is a voltmeter or an ammeter, a clock or a balance. In order to obtain any information of the outside world, in order to make any measurement or observation, it is necessary that one already possess a crude knowledge of his surroundings. It is true that this crude knowledge usually comes from other observations, but this only transfers the problem one step further back. Evidently, there is another chain here, similar to that described before, and again the end of the chain—the acquisition of our original and most crude knowledge of the innumerable laws of behavior of our surroundings—is shrouded in mystery. It is probably not only cotemporaneous with, but also part of, the awakening of our consciousness, the most mysterious process of all.

Viewing the role of science in this way, one arrives at a much more modest judgment of the role which it plays in our whole body of knowledge. Scientific knowledge always leans on, and is impossible without, the type of knowledge which we acquired in babyhood. Furthermore, this original knowledge was probably not acquired by us in the active sense; most of it must have been given to us in the same mysterious way as, and probably as part of, our consciousness. As to content and usefulness, scientific knowledge is an infinitesimal fraction of the natural knowledge. However, it is a knowledge the structure of which is endowed with beauty because it satisfies abstractions derived from natural knowledge much more clearly than does natural knowledge itself, and we are justly proud of it because we can call it our own creation. It taught us clear thinking and the extent to which clear thinking helps us to order our sensations is a marvel which "fills the mind with ever new and increasing admiration and awe."

Why Are Some Realities of the Second Type So Pervasive?

Another fact that is difficult to understand is the existence of realities of the second type as useful and indispensable as that of material objects. If a little thinking did not make it clear, a recollection of almost every dream would convince us that it could be otherwise, that everything could have a more shadowy existence than do the common objects around us. It is remarkable that, if we look for our glasses, there is no doubt in our mind that they could be found, and one at once stops looking for them on the second floor if one's wife finds them on the first. The fact that this is not so in our dreams shows—if it has to be shown—that reality is a composite empirical fact. Almost equally surprising is the degree of the reality of scientific concepts, facts such as that, if a radio which we put together fails to work, we look for a loose contact and do not suspect the theory.

The question comes up naturally whether it ever will be possible to understand the reality of the second kind, both that given to us by nature, and that acquired by us. Admittedly, the task looks difficult now but so did, only fifty years ago, the task of understanding the properties of materials, such as glass or copper. By understanding, we mean in science the coordination with a larger group of phenomena and the ensuing subordination to a deeper, more general principle. As to the possibility of this, we need not despair even though the problem of the reality of the second kind, the emergence of almost infallible and decisively important concepts, probably lies several layers deeper than could be reached by our present search into the laws of nature.

Perhaps one could find a body of phenomena which would make our concept-building ability less of a single stark fact by studying the concept-forming ability of animals. Perhaps the consciousness of animals is more shadowy than ours and perhaps their perceptions are always dreamlike. On the opposite side, whenever I talked with the sharpest intellect whom I have known—with von Neumann—I always had the impression that only he was fully awake, that I was halfway in a dream.

Let me try to summarize what I have attempted to say here. First, that it seems not only possible but rather easy to tell what is real and that there are two kinds of reality. These are so different that they should have different names. The reality of my perceptions, sensations, and consciousness is immediate and absolute. The reality of everything else consists in the usefulness of thinking in terms of it; this reality is relative and changes from object to object, from concept to concept. This is not in conflict with the fact that it would be virtually impossible to live without accepting the reality of some of these objects, such as our surroundings, practically uninterruptedly; in these cases we cannot really avoid thinking in terms of the objects in question. Their reality, although of the second category, is almost complete. It seems to me that these statements follow from a simple analysis of what we call "real." On the contrary, the reason for the existence of any of these things, the consistency and accuracy of our picture of the world, is profoundly baffling. The same is true, perhaps to an even greater extent, of the reality of the concepts of science.

15

The Probability of the Existence of
a Self-Reproducing Unit

General Remarks

In his "Analytical Study" of life and the multiplication of organisms,[1] Elsasser analyzes the way in which the information is stored in the germ-cells which enables these germ-cells to develop into organisms similar to the parent—similar also in their ability to produce, in their turn, germ-cells containing the same type of information. Although no clear-cut proof is presented, a good deal of weighty evidence is adduced[2] to show "that the structure of a butterfly, a snake, a tree, or a bird cannot be deduced mathematically from some relatively compact body of basic data stored in the chromosomes"; the "maintenance of information is . . . not adequately described in terms of the mechanistic approximation." The present writer has also been baffled by the miracle that there are organisms—that is, from the point of view of the physical scientist, structures—which, if brought into contact with certain nutrient materials, multiply, that is, produce further structures identical with themselves. He felt that it is, according to the known laws of physics, infinitely unlikely that structures of this nature exist and the present

Reprinted by permission from *The Logic of Personal Knowledge: Essays in Honor of Michael Polanyi,* Chapter 19 (London: Routledge and Kegan Paul Ltd., 1961).

[1] Walter M. Elsasser, *The Physical Foundations of Biology* (London: Pergamon Press, 1958).

[2] Since the whole book (cf. Ref. 1) is built around this theme, it is not possible to point to definite passages which contain all the evidence presented. Nevertheless, pages 124-132 are perhaps most characteristic of the trend of thought.

article is a report on the considerations and calculations which he undertook in this connection.[3] Actually, the point of view is somewhat different from Elsasser's: Elsasser considers the way in which the information necessary to develop the adult specimen is stored in the germ-cells and shows that the germ-cells do not have properties which the physicist would expect to be suitable for storing large amounts of information. We shall be concerned, on the other hand, with what appears to be a miracle from the point of view of the physicist: that there are structures which produce further identical structures.[4]

Elsasser's book does not spell out very explicitly a proposition for the resolution of the problem to which he points. He postulates, on the one hand, further laws of nature not contained in the laws of physics and quantum mechanics. He calls these laws *biotonic*. On the other hand, he maintains that the validity of the laws of quantum mechanics is not impaired by the new laws. Inasmuch as quantum mechanics claims to apply to all situations, and to provide all meaningful predictions, this seems to be a contradiction. The only resolution of this contradiction which appears consistent with the ideas expressed by Elsasser is that the biological units are so complicated that it is *in principle* impossible to calculate their behavior on the basis of the laws of quantum mechanics. Elsasser concludes that a computing machine which could store all the information contained in a germ-cell would be inconceivably large. Even this interpretation is questionable: it is quite possible that one can deduce, by abstract reasoning, consequences of the quantum mechanical equations which either reproduce, or contradict, important properties of living organisms. The present study will make an attempt in this direction. After all, we can explain, by means of quantum mechanical theory, at least a large number of the properties of solids and liquids, and the accurate description of these does contain as much information as can be stored in a germ-cell. Alternatively, one could derive, again by abstract reasoning, intermediate theorems which would greatly simplify the task of the computing machines. For all these reasons, it does not appear very likely that the aforementioned contradic-

---

[3] The results of these considerations have already been mentioned in the author's article "The Unreasonable Effectiveness of Mathematics in the Natural Sciences," *Communications in Pure and Applied Mathematics*, 13, 1 (1960), reprinted in this volume.

[4] M. Polanyi's review of G. Himmelfarb's *Darwin and the Darwinian Revolution*, *The New Leader*, 31, 24 (1959), expresses similar doubts concerning the possibility of explaining the phenomenon of life on mechanistic grounds.

tion can be resolved. It is more likely that the present laws and concepts of quantum mechanics will have to undergo modifications before they can be applied to the problems of life.

For reasons which are not quite clear, the phenomenon of consciousness has become tabu in scientific discussions. Nevertheless, as one can see, for instance, from von Neumann's brilliant discussion of the process of quantum mechanical measurement,[5] even the laws of quantum mechanics itself cannot be formulated, with all their implications, without recourse to the concept of consciousness.[6] It is very likely that those who deny the reality of consciousness only mean that the external world can be completely described without reference to the consciousness of others, that is, that the motion of matter (in the broadest sense of this word) is not influenced by consciousness, even though consciousness is obviously influenced by the motion of matter. According to the view attributed in the preceding paragraph to Elsasser, this view is neither correct, nor false, but meaningless, because it is, even in principle, impossible to describe the motion of all matter by the laws of physics. In particular, it should be impossible to describe living matter in terms of the laws of physics. It seems more likely, however, that this view is incorrect and that living matter is actually influenced by what it clearly influences: consciousness. The description of this phenomenon clearly needs incorporation of concepts into our laws of nature which are foreign to the present laws of physics. Perhaps the relation of consciousness to matter is not too dissimilar to the relation of light to matter, as it was known in the last century: matter clearly influenced the motion of light but no phenomenon such as the Compton effect was known at that time which would have shown that light can directly influence the motion of matter. Nevertheless, the "reality" of light was never doubted.

[5] J. von Neumann, *Mathematische Grundlagen der Quantenmechanik* (Berlin: Julius Springer, 1932); English translation (Princeton, N.J.: Princeton University Press, 1955), Chapter VI. Heisenberg [*Daedalus*, 87, 100 (1958)] puts it even more concisely and picturesquely: "The conception of objective reality . . . has thus evaporated . . . into the transparent clarity of a mathematics that represents no longer the behavior of elementary particles but rather our knowledge of this behavior."

[6] It is interesting from a psychological-epistemological point of view that, although consciousness is the only phenomenon for which we have direct evidence, many people deny its reality. The question: "If all that exists are some complicated chemical processes in your brain, why do you care what those processes are?" is countered with evasion. One is led to believe that, as explained in the text, the word "reality" does not have the same meaning for all of us.

Calculation of the Probability That There Be
Reproducing States

The preceding, very general and speculative considerations will be supported below by a definite argument. As will be discussed in the last section, the argument to be presented is not truly conclusive. Nevertheless, it is at least indicative. It purports to show that, according to standard quantum mechanical theory, the probability is zero for the existence of self-reproducing states. The discussion of this result and of its implications will be reserved for the last section; the present section will contain only the derivation of the result. The derivation is not a rigorous one: it will be based on an assumption which is analogous to our belief that in no system of any complexity is there any "accidental degeneracy."[7] It is even more closely similar to the assumption on the basis of which the second law of thermodynamics was derived.[8] The assumption is that the Hamiltonian which governs the behavior of a complicated system is a random symmetric matrix, with no particular properties except for its symmetric nature. It is by assuming this property for the Hamiltonian, when written in the co-ordinate system in which the observables are diagonal, that von Neumann proved the second law of thermodynamics to be a consequence of quantum mechanical theory. A second, probably less important, assumption will be introduced later.

The calculation will be carried out in two steps. First, it will be assumed that "the living state" is completely given in the quantum mechanical sense: it has one definite state vector with the components v_k. Clearly, there must exist at least one state of the nutrient which permits the organism to multiply. The state vector of this state will be denoted by w. There should be, as a matter of fact, many states of the nutrient on which the organism can feed but a contradiction will be obtained already by assuming a single such state. Before multiplication, the state vector of the system, organism + nutrient, is

$$\Phi = v \times w, \tag{1}$$

---

[7] For this concept, see, e.g., E. Wigner, *Gruppentheorie*, etc. (Braunschweig: Friedr. Vieweg, 1931); English translation (New York: Academic Press, Inc., 1959), Chapter XII.

[8] J. von Neumann, *op. cit.*, Chapter V.

the cross denoting the direct (Kronecker) product. When multiplication has taken place, the state vector will have to have the form

$$\Psi = v \times v \times r, \tag{2}$$

that is, two organisms, each with the state vector v, will be present; the vector r describes both the rest of the system which is the rejected part of the nutrient and also the position, etc., co-ordinates of the two organisms. Introducing a co-ordinate system in Hilbert space which corresponds to the decomposition (2), this reads

$$\Psi_{\kappa\lambda\mu} = v_\kappa v_\lambda r_\mu. \tag{3}$$

The first index (κ) substitutes for the variables which describe the part of the system contained in the "parent," the second index (λ) substitutes for the variables which describe the "child," the last index (μ) substitutes for the variables in terms of which the rejected part of the nutrient is described. In the same co-ordinate system, (1) reads in terms of its components

$$\Phi_{\kappa\lambda\mu} = v_\kappa w_{\lambda\mu} \tag{4}$$

and we have a double index for the specification of the state of the nutrient.

The two assumptions which were mentioned before will now be introduced in precise language. The second and less important of these is the replacement of Hilbert space by a finite dimensional space. In particular, the space of the organism shall have N dimensions, the space which describes the rejected part of the nutrient shall have R dimensions. Then κ and λ can assume N values each, μ can assume R values; the state of the organism is a vector in N-dimensional (rather than infinite dimensional) space. Since no assumptions will be made concerning the magnitude of N and R, both of which surely must be assumed to be very large, this assumption appears harmless enough. It is made to make the mathematical analysis easy and can be justified since, as the total energy available is finite, both parts of the system are restricted to a finite number of states. The state of the nutrient is a vector in NR dimensional space; i.e., it is a much more specialized state than the state of the organism. This is surprising at first but must be true, since the life and multiplication of the organism is connected with an increase in entropy; i.e., the final state is less specialized than the original state.

The more relevant and more questionable assumption is that the "collision matrix" which gives the final state resulting from the interaction of the organism and the nutrient, and which will be denoted by S, has no particular properties but is a random matrix. Since it transforms the Φ of (4) into the Ψ of (3), we have

$$v_\kappa \, v_\lambda \, r_\mu = \sum_{\kappa'\lambda'\mu'} S_{\kappa\lambda\mu \, ; \, \kappa'\lambda'\mu'} \, v_\kappa \, w_{\lambda'\mu'} \tag{5}$$

S, so to say, embodies the laws of interaction between any state of the material which makes up the organism and any state of the material which makes up the nutrient. "Any state" must, however, be interpreted in the light of the preceding remark; it is any of a finite number of states. S is completely determined by the laws of quantum mechanics; it is the quantity which, according to Elasser, actually cannot be calculated. What we shall ask is, then: Given an S, is it in general possible to find N numbers v_κ, which, together with suitably chosen R numbers r_μ and NR numbers $w_{\lambda\mu}$, satisfy (5)? We shall decide this question simply by counting the number of equations and the number of unknowns. We shall find that the former number is greater.

Since (5) must be valid for any κ, λ, and μ, we have actually $N^2 R$ complex, or $2N^2 R$ real, equations. There are several identities between these but since N^2 is a tremendously large number, this fact will be disregarded. There are N unknown v-components, r has R unknown components, and w has NR unknown components. Altogether, there are $N + R + NR$ complex or twice as many real unknowns—very much fewer than equations—so that "it would be a miracle" if (5) could be satisfied.

Evidently, the preceding calculation cannot be taken too seriously because surely an organism is not completely determined in the quantum mechanical sense. There must be many states v all of which represent a living organism. Their number will be denoted by n. This number is, however, much smaller than the number N of states which the matter constituting the organism can assume: evidently most of the states of this matter are not living. Hence $n \ll N$. Let us denote the n vectors which represent living organisms by v^k, the index k running from 1 to n. Then every linear combination of the v^k will also represent a living state. As a result, n initial states will have to be considered:

$$\Phi^{(j)} = v^{(j)} \times w \qquad \text{or} \qquad \Phi^{(j)}_{\kappa\lambda\mu} = v^{(j)}_{\kappa} w_{\lambda\mu}. \tag{6}$$

The final state, obtained from the interaction of the state $v^{(j)}$ and the nutrient (for which we continue to postulate only a single state w), will be denoted by $\Psi^{(j)}$. As far as the dependence of $\Psi^{(j)}$ on the first two indices is concerned, this may be an arbitrary linear combination of the n^2 vectors $v^{(\kappa)} \times v^{(l)}$. Hence

$$\Psi^{(j)}_{\kappa\lambda\mu} = \sum_{kl} u^{jkl}_{\mu} v^{(k)}_{\kappa} v^{(l)}_{\lambda} \tag{7}$$

and we have instead of (5)

$$\sum_{kl} u^{jkl}_{\mu} v^{(k)}_{\kappa} v^{(l)}_{\lambda} = \sum_{\kappa'\lambda'\mu'} S_{\kappa\lambda\mu;\kappa'\lambda'\mu'} v^{(j)}_{\kappa'} w_{\lambda'\mu'}. \tag{8}$$

This equation must be valid for every j and, as before, for every κ, λ, and μ. Altogether, we have nN^2R complex or $2nN^2R$ real equations.

The unknowns are the v, the w, and the u. There are nN quantities v and, as before, NR quantities w. The number of constants u is, on the other hand, n^3R because j, k, l can assume n values each and μ can assume R values. Disregarding the possibility that neither the unknowns nor the variables may be independent of each other, the number of unknowns will be equal to the number of variables if

$$nN^2R = nN + NR + n^3R \tag{9}$$

Because of $n \ll N$, the left side is still very much larger than the right side and the equation is not satisfied. Even if one allows for the possibility that *one* of the products be arbitrary (i.e., that $v^{(l)}$ in (8) be any state, living or not living), the number of unknown u will increase only to n^2NR and the right side will still be much smaller than the left. We arrive at the result that, if the interaction S is not "tailored" so as to permit reproduction, it is infinitely unlikely that there be *any* state of the nutrient which would permit the multiplication of any set of states which is much smaller than all the possible states of the system.

As was mentioned before, the preceding calculation disregards the fact that the equations (8) are not independent of each other and also the fact that the unknowns cannot be chosen freely. Both relations are consequences of the unitary nature of S. A more detailed calculation shows, however, that the relations between the equations are just about equal to the number of relations between the unknowns and, as long as $n \ll N$, neither of them affects (9) appreciably. The conclusion of the preceding paragraph stands, therefore, in spite of these relations.

Limitations of the Preceding Calculation*

Even the preceding calculation, which assumes that many quantum mechanical states represent life, is far from realistic. The difficulty is that it stipulates that at least one organism *surely* survives the interaction with the nutrient. There is no clear reason to believe this. A realistic model would permit, rather, any final state, but would demand that the sum of the probabilities of the states with two living organisms be well in excess of $\frac{1}{2}$. This would lead, instead of to (8), to certain inequalities the mathematical discussion of which is much more difficult than the discussion of the equalities (8) and has not been concluded and will not be reproduced here. It remains noteworthy that the chances are nil for the existence of a set of "living" states for which one can find a nutrient of such nature that the inter-action *always* leads to muliplication.

The preceding result seems to be in conflict with von Neumann's well known construction of self-duplicating machines.[9] If one tries to confront the evidence of the preceding section with von Neumann's explicit construction, one finds that such a confrontation is not possible because the model used by von Neumann (based on Turing's universal automaton) can assume only a discrete set of states, whereas all our variables (v, w) are continuous. This permits the postulation of an ideal behavior of the system and the "tailoring" of the substitutes for the equations of motion in such a way that they permit reproduction. The question which is in the foreground of the present discussion is whether the real equations of motion can be expected to give reproduction. The difference between a truly macroscopic "hard" system, for which one can assume with a little goodwill any law of motion, and the "soft" systems which really undergo multiplication has been stressed already by Elsasser.[10] Actually, the inapplicability of his model to biological considerations was also recognized by von Neumann.

---

* Professor Wigner suggests that the reader pay careful attention to these limitations. *Eds.*

[9] The only paper that is available on this subject seems to be "The General and Logical Theory of Automata" in *The Hixon Symposium,* L. A. Jeffress, ed. (New York: John Wiley and Sons, 1951), p. 1. However, C. E. Shannon's discussion of von Neumann's work, *Bull. Am. Math. Soc.,* 64, 123 (1958), draws attention to further unpublished papers. In connection with the reliability problem, to be discussed below, see "Probabilistic Logics and the Synthesis of Reliable Organisms from Unreliable Components," in *Automata Studies,* C. E. Shannon and J. McCarthy, eds. (Princeton, N.J.: Princeton University Press, 1956), p. 43.

[10] Elsasser, *op. cit.,* p. 129.

The second piece of conflicting information is the model which Crick and Watson suggested for reproduction and which proposes a definite mechanism for the transfer of the properties to the progeny.[11] This model is also based on classical rather than quantum concepts. It is indeed an ingenious and realistic-looking model which suggests the view that it may have been difficult to find a system with equations of motion which permit reproduction, but, in spite of the adverse odds, the difficult feat has in fact been accomplished. It is not intended to contradict this view absolutely. It is necessary to point out, nevertheless, that the details of the functioning of the model do not appear to have been worked out completely. Similarly, the reliability of the model, that is, the probability of its malfunctioning, has not been evaluated and compared with experience. One may incline, therefore, to the view, implicit also in Elsasser's ideas, that the type of reproduction for which the model of Crick and Watson seems to apply can, as can all similar processes, be described by the known laws of nature, but only approximately. However, the apparently virtually absolute reliability of the functioning of the model is the consequence of a biotonic law.

The writer does not wish to close this article without admitting that his firm conviction in the existence of biotonic laws stems from the overwhelming phenomenon of consciousness. As to the arguments presented here, they are suggestive but not conclusive. The possibility that we overlook the influence of biotonic phenomena, as one immersed in the study of the laws of macroscopic mechanics could have overlooked the influence of light on his macroscopic bodies, is real. This does not, however, render the arguments here presented conclusive, because, in their present form, *they are based on the assumption that the laws of reproduction are absolute.* This may be just as little true, or may be just as misleading, as was Leibniz's conclusion of the incorrectness of atomic theory which he inferred from the impossibility of finding two identical blades of grass.[12]

---

[11] It must suffice to mention a few of the pertinent papers here, and the knowledge of most of these I owe to Dr. H. Jehle of George Washington University: F. H. C. Crick and J. D. Watson, *Nature*, 171, 737 (1953); *Proc. Roy. Soc.* (London), A223, 80 (1954); G. Gamow, *Biol. Medd. Danske Vid. Selskab*, 22, No. 2 (1954); 22, No. 8 (1955); F. H. C. Crick, J. S. Griffith, and L. E. Orgel, *Proc. Natl. Acad. Sci. U.S.*, 43, 416 (1957); M. Delbrück, S. W. Golomb, L. R. Welch, *Biol. Medd. Danske Vid. Selskab*, 23, No. 9 (1958). See also H. J. Muller, *Proc. Roy. Soc.* (London), B134, 1 (1947).

[12] P. Morrison, *Am. J. Phys.*, 26, 358 (1958).

IV

REFLECTIONS

16

The Limits of Science

The present discussion is not put forward with the usual pride of the scientist who feels that he can make an addition, however small, to a problem which has aroused his and his colleagues' interest. Rather, it is a speculation of a kind which all of us feel a great reluctance to undertake: much like the speculation on the ultimate fate of somebody who is very dear to us. It is a speculation on the future of science itself, whether it will share, at some very distant future, the fate of "Alles was entsteht ist wert dass es zu Grunde geht." Naturally, in such a speculation one wishes to assume the best of conditions for one's subject and disregard the danger of an accident that may befall it, however real that danger may be.

The Growth of Science

The most remarkable thing about Science is its youth. The earliest beginning of chemistry, as we now know it, certainly does not antedate Boyle's *Sceptical Chemist*, which appeared in 1661. More probably, one would place the birthyear of chemistry around the years of activity of Lavoisier, between 1770 and 1790, or count its years from Dalton's law in 1808. Physics is somewhat older; Newton's *Principia*, a rather finished work, became available in 1687. Archimedes discovered laws of physics around 250 B.C., but his discoveries hardly can be called the real begin-

Reprinted by permission from the *Proceedings of the American Philosophical Society,* Vol. 94, No. 5 (October, 1950).

ning of physics. On the whole, one is probably safe in saying that Science is less than 300 years old. This number has to be compared with the age of Man, which is certainly greater than 100,000 years.

The number of people who devote years of their life to the acquisition of knowledge had an equally spectacular rise. Thus, about ten per cent of the American youth are graduated from college, a percentage that has lately doubled in every twenty years. Harvard College was founded in 1636 and it was certainly not a scientific college at that time. The American Association for the Advancement of Science is one hundred years old and had originally 461 members. Today, it has more than half a million and its membership increased by almost 10,000 in a single half year. The growth of college attendance was less spectacular in some other countries, probably more spectacular in Russia.

Man's increased mastery of the Earth can be directly traced to his increased knowledge of the laws of nature. The surface of the Earth, as a whole, was not affected by man for 99,700 years but vast areas have been deforested or the surface's store of some minerals depleted since the birth of science. For 99,700 years, a man equipped with a good telescope on the moon might not have discovered man's existence on the Earth. He could not have overlooked it during the last three hundred years. There is no natural phenomenon that is comparable with the sudden and apparently accidentally timed development of science, except perhaps the condensation of a super-saturated gas or the explosion of some unpredictable explosives. Will the fate of science show some similarity to one of these phenomena?

Actually, if one views detachedly the rapid growth of science, and of the power of man, one cannot help fearing the second alternative. Surely man has not been able to adjust his spiritual outlook to the responsibility which his increased power imposed on him and one has to fear a catastrophe as a consequence of this maladjustment. This has come to be so well recognized recently, particularly as a result of the development of atomic weapons and the subsequent failure of man to cope, or even to come to grips, with the problems created by these weapons, that it is almost a commonplace. Nevertheless, this possibility will be disregarded here, and the limits of the growth of science will be considered under the assumption that no cataclysmic effect will interrupt this growth. The following speculations therefore apply only if we should be able to avoid the cataclysm which threatens us, and science can develop in a

relatively peaceful atmosphere. They will look for the inherent limitations of science, rather than the limitations imposed by external effects,
whether or not these external effects are influenced by science.

What Can We Call "Our Science"

What might be considered as the natural limit of our science will become perhaps best apparent if we try to define what "our science" is.
It is our store of knowledge of natural phenomena. The question then is,
what is "our" store? This question will be approached by giving both
too broad and too narrow definitions and then attempting an acceptable
compromise. A set of volumes, containing information and theories, certainly does not become our store of knowledge by our mere possession
of it: the renaissance, or rather the preceding dark ages, teach us that
physical possession is not enough. Is it then necessary that anybody
know all the contents of those volumes before they can be called "our
science"? This may be a defensible point of view but if it were accepted
science would have reached its limits already, might have reached them
quite some time ago. Is it then enough that there be, in our society, for
every volume a person who is fully familiar with it? No, because there
may be contradictions between the statements of the various volumes
which would remain hidden if everyone knew only part of them. Science is an edifice, not a pile of bricks, valuable as such a pile may be.

I would say that a store of knowledge can reasonably be called "our
science" if there are people who are competent to learn and use any
part of it, who would like to know each part of it even if they realize
that they cannot, and if one has good assurance that the parts are not
contradictory but form a whole. The section on elasticity must use the
same picture of the structure of iron on which the section on magnetism
is based.

Limits of "Our Science"

If the above is accepted as a fair description of what may be called
"our science" then its limitations are in the human intellect, in its capacity for interest and learning, in its memory and facilities for communication. All these are surely related to the finite span of the human life.
In fact, if we accept the above, science is already changing not only by

acquiring new territories, but partly also by shifting from older to new fields. We forget things and focus our attention on more recent developments. Right now, the older parts of science cease to be parts of our science not so much because we have no assurance that they fit into the new picture—I believe they do—but rather because nobody has a strong desire to know them, at least nobody who is interested in the new parts.

Surely, the possibilities of this type of growth are very far from being exhausted. Today, we are neglecting the theory of solids, in which a student has to study perhaps six hundred papers before he reaches the frontiers and can do research on his own; we concentrate instead on quantum electrodynamics, in which he has to study six papers. Tomorrow, we may give up a whole science, such as chemistry, and concentrate on something that is less explored. These changes in interest are, furthermore, surely not arbitrary but in most cases well justified, inasmuch as the new subject is deeper than the abandoned one, starts from more fundamental realizations, and embraces the old one. The properties of solids follow from the principles of quantum electrodynamics and this discipline is, in addition, able to deal with many phenomena besides those important for solids.

One should realize, nevertheless, that the embracing of the old subject by the new discipline is somewhat illusory. Thus the theory of solids is relinquished by the student of quantum electrodynamics in a very real sense because the human intellect is not powerful enough to derive the important properties of solids from quantum theory, unless it has made a particular, both experimental and theoretical, study to develop the idealizations and approximations which are useful for the description of solids. Only an unusual intellect could guess on the basis of the principles of ordinary quantum theory that there are solids and that they consist of regular lattice-like arrangements of the atoms. No human intellect could overlook, as a matter of course, the significance and role of the defects of these lattices. The equations of quantum theory may form the words of a magic oracle which describes the phenomena of crystal physics in a wonderfully condensed fashion. However, no human intellect can understand this oracle without using a commentary to its words, the length of this commentary being in the same proportion to the condensate of the oracle as is the whole Bible to Leviticus 19: 18. There is clearly a limit beyond which condensation, elevating though it may be as a purpose *per se*, is not useful for storing information. Present day condensation in physics has certainly reached this limit.

Shift of the Second Type

The question now comes up whether science will at least be able to continue the type of shifting growth indefinitely in which the new discipline is deeper than the older one and embraces it at least virtually. The answer is, in my opinion, no, because the shifts in the above sense always involve digging one layer deeper into the "secrets of nature," and involve a longer series of concepts based on the previous ones, which are thereby recognized as "mere approximations." Thus, in the example above, first ordinary mechanics had to be replaced by quantum mechanics, thus recognizing the approximate nature and limitation of ordinary mechanics to macroscopic phenomena. Then, ordinary mechanics had to be recognized to be inadequate from another point of view and replaced by field theories. Finally, the approximate nature and limitation to small velocities of all of the above concepts had to be uncovered. Thus, relativistic quantum theory is at least four layers deep; it operates with three successive types of concepts all of which are recognized to be inadequate and are replaced by a more profound one in the fourth step. This is, of course, the charm and beauty of the relativistic quantum theory and of all fundamental research in physics. However, it also shows the limits of this type of development. The recognizing of an inadequacy in the concepts of the tenth layer and the replacing of it with the more refined concepts of the eleventh layer will be much less of an event than the discovery of the theory of relativity was. It will, furthermore, require a much more elaborate and a much longer study to arrive at an understanding of the roots of the evil than was the study needed to appreciate the discrepancies which were eliminated by the theory of relativity. It is not difficult to imagine a stage in which the new student will no longer be interested, perhaps will not be able any more, to dig through the already accumulated layers in order to do research at the frontier. The number of physics graduate students will then drop and the shift of science to new territories will be more drastic than the shifts we are accustomed to: the new discipline in fashion will not embrace physics any more in the same way, as, for instance, quantum theory embraces classical physics. I will call this type of shift the shift of the second type.

The above picture assumes that, in order to understand a growing body of phenomena, it will be necessary to introduce deeper and deeper concepts into physics and that this development will not end by the discovery of the final and perfect concepts. I believe that this is true: we have no right to expect that our intellect can formulate perfect concepts for the full understanding of inanimate nature's phenomena. However, the second type of shift will occur also if we do, because science does not seem to be viable if no research is being done on its outskirts and the interest will soon flag in a completed subject. It is possible also that neither of the two alternatives will come to pass, that it will never be decided whether the concepts of the tenth layer are adequate "in principle" for the understanding of the inanimate world. Absence of interest and the weakness of the human intellect may easily combine to postpone indefinitely the determination of the full adequacy of the nth layer of concepts. In that case physics will be left by the wayside, in a somewhat similar fashion to the way in which the phenomena connected with superconductivity are apparently being left by the wayside, most physicists not feeling an acute sense of unhappiness about it.

The second type of shift will not be all resignation. In fact, many feel nowadays that the life sciences and the science of the minds of both animals and men have already been neglected too long. Our picture of the world would surely be more rounded if we knew more about the minds of men and animals, their customs and habits. The second type of shift may mean, however, the acknowledgment that we are unable to arrive at the full understanding of even the inanimate world, just as, a few centuries ago, man came to the conclusion that he has no very good chance to foresee what will happen to his soul after the death of his body. We all continue to feel a frustration because of our inability to foresee our soul's ultimate fate. Although we do not speak about it, we all know that the objectives of our science are, from a general human point of view, much more modest than the objectives of, say, the Greek science were; that our science is more successful in giving us power than in giving us knowledge of truly human interest. The development of the natural sciences was, however, not less vigorous because of the ensuing sense of frustration. Similarly, the vigor of work in the fields to which shifts of the second type will lead will not be smaller because we shall have abandoned the full realization of our dreams concerning an earlier field.

However, the second type of shift will mean some new resignation and also mark a turning point in the existence of science, taking science in the sense of our definition. When shifts of the second type will have occurred in relevant numbers, science will lose some of the attraction on the young mind which it now holds. It will be something altogether different, a bit less fascinating. The wonderful elation which we scientists now are experiencing, and which comes from the new feeling of the power of our intellect, will be somewhat dampened by the recognition of the limits of that power. We will have to acquiesce in the fact that our intellect's toil cannot give us a satisfactory picture of the world such as the Greeks dreamed to attain, in an effortless way, by easy speculation.

Stabilizing Forces

Many of us will be inclined to make light of the preceding argument and say that science has a natural vitality by which it will overcome the limits which we, small minds of today, imagine to perceive in its path. There surely is much truth in this statement and we shall shortly turn to elements of elasticity in the whole picture which support it. However, I believe that the darker picture is the fundamentally correct one and that our instinctive desire not to believe it is the desire and ability of the human mind not to think of repugnant events in the future if their threat has no accurately foreseeable date. However, great changes, and often very unwanted changes, do take place and the elasticity of nature only delays them: buffaloes did die out as sources of food; the role of the individual warrior has vanished; the detailed explanation of the holy writings, once the only subject worthy of human studies, has ceased to be an element of our culture; Malthus' dire predictions are sure to come true at least in some respects. All the forecasts predicting these events were once resented by large groups just as we resent and resist the statement of the insufficiency of science.

Can we see even today signals of the crisis in science? Perhaps. The difficulty in penetrating to the frontiers of physics has been mentioned before. It is already so serious for the average human mind that only a negligible fraction of our contemporaries really feels the force of the arguments of quantum and relativity theories. Chemistry has grown so big that very few people can keep an even loose acquaintance with all its ramifications. Shifts of the first type are going on in these sciences constantly, some of them being the butts of constant jokes.

The clearest sign of the growing realization that the capacity of our intellect limits the volume of science is the number of queries which we hear every day, whether this or that piece of research "is worth doing." In almost all such cases, the problem posed is interesting, the proposed method of attack shows elements of ingenuity, and the answer, whatever it may turn out to be, can be expected to be worth remembering. However, the questioner realizes how great is the number of problems of similar importance, how limited the time and memory of those to whom the results will be of interest. He wonders whether his proposed work would not remain submerged in the mass of literature, with nobody taking time and energy fully to understand and appreciate it. Hence the query. Similar doubts on the "worth" of some proposed research must have arisen at all times. It seems to me doubtful, however, that they ever were as deep as they are now, and concerned as intrinsically interesting problems. I believe I have observed an increase in the frequency of these queries and doubts even during my own short scientific life.

Recently, M. Fierz, in a very thoughtful article, has pointed to what may well become in time a shift of the second type. He pointed out that both physics and psychology claim to be all-embracing disciplines: the first because it endeavors to describe all nature; the second because it deals with all mental phenomena, and nature exists for us only because we have cognizance of it. Fierz points out that the pictures of the world which these two disciplines project into us are not necessarily contradictory. However, it surely is difficult if not impossible to recognize the two pictures as only different aspects of the same thing. Furthermore, it is hardly an exaggeration to say that no psychologist understands the philosophy of modern physics. Conversely, only the exceptional physicist understands the language of the psychologist. Of course, psychology's philosophy is as yet too vague to draw definite conclusions. However, it is not impossible that we, or our students, are going to witness a real split of science right here.

It would be foolish to draw far reaching conclusions from the emergence of two sciences, both of which may claim to be all embracing and between the concepts and statements of which one cannot, at present, see any real similarity. Both may yet be united into a deeper common discipline without overtaxing our mind's capacity for abstraction. Altogether, there are many favorable stabilizing effects which can delay the balkanization of science for very long periods. Some of these are methodological: as we understand discoveries more fully, we will be able to explain them better. It is certainly no accident that we have scores of excellent books on thermodynamics but had surely until recently nothing comparable in quantum theory. Relativity theory was understood, so it was claimed, twenty-five years ago only by two—today we teach its principles to undergraduates. Examples of improving teaching techniques by both minor simplifications and by spectacular "condensations" and generalizations are in fact too obvious to bear enumeration.

Another important stabilizing effect will be the reduction of the size of disciplines by elimination of parts of it. An example which must have struck everyone of my age is that the theory of elliptic functions—a theory as spectacular in its methods and successes as any part of modern mathematics—is right now falling into oblivion. This is a shift of the first kind to which even the queen of sciences is not immune. As such it keeps mathematics more learnable.

Finally, it is not impossible that we'll breed during the coming centuries a human whose power of recollection, whose facility of abstraction, is greater than ours. Or at least that we make a greater and more aptly guided effort to select among the young those best suited for furthering science.

There is, on the other hand, a circumstance which will undoubtedly have an opposite effect. Thirst for knowledge, curiosity concerning the extent of one's mental faculties, and a healthy sense of rivalry, are strong stimulants of the young scientist and will continue to spur him along also in the future. They are, however, not his only motives: the desire to improve the lot of mankind, to extend its power, is also a traditional trait of scientists. These latter incentives are, however, waning, at least as far as the natural sciences are concerned, with the advent of man's full mastery of the elements, with the increasing realization that the economic welfare of man is a question of organization rather than a problem of production. The effect of the loss of this incentive will certainly be present; its magnitude is unpredictable.

Cooperative Research

If science is expected to grow so great, both in the comprehensiveness of its subject and also in depth, that the human mind will not be able to embrace it, that the life span of man will not be long enough to penetrate to its fringes in time to enlarge it, could several people not form a team and accomplish jointly what no single person can accomplish? Instead of returning with Shaw to Methuselah, can we find a new way to enlarge the capacity of human intellect by the juxtaposition of several individual intellects rather than by extending a single one? This is a possibility which is so little explored that all that one may say about it must remain highly speculative—much more speculative, I believe, than the rest of this article. The possibilities of cooperative research have to be explored, however, to a much greater extent than they have been so far because they form the only visible hope for a new lease on life for science when it will have grown too large for a single individual.

Most of us scientists are too individualistic to take cooperative research too seriously. As the founder of relativity theory once remarked, he cannot imagine how relativity theory could have been conceived by a group. Indeed, if we think of the present day research groups, working under a group leader who received his assignment through a section chief, the idea becomes amusingly absurd. Clearly, no fundamental change in our way of thinking can come about that way and no such fundamental change is intended by the groups referred to.

The case against group research can be stated more rationally on the basis of Poincaré's keen analysis of the nature of mathematical discovery. It is, I believe, our intuitive awareness of the facts which he and Hadamard have expressed so aptly which makes us smile at the idea of group research. Poincaré and Hadamard have recognized that, unlike most thinking which goes on in the upper consciousness, the really relevant mathematical thinking is not done in words. In fact, it happens somewhere so deep in the subconscious that the thinker is usually not even aware of what is going on inside of him.

It is my opinion that the role of subconscious thinking is equally important in other sciences, that it is decisive even in the solution of apparently trivial technical details. An experimentalist friend once told me (this was some twenty years ago) that if he could not find the leak in his vacuum system he usually felt like going for a walk, and very often, when he returned from the walk, he knew exactly where the leak was. The problem of group research is, therefore, to give free rein to the inventiveness of the subconscious of the individual but, at the same time, have available for him the whole store of knowledge of the group.

It is certainly impossible to tell now whether and how this can be accomplished. It will surely need a much more intimate symbiosis between collaborators than has been established to date. Part, but only part, of this more intimate symbiosis will be a higher faculty for the communication of ideas and information than we have developed so far. If group research is to be fully effective, it will also need a much deeper understanding of the functioning of the human mind than we now have. However, neither of these is impossible; in fact, we may be closer to both than we suspect.

Meanwhile, we should keep two facts in mind. The first is that the difficulty in the future development of science, which we have envisaged before, is based in the first place on the limited capacity of the human mind, not on its limited depth. Even if the depth, which is more intimately based on subconscious thinking, could not be increased, the first obstacle, the limitation of the capacity, might well be cut back by teamwork. Second, we should not forget that while it is true that relativity theory could not have been conceived by teamwork, the structure of the George Washington Bridge, and probably even that of the Hanford nuclear reactors, could not have been thought out by a single individual. The problem of group research is to avoid suppressing the subconscious thinking of the individual but to make available for him the information and to some degree even the unfinished ideas of his collaborators. Success of this may mean that the limitations of "our science" which were described above are limitations only for individualist science.

It is depressing for every scientist and for every person to have to conclude that his principal motive, or that of his epoch, is not here to stay. However, humanity's goals and ideals have shifted already several times during our known history. In addition, it must fill us with pride to believe that we are living in the heroic age of science, in the epoch in which the individual's abstract knowledge of nature, and, we may hope, also of himself, is increasing more rapidly and perhaps to a higher level than it ever has before or will afterwards. It is uncomfortable to believe that our ideals may pass as the Round Table's illusions disappeared. Still, we live in the heroic age of these ideals.

17

The Unreasonable Effectiveness of
Mathematics in the Natural Sciences

"and it is probable that there is some secret here which
remains to be discovered." —C. S. Peirce

There is a story about two friends, who were classmates in high school,
talking about their jobs. One of them became a statistician and was
working on population trends. He showed a reprint to his former classmate. The reprint started, as usual, with the Gaussian distribution and
the statistician explained to his former classmate the meaning of the
symbols for the actual population, for the average population, and so
on. His classmate was a bit incredulous and was not quite sure whether
the statistician was pulling his leg. "How can you know that?" was his
query. "And what is this symbol here?" "Oh," said the statistician, "this
is π." "What is that?" "The ratio of the circumference of the circle to
its diameter." "Well, now you are pushing your joke too far," said the
classmate, "surely the population has nothing to do with the circumference of the circle."

Naturally, we are inclined to smile about the simplicity of the classmate's approach. Nevertheless, when I heard this story, I had to admit
to an eerie feeling because, surely, the reaction of the classmate be-
trayed only plain common sense. I was even more confused when, not

Richard Courant Lecture in Mathematical Sciences delivered at New York Uni-
versity, May 11, 1959. Reprinted by permission from *Communications in Pure and
Applied Mathematics*, Vol. 13, No. 1 (February, 1960). Copyright by John Wiley &
Sons, Inc.

many days later, someone came to me and expressed his bewilderment[1] with the fact that we make a rather narrow selection when choosing the data on which we test our theories. "How do we know that, if we made a theory which focuses its attention on phenomena we disregard and disregards some of the phenomena now commanding our attention, that we could not build another theory which has little in common with the present one but which, nevertheless, explains just as many phenomena as the present theory?" It has to be admitted that we have no definite evidence that there is no such theory.

The preceding two stories illustrate the two main points which are the subjects of the present discourse. The first point is that mathematical concepts turn up in entirely unexpected connections. Moreover, they often permit an unexpectedly close and accurate description of the phenomena in these connections. Secondly, just because of this circumstance, and because we do not understand the reasons of their usefulness, we cannot know whether a theory formulated in terms of mathematical concepts is uniquely appropriate. We are in a position similar to that of a man who was provided with a bunch of keys and who, having to open several doors in succession, always hit on the right key on the first or second trial. He became skeptical concerning the uniqueness of the coordination between keys and doors.

Most of what will be said on these questions will not be new; it has probably occurred to most scientists in one form or another. My principal aim is to illuminate it from several sides. The first point is that the enormous usefulness of mathematics in the natural sciences is something bordering on the mysterious and that there is no rational explanation for it. Second, it is just this uncanny usefulness of mathematical concepts that raises the question of the uniqueness of our physical theories. In order to establish the first point, that mathematics plays an unreasonably important role in physics, it will be useful to say a few words on the question, "What is mathematics?", then, "What is physics?", then, how mathematics enters physical theories, and last, why the success of mathematics in its role in physics appears so baffling. Much less will be said on the second point: the uniqueness of the theories of physics. A proper answer to this question would require elaborate experimental and theoretical work which has not been undertaken to date.

---

[1] The remark to be quoted was made by F. Werner when he was a student in Princeton.

What Is Mathematics?

Somebody once said that philosophy is the misuse of a terminology which was invented just for this purpose.[2] In the same vein, I would say that mathematics is the science of skillful operations with concepts and rules invented just for this purpose. The principal emphasis is on the invention of concepts. Mathematics would soon run out of interesting theorems if these had to be formulated in terms of the concepts which already appear in the axioms. Furthermore, whereas it is unquestionably true that the concepts of elementary mathematics and particularly elementary geometry were formulated to describe entities which are directly suggested by the actual world, the same does not seem to be true of the more advanced concepts, in particular the concepts which play such an important role in physics. Thus, the rules for operations with pairs of numbers are obviously designed to give the same results as the operations with fractions which we first learned without reference to "pairs of numbers." The rules for the operations with sequences, that is, with irrational numbers, still belong to the category of rules which were determined so as to reproduce rules for the operations with quantities which were already known to us. Most more advanced mathematical concepts, such as complex numbers, algebras, linear operators, Borel sets—and this list could be continued almost indefinitely—were so devised that they are apt subjects on which the mathematician can demonstrate his ingenuity and sense of formal beauty. In fact, the definition of these concepts, with a realization that interesting and ingenious considerations could be applied to them, is the first demonstration of the ingeniousness of the mathematician who defines them. The depth of thought which goes into the formulation of the mathematical concepts is later justified by the skill with which these concepts are used. The great mathematician fully, almost ruthlessly, exploits the domain of permissible reasoning and skirts the impermissible. That his recklessness does not lead him into a morass of contradictions is a miracle in itself: certainly it is hard to believe that our reasoning power was brought, by Darwin's process of natural selection, to the perfection which it seems to possess. However, this is not our present subject. The principal point which will have to be recalled later is that the mathematician could

[2] This statement is quoted here from W. Dubislav's *Die Philosophie der Mathematik in der Gegenwart* (Berlin: Junker and Dünnhaupt Verlag, 1932), p. 1.

formulate only a handful of interesting theorems without defining concepts beyond those contained in the axioms and that the concepts outside those contained in the axioms are defined with a view of permitting ingenious logical operations which appeal to our aesthetic sense both as operations and also in their results of great generality and simplicity.[3]

The complex numbers provide a particularly striking example for the foregoing. Certainly, nothing in our experience suggests the introduction of these quantities. Indeed, if a mathematician is asked to justify his interest in complex numbers, he will point, with some indignation, to the many beautiful theorems in the theory of equations, of power series, and of analytic functions in general, which owe their origin to the introduction of complex numbers. The mathematician is not willing to give up his interest in these most beautiful accomplishments of his genius.[4]

What Is Physics?

The physicist is interested in discovering the laws of inanimate nature. In order to understand this statement, it is necessary to analyze the concept, "law of nature."

The world around us is of baffling complexity and the most obvious fact about it is that we cannot predict the future. Although the joke attributes only to the optimist the view that the future is uncertain, the optimist is right in this case: the future is unpredictable. It is, as Schrödinger has remarked, a miracle that in spite of the baffling complexity of the world, certain regularities in the events could be discovered (1).* One such regularity, discovered by Galileo, is that two rocks, dropped at the same time from the same height, reach the ground at the same time. The laws of nature are concerned with such regularities. Galileo's regularity is a prototype of a large class of regularities. It is a surprising regularity for three reasons.

The first reason that it is surprising is that it is true not only in Pisa, and in Galileo's time, it is true everywhere on the Earth, was always

[3] M. Polanyi, in his *Personal Knowledge* (Chicago: University of Chicago Press, 1958), says: "All these difficulties are but consequences of our refusal to see that mathematics cannot be defined without acknowledging its most obvious feature: namely, that it is interesting" (page 188).

[4] The reader may be interested, in this connection, in Hilbert's rather testy remarks about intuitionism which "seeks to break up and to disfigure mathematics," *Abh. Math. Sem.*, Univ. Hamburg, 157 (1922), or *Gesammelte Werke* (Berlin: Springer, 1935), p. 188.

* The numbers in parentheses refer to the References at the end of the article.

true, and will always be true. This property of the regularity is a recognized invariance property and, as I had occasion to point out some time ago (2), without invariance principles similar to those implied in the preceding generalization of Galileo's observation, physics would not be possible. The second surprising feature is that the regularity which we are discussing is independent of so many conditions which could have an effect on it. It is valid no matter whether it rains or not, whether the experiment is carried out in a room or from the Leaning Tower, no matter whether the person who drops the rocks is a man or a woman. It is valid even if the two rocks are dropped, simultaneously and from the same height, by two different people. There are, obviously, innumerable other conditions which are all immaterial from the point of view of the validity of Galileo's regularity. The irrelevancy of so many circumstances which *could* play a role in the phenomenon observed has also been called an invariance (2). However, this invariance is of a different character from the preceding one since it cannot be formulated as a general principle. The exploration of the conditions which do, and which do not, influence a phenomenon is part of the early experimental exploration of a field. It is the skill and ingenuity of the experimenter which show him phenomena which depend on a relatively narrow set of relatively easily realizable and reproducible conditions.[5] In the present case, Galileo's restriction of his observations to relatively heavy bodies was the most important step in this regard. Again, it is true that if there were no phenomena which are independent of all but a manageably small set of conditions, physics would be impossible.

The preceding two points, though highly significant from the point of view of the philosopher, are not the ones which surprised Galileo most, nor do they contain a specific law of nature. The law of nature is contained in the statement that the length of time which it takes for a heavy object to fall from a given height is independent of the size, material, and shape of the body which drops. In the framework of Newton's second "law," this amounts to the statement that the gravitational force which acts on the falling body is proportional to its mass but independent of the size, material, and shape of the body which falls.

---

[5] See, in this connection, the graphic essay of M. Deutsch, *Daedalus*, 87, 86 (1958). A. Shimony has called my attention to a similar passage in C. S. Peirce's *Essays in the Philosophy of Science* (New York: The Liberal Arts Press, 1957), p. 237.

The preceding discussion is intended to remind us, first, that it is not at all natural that "laws of nature" exist, much less that man is able to discover them.[6] The present writer had occasion, some time ago, to call attention to the succession of layers of "laws of nature," each layer containing more general and more encompassing laws than the previous one and its discovery constituting a deeper penetration into the structure of the universe than the layers recognized before (3). However, the point which is most significant in the present context is that all these laws of nature contain, in even their remotest consequences, only a small part of our knowledge of the inanimate world. All the laws of nature are conditional statements which permit a prediction of some future events on the basis of the knowledge of the present, except that some aspects of the present state of the world, in practice the overwhelming majority of the determinants of the present state of the world, are irrelevant from the point of view of the prediction. The irrelevancy is meant in the sense of the second point in the discussion of Galileo's theorem.[7]

As regards the present state of the world, such as the existence of the earth on which we live and on which Galileo's experiments were performed, the existence of the sun and of all our surroundings, the laws of nature are entirely silent. It is in consonance with this, first, that the laws of nature can be used to predict future events only under exceptional circumstances—when all the relevant determinants of the present state of the world are known. It is also in consonance with this that the construction of machines, the functioning of which he can foresee, constitutes the most spectacular accomplishment of the physicist. In these machines, the physicist creates a situation in which all the relevant coordinates are known so that the behavior of the machine can be predicted. Radars and nuclear reactors are examples of such machines.

The principal purpose of the preceding discussion is to point out that the laws of nature are all conditional statements and they relate only to a very small part of our knowledge of the world. Thus, classical mechanics, which is the best known prototype of a physical theory, gives the second derivatives of the positional coordinates of all bodies, on

[6] E. Schrödinger, in his *What Is Life* (Cambridge: Cambridge University Press, 1945), p. 31, says that this second miracle may well be beyond human understanding.

[7] The writer feels sure that it is unnecessary to mention that Galileo's theorem, as given in the text, does not exhaust the content of Galileo's observations in connection with the laws of freely falling bodies.

the basis of the knowledge of the positions, etc., of these bodies. It gives no information on the existence, the present positions, or velocities of these bodies. It should be mentioned, for the sake of accuracy, that we discovered about thirty years ago that even the conditional statements cannot be entirely precise: that the conditional statements are probability laws which enable us only to place intelligent bets on future properties of the inanimate world, based on the knowledge of the present state. They do not allow us to make categorical statements, not even categorical statements conditional on the present state of the world. The probabilistic nature of the "laws of nature" manifests itself in the case of machines also, and can be verified, at least in the case of nuclear reactors, if one runs them at very low power. However, the additional limitation of the scope of the laws of nature[8] which follows from their probabilistic nature will play no role in the rest of the discussion.

The Role of Mathematics in Physical Theories

Having refreshed our minds as to the essence of mathematics and physics, we should be in a better position to review the role of mathematics in physical theories.

Naturally, we do use mathematics in everyday physics to evaluate the results of the laws of nature, to apply the conditional statements to the particular conditions which happen to prevail or happen to interest us. In order that this be possible, the laws of nature must already be formulated in mathematical language. However, the role of evaluating the consequences of already established theories is not the most important role of mathematics in physics. Mathematics, or, rather, applied mathematics, is not so much the master of the situation in this function: it is merely serving as a tool.

Mathematics does play, however, also a more sovereign role in physics. This was already implied in the statement, made when discussing the role of applied mathematics, that the laws of nature must have been formulated in the language of mathematics to be an object for the use of applied mathematics. The statement that the laws of nature are written in the language of mathematics was properly made three hundred years ago[9]; it is now more true than ever before. In order to show the importance which mathematical concepts possess in the formulation

[8] See, for instance, E. Schrödinger, reference (1).
[9] It is attributed to Galileo.

of the laws of physics, let us recall, as an example, the axioms of quantum mechanics as formulated, explicitly, by the great mathematician, von Neumann, or, implicitly, by the great physicist, Dirac (4, 5). There are two basic concepts in quantum mechanics: states and observables. The states are vectors in Hilbert space, the observables self-adjoint operators on these vectors. The possible values of the observations are the characteristic values of the operators—but we had better stop here lest we engage in a listing of the mathematical concepts developed in the theory of linear operators.

It is true, of course, that physics chooses certain mathematical concepts for the formulation of the laws of nature, and surely only a fraction of all mathematical concepts is used in physics. It is true also that the concepts which were chosen were not selected arbitrarily from a listing of mathematical terms but were developed, in many if not most cases, independently by the physicist and recognized then as having been conceived before by the mathematician. It is not true, however, as is so often stated, that this had to happen because mathematics uses the simplest possible concepts and these were bound to occur in any formalism. As we saw before, the concepts of mathematics are not chosen for their conceptual simplicity—even sequences of pairs of numbers are far from being the simplest concepts—but for their amenability to clever manipulations and to striking, brilliant arguments. Let us not forget that the Hilbert space of quantum mechanics is the complex Hilbert space, with a Hermitean scalar product. Surely to the unpreoccupied mind, complex numbers are far from natural or simple and they cannot be suggested by physical observations. Furthermore, the use of complex numbers is in this case not a calculational trick of applied mathematics but comes close to being a necessity in the formulation of the laws of quantum mechanics. Finally, it now begins to appear that not only complex numbers but so-called analytic functions are destined to play a decisive role in the formulation of quantum theory. I am referring to the rapidly developing theory of dispersion relations.

It is difficult to avoid the impression that a miracle confronts us here, quite comparable in its striking nature to the miracle that the human mind can string a thousand arguments together without getting itself into contradictions, or to the two miracles of the existence of laws of nature and of the human mind's capacity to divine them. The observation which comes closest to an explanation for the mathematical concepts' cropping up in physics which I know is Einstein's statement that the only physical theories which we are willing to accept are the beautiful ones. It stands to argue that the concepts of mathematics, which invite the exercise of so much wit, have the quality of beauty. However, Einstein's observation can at best explain properties of theories which we are willing to believe and has no reference to the intrinsic accuracy of the theory. We shall, therefore, turn to this latter question.

Is the Success of Physical Theories Truly Surprising?

A possible explanation of the physicist's use of mathematics to formulate his laws of nature is that he is a somewhat irresponsible person. As a result, when he finds a connection between two quantities which resembles a connection well-known from mathematics, he will jump at the conclusion that the connection *is* that discussed in mathematics simply because he does not know of any other similar connection. It is not the intention of the present discussion to refute the charge that the physicist is a somewhat irresponsible person. Perhaps he is. However, it is important to point out that the mathematical formulation of the physicist's often crude experience leads in an uncanny number of cases to an amazingly accurate description of a large class of phenomena. This shows that the mathematical language has more to commend it than being the only language which we can speak; it shows that it is, in a very real sense, the correct language. Let us consider a few examples.

The first example is the oft-quoted one of planetary motion. The laws of falling bodies became rather well established as a result of experiments carried out principally in Italy. These experiments could not be very accurate in the sense in which we understand accuracy today partly because of the effect of air resistance and partly because of the impossibility, at that time, to measure short time intervals. Nevertheless, it is not surprising that, as a result of their studies, the Italian natural scientists acquired a familiarity with the ways in which objects travel through the atmosphere. It was Newton who then brought the law of freely falling objects into relation with the motion of the moon, noted that the parabola of the thrown rock's path on the earth and the circle of the moon's path in the sky are particular cases of the same mathematical object of an ellipse, and postulated the universal law of gravitation on the basis of a single, and at that time very approximate, numerical coincidence. Philosophically, the law of gravitation as formulated by Newton was repugnant to his time and to himself. Empirically, it was based on very scanty observations. The mathematical language in which it was formulated contained the concept of a second derivative and those of us who have tried to draw an osculating circle to a curve know that the second derivative is not a very immediate concept. The law of gravity which Newton reluctantly established and which he could verify with an accuracy of about 4% has proved to be accurate to less than a ten thousandth of a per cent and became so closely associated with the idea of absolute accuracy that only recently did physicists become again bold enough to inquire into the limitations of its accuracy.[10] Certainly, the example of Newton's law, quoted over and over again, must be mentioned first as a monumental example of a law, formulated in terms which appear simple to the mathematician, which has proved accurate beyond all reasonable expectations. Let us just recapitulate our thesis on this example: first, the law, particularly since a second derivative appears in it, is simple only to the mathematician, not to common sense or to non-mathematically-minded freshmen; second, it is a conditional law of very limited scope. It explains nothing about the earth which attracts Galileo's rocks, or about the circular form of the moon's orbit, or about the planets of the sun. The explanation of these initial conditions is left to the geologist and the astronomer, and they have a hard time with them.

The second example is that of ordinary, elementary quantum mechanics. This originated when Max Born noticed that some rules of computation, given by Heisenberg, were formally identical with the rules of computation with matrices, established a long time before by mathematicians. Born, Jordan, and Heisenberg then proposed to replace by matrices the position and momentum variables of the equations of classical mechanics (6). They applied the rules of matrix mechanics to a few highly idealized problems and the results were quite satisfactory. However, there was, at that time, no rational evidence that their matrix mechanics would prove correct under more realistic conditions. Indeed, they say "if the mechanics as here proposed should already be correct in its essential traits." As a matter of fact, the first application of their mechanics to a realistic problem, that of the hydrogen atom, was given several months later, by Pauli. This application gave results in agreement with experience. This was satisfactory but still understandable because Heisenberg's rules of calculation were abstracted from prob-

---

[10] See, for instance, R. H. Dicke, *Am. Sci.*, 25 (1959).

lems which included the old theory of the hydrogen atom. The miracle occurred only when matrix mechanics, or a mathematically equivalent theory, was applied to problems for which Heisenberg's calculating rules were meaningless. Heisenberg's rules presupposed that the classical equations of motion had solutions with certain periodicity properties; and the equations of motion of the two electrons of the helium atom, or of the even greater number of electrons of heavier atoms, simply do not have these properties, so that Heisenberg's rules cannot be applied to these cases. Nevertheless, the calculation of the lowest energy level of helium, as carried out a few months ago by Kinoshita at Cornell and by Bazley at the Bureau of Standards, agrees with the experimental data within the accuracy of the observations, which is one part in ten million. Surely in this case we "got something out" of the equations that we did not put in.

The same is true of the qualitative characteristics of the "complex spectra," that is, the spectra of heavier atoms. I wish to recall a conversation with Jordan, who told me, when the qualitative features of the spectra were derived, that a disagreement of the rules derived from quantum mechanical theory and the rules established by empirical research would have provided the last opportunity to make a change in the framework of matrix mechanics. In other words, Jordan felt that we would have been, at least temporarily, helpless had an unexpected disagreement occurred in the theory of the helium atom. This was, at that time, developed by Kellner and by Hilleraas. The mathematical formalism was too clear and unchangeable so that, had the miracle of helium which was mentioned before not occurred, a true crisis would have arisen. Surely, physics would have overcome that crisis in one way or another. It is true, on the other hand, that physics as we know it today would not be possible without a constant recurrence of miracles similar to the one of the helium atom, which is perhaps the most striking miracle that has occurred in the course of the development of elementary quantum mechanics, but by far not the only one. In fact, the number of analogous miracles is limited, in our view, only by our willingness to go after more similar ones. Quantum mechanics had, nevertheless, many almost equally striking successes which gave us the firm conviction that it is, what we call, correct.

The last example is that of quantum electrodynamics, or the theory of the Lamb shift. Whereas Newton's theory of gravitation still had obvious connections with experience, experience entered the formulation of matrix mechanics only in the refined or sublimated form of Heisenberg's prescriptions. The quantum theory of the Lamb shift, as conceived by Bethe and established by Schwinger, is a purely mathematical theory and the only direct contribution of experiment was to show the existence of a measurable effect. The agreement with calculation is better than one part in a thousand.

The preceding three examples, which could be multiplied almost indefinitely, should illustrate the appropriateness and accuracy of the mathematical formulation of the laws of nature in terms of concepts chosen for their manipulability, the "laws of nature" being of almost fantastic accuracy but of strictly limited scope. I propose to refer to the observation which these examples illustrate as the empirical law of epistemology. Together with the laws of invariance of physical theories, it is an indispensable foundation of these theories. Without the laws of invariance the physical theories could have been given no foundation of fact; if the empirical law of epistemology were not correct, we would lack the encouragement and reassurance which are emotional necessities, without which the "laws of nature" could not have been successfully explored. Dr. R. G. Sachs, with whom I discussed the empirical law of epistemology, called it an article of faith of the theoretical physicist, and it is surely that. However, what he called our article of faith can be well supported by actual examples—many examples in addition to the three which have been mentioned.

The Uniqueness of the Theories of Physics

The empirical nature of the preceding observation seems to me to be self-evident. It surely is not a "necessity of thought" and it should not be necessary, in order to prove this, to point to the fact that it applies only to a very small part of our knowledge of the inanimate world. It is absurd to believe that the existence of mathematically simple expressions for the second derivative of the position is self-evident, when no similar expressions for the position itself or for the velocity exist. It is therefore surprising how readily the wonderful gift contained in the empirical law of epistemology was taken for granted. The ability of the human mind to form a string of 1000 conclusions and still remain "right," which was mentioned before, is a similar gift.

Every empirical law has the disquieting quality that one does not know its limitations. We have seen that there are regularities in the events in the world around us which can be formulated in terms of mathematical concepts with an uncanny accuracy. There are, on the other hand, aspects of the world concerning which we do not believe in the existence of any accurate regularities. We call these initial conditions. The question which presents itself is whether the different regularities, that is, the various laws of nature which will be discovered, will fuse into a single consistent unit, or at least asymptotically approach such a fusion. Alternatively, it is possible that there always will be some laws of nature which have nothing in common with each other. At present, this is true, for instance, of the laws of heredity and of physics. It is even possible that some of the laws of nature will be in conflict with each other in their implications, but each convincing enough in its own domain so that we may not be willing to abandon any of them. We may resign ourselves to such a state of affairs or our interest in clearing up the conflict between the various theories may fade out. We may lose interest in the "ultimate truth," that is, in a picture which is a consistent fusion into a single unit of the little pictures, formed on the various aspects of nature.

It may be useful to illustrate the alternatives by an example. We now have, in physics, two theories of great power and interest: the theory of quantum phenomena and the theory of relativity. These two theories have their roots in mutually exclusive groups of phenomena. Relativity theory applies to macroscopic bodies, such as stars. The event of coincidence, that is, in ultimate analysis of collision, is the primitive event in the theory of relativity and defines a point in space-time, or at least would define a point if the colliding particles were infinitely small. Quantum theory has its roots in the microscopic world and, from its point of view, the event of coincidence, or of collision, even if it takes place between particles of no spatial extent, is not primitive and not at all sharply isolated in space-time. The two theories operate with different mathematical concepts—the four dimensional Riemann space and the infinite dimensional Hilbert space, respectively. So far, the two theories could not be united, that is, no mathematical formulation exists to which both of these theories are approximations. All physicists believe that a union of the two theories is inherently possible and that we shall find it. Nevertheless, it is possible also to imagine that no union of the two theories can be found. This example illustrates the two possibilities, of union and of conflict, mentioned before, both of which are conceivable.

In order to obtain an indication as to which alternative to expect ultimately, we can pretend to be a little more ignorant than we are and place ourselves at a lower level of knowledge than we actually possess. If we can find a fusion of our theories on this lower level of intelligence, we can confidently expect that we will find a fusion of our theories also at our real level of intelligence. On the other hand, if we would arrive at mutually contradictory theories at a somewhat lower level of knowledge, the possibility of the permanence of conflicting theories cannot be excluded for ourselves either. The level of knowledge and ingenuity is a continuous variable and it is unlikely that a relatively small variation of this continuous variable changes the attainable picture of the world from inconsistent to consistent.[11]

Considered from this point of view, the fact that some of the theories which we know to be false give such amazingly accurate results is an adverse factor. Had we somewhat less knowledge, the group of phenomena which these "false" theories explain would appear to us to be large enough to "prove" these theories. However, these theories are considered to be "false" by us just for the reason that they are, in ultimate analysis, incompatible with more encompassing pictures and, if sufficiently many such false theories are discovered, they are bound to prove also to be in conflict with each other. Similarly, it is possible that the theories, which we consider to be "proved" by a number of numerical agreements which appears to be large enough for us, are false because they are in conflict with a possible more encompassing theory which is beyond our means of discovery. If this were true, we would have to expect conflicts between our theories as soon as their number grows beyond a certain point and as soon as they cover a sufficiently large number of groups of phenomena. In contrast to the article of faith of the theoretical physicist mentioned before, this is the nightmare of the theorist.

---

[11] This passage was written after a great deal of hesitation. The writer is convinced that it is useful, in epistemological discussions, to abandon the idealization that the level of human intelligence has a singular position on an absolute scale. In some cases it may even be useful to consider the attainment which is possible at the level of the intelligence of some other species. However, the writer also realizes that his thinking along the lines indicated in the text was too brief and not subject to sufficient critical appraisal to be reliable.

Let us consider a few examples of "false" theories which give, in view of their falseness, alarmingly accurate descriptions of groups of phenomena. With some goodwill, one can dismiss some of the evidence which these examples provide. The success of Bohr's early and pioneering ideas on the atom was always a rather narrow one and the same applies to Ptolemy's epicycles. Our present vantage point gives an accurate description of all phenomena which these more primitive theories can describe. The same is not true any longer of the so-called free-electron theory, which gives a marvellously accurate picture of many, if not most, properties of metals, semiconductors, and insulators. In particular, it explains the fact, never properly understood on the basis of the "real theory," that insulators show a specific resistance to electricity which may be 10^{26} times greater than that of metals. In fact, there is no experimental evidence to show that the resistance is not infinite under the conditions under which the free-electron theory would lead us to expect an infinite resistance. Nevertheless, we are convinced that the free-electron theory is a crude approximation which should be replaced, in the description of all phenomena concerning solids, by a more accurate picture.

If viewed from our real vantage point, the situation presented by the free-electron theory is irritating but is not likely to forebode any inconsistencies which are unsurmountable for us. The free-electron theory raises doubts as to how much we should trust numerical agreement between theory and experiment as evidence for the correctness of the theory. We are used to such doubts.

A much more difficult and confusing situation would arise if we could, some day, establish a theory of the phenomena of consciousness, or of biology, which would be as coherent and convincing as our present theories of the inanimate world. Mendel's laws of inheritance and the subsequent work on genes may well form the beginning of such a theory as far as biology is concerned. Furthermore, it is quite possible that an abstract argument can be found which shows that there is a conflict between such a theory and the accepted principles of physics. The argument could be of such abstract nature that it might not be possible to resolve the conflict, in favor of one or of the other theory, by an experiment. Such a situation would put a heavy strain on our faith in our theories and on our belief in the reality of the concepts which we form. It would give us a deep sense of frustration in our search for what I called "the ultimate truth." The reason that such a situation is conceivable is that, fundamentally, we do not know why our theories work so well. Hence, their accuracy may not prove their truth and consistency. Indeed, it is this writer's belief that something rather akin to the situation which was described above exists if the present laws of heredity and of physics are confronted.

Let me end on a more cheerful note. The miracle of the appropriateness of the language of mathematics for the formulation of the laws of physics is a wonderful gift which we neither understand nor deserve. We should be grateful for it and hope that it will remain valid in future research and that it will extend, for better or for worse, to our pleasure, even though perhaps also to our bafflement, to wide branches of learning.

The writer wishes to record here his indebtedness to Dr. M. Polanyi, who, many years ago, deeply influenced his thinking on problems of epistemology, and to V. Bargmann, whose friendly criticism was material in achieving whatever clarity was achieved. He is also greatly indebted to A. Shimony for reviewing the present article and calling his attention to C. S. Peirce's papers.

References

(1) Schrödinger, E., *Über Indeterminismus in der Physik* (Leipzig: J. A. Barth, 1932); also Dubislav, W., *Naturphilosophie* (Berlin: Junker und Dünnhaupt, 1933), Chap. 4.

(2) Wigner, E. P., "Invariance in Physical Theory," *Proc. Am. Phil. Soc.*, 93, 521-526 (1949), reprinted in this volume.

(3) Wigner, E. P., "The Limits of Science," *Proc. Am. Phil. Soc.*, 94, 422 (1950); also Margenau, H., *The Nature of Physical Reality* (New York: McGraw-Hill, 1950), Ch. 8, reprinted in this volume.

(4) Dirac, P. A. M., *Quantum Mechanics*, 3rd ed. (Oxford: Clarendon Press, 1947).

(5) von Neumann, J., *Mathematische Grundlagen der Quantenmechanik* (Berlin: Springer, 1932). English translation (Princeton, N.J.: Princeton Univ. Press, 1955).

(6) Born, M., and Jordan, P., "On Quantum Mechanics," *Z. Physik*, 34, 858-888 (1925). Born, M., Heisenberg, W., and Jordan, P., "On Quantum Mechanics," Part II, *Z. Physik*, 35, 557-615 (1926). (The quoted sentence occurs in the latter article, page 558.)

18

Twentieth Birthday of the Atomic Age

Though it had been coming for nearly half a century, the Atomic Age began 20 years ago—on Dec. 2, 1942—when a man-made nuclear chain reaction was established for the first time. The event took place in a converted squash court, underneath the west stands of the University of Chicago's Stagg Field. While those of us who carried out the experiment were aware of its possible long-term significance, our principal concern was for its effectiveness as a step toward victory over Germany and Japan—an outcome which, at the time, seemed far from certain. That very morning, The New York Times carried on its front page reports about bitter air battles over Tunisia and Guadalcanal, and the discouraging headline: *"President Refuses To Prophesy On War."*

As part of the Uranium Project that ultimately led to development of the atomic bomb, the Stagg Field experiment had been prepared in secrecy, and consequently not many were present to witness it. Arthur H. Compton, director of the project, was there; so, of course, was Enrico Fermi, the head of our group and chief planner of the experiment. Others included Fermi's trusted lieutenants: Herbert Anderson, Harold Lichtenberger, John Marshall, George Weil, Walter Zinn, and some others. Also, Compton had asked me to bring along Crawford H. Greenewalt, later president of the du Pont Company and at that time in charge of its negotiations toward the large-scale application of the chain reaction we were trying to achieve.

Reprinted by permission from *The New York Times Magazine*, Dec. 2, 1962, p. 34.

The theory of uranium fission had been firmly established several years before. A neutron penetrates the heavy nucleus of uranium. The nucleus breaks up, releasing its *own* neutrons which penetrate other nuclei in turn. If the piece of uranium is large enough (of "critical" size), fission will carry on by itself in a continuous chain. The uranium can be "burned" very quickly, releasing vast amounts of energy—and that is an atomic bomb. Or it can be "burned" slowly, in an atomic "pile," or reactor, to provide a convertible source of power.

Considering the crucial nature of the experiment, the materials used in it would have seemed quite unimpressive to an outsider. They consisted of a few thousand cubic feet of graphite in the form of rectangular columns 4 inches thick and 60 inches long, and several thousand slugs of uranium. The graphite columns were laid horizontally, and had holes of about 2 inches in diameter in the upper surface. The uranium slugs were inserted into these holes as the columns were piled up, one layer on top of the other: hence the name "pile" for the chain reactor. The completed graphite structure had a shape similar to a house, about 15 feet long on each side and approximately the same height.

As the structure grew, the number of neutrons it emitted (the so-called neutron background) increased, and this led to an increased frequency of the clicking of counters placed near the surface of the pile. As the pile's size approached the "critical" or chain-reacting stage, the addition of even a small amount of material increased the background considerably. "Control rods" were therefore inserted to absorb the neutrons and thus hold the pile in check.

When our group assembled on that 2d of December, the pile was large enough so that it would have been chain-reacting without the control rods. We stood on the balcony of the court and Fermi directed the withdrawal of the rods in steps of about a foot each. After each step, the clicking of the counters started to speed up, but soon leveled off and reached a steady value. This steady clicking rate became higher and higher as the control rods were pulled out further and further. However, this was still "background," for the counting rate was still leveling off. Finally, at the last stage, the clicking (thus the flow of neutrons inside the pile) continued to increase and did not seem to approach a steady state. Left alone, in another few minutes the neutron count would have doubled, then doubled again during the same interval, and so on.

This meant that the self-sustaining chain reaction was established; the pile was "critical." When it was certain that this stage had been reached, Fermi had the control rods reinserted and the clicking died down.

Nothing very spectacular had happened. Nothing had moved and the pile itself had given no sound. Nevertheless, when the rods were pushed back and the clicking died down, we suddenly experienced a let-down feeling, for all of us understood the language of the counters. Even though we had anticipated the success of the experiment, its accomplishment had a deep impact on us. For some time we had known that we were about to unlock a giant; still, we could not escape an eerie feeling when we knew we had actually done it. We felt as, I presume, everyone feels who has done something that he knows will have very far-reaching consequences which he cannot foresee.

I produced a bottle of imported Chianti from a brown paper bag on the balcony floor. Italian wine was appropriate because our leader, Fermi, was of Italian birth. He uncorked the bottle and we toasted the success of the experiment. As we drank the wine from paper cups, we sent up silent prayers that what we had done was the right thing to do. I do not remember whether any of us gave expression to his sentiments but we knew each other too well not to sense what was in the others' minds.

The physical phenomenon on which our work was based, uranium fission, had been discovered in Germany at the beginning of 1939 and the potentialities of the discovery were soon apparent to the community of physicists. Many of us, fearing that the German Government would seize upon the process as a military means toward the conquest of the world, urged our Government to support work on it on a larger scale. As spokesman, Einstein signed an urgent message to President Roosevelt in mid-1939.

In spite of this, little was done at first, and we feared that Germany was far ahead in uranium research. We knew that Hitler had stopped the sale of uranium from the rich mines of Czechoslovakia which he had taken over, and had increased the production of heavy water (used as a moderator in reactors) at his captured refinery in Norway—in 1940 the world's only heavy-water refinery. Furthermore, we heard reports that German nuclear experts—some of the world's leading physicists—had been brought together from laboratories all over Germany to concentrate on hitching the atom to Hitler's juggernaut.

Those of us in the American scientific community who were most alarmed by these reports knew very well the destructive power which was involved: that a single pound of uranium-235 contains as much energy as 10,000 tons of TNT, and may produce an explosive pressure many million times greater. The fear that Hitler might be the first to acquire so decisive a military advantage drove us to feverish efforts.

But despite the hectic pace dictated by our fears, there was little haphazard about our Dec. 2 results. From theoretical calculations and preliminary experiments, we knew that the chain reaction could be established with natural uranium. Indeed, Fermi's "pile" was running less than 24 hours after the arrival of the necessary materials. For months we had been so sure that this would happen that some jokester remarked afterward that it had required more foresight to buy the Chianti before imported Italian wine became scarce than to predict that the bottle would be needed before 1942 was out.

Do we then exaggerate the importance of Fermi's famous experiment? I may have thought so sometime in the past, but do not believe it now. The experiment *was* the culmination of the efforts to prove the chain reaction. The elimination of the last doubts in the information on which our further work had to depend had a decisive influence on our effectiveness in tackling the second problem of the Chicago project: the design and realization of a large-scale reactor to produce the nuclear explosive plutonium. This objective could now be pursued with all the energy and imagination which the project could muster.

Even though our hearts were by no means light when we sipped our wine around Fermi's pile, our fears were undefined, like the vague apprehensions of a man who has done something bigger than he ever expected to. Our forebodings did not concern concrete events. In fact, our hopes, some of them very far-reaching, preponderated.

How perceptive were our speculations, some two decades ago, at the threshold of the atomic age? In several particulars, we turned out to be right—or on the right track. In at least two important ways, we misjudged badly.

To begin with the positive side, it is worth repeating that our prime objective in 1942 was victory over Germany and Japan. We did not underestimate the wartime importance of controlling nuclear energy. As for postwar applications, we were quite correct in predicting that the uranium project would stimulate the use of such radioactive elements as tracers and indicators. It is hard to find a modern laboratory or research institution which does not make use of these tools: they are as commonplace as electric furnaces.

While radioisotopes have specific significance for research, by far the most important social and economic effect of our achievement has been the postwar support for, and influence of, science in general. We expected some such burgeoning, but our forecasts have been exceeded many times. Indeed, the recognition of science as a decisive factor on the national and international scene has led to a massive increase of the influence of scientists in government and industry.

Whether the scientific community's increased prestige has helped science in a true sense is not an easy question to answer. Many of us find it difficult to give the undivided attention to our scientific problems which we were able to give them in the old "ivory tower" days, when we had neither the opportunity nor the responsibility of counseling government. And further, since our judgment and advice as counselors cannot be independent of our political views, and since scientists, like other intellectuals, are individualistic, disagreements have arisen among us. As a result, the coherence of the scientific community and the respect of scientists for one another have suffered. It is not surprising that a song which has long been popular in scientific circles contains the phrase: "Take back your billion dollars. . . ."

Nevertheless, the increased prestige and freer flow of dollars has helped to speed up scientific progress: an outcome which, though on a much more modest scale, we foresaw correctly 20 years ago.

Of our two regrettably inaccurate predictions, the first is economic, the second political. Our economic expectations concerning cheap nuclear power have, so far at any rate, failed us rather completely. The long experience of our engineers in the building and operating of coal- or oil-fired power plants allowed a reduction of the investment and operating costs of these plants to a degree which cannot now be duplicated by the young nuclear-power industry. These items more than compensate for the lower fuel cost of nuclear-power plants, except perhaps in areas where the price of coal and oil is particularly high.

In addition, there are secondary cost items, such as increased insurance rates, which militate against the economy of nuclear power. Finally, we greatly overestimated the importance of power, or rather of fuel, in the national economy. The value of coal and oil from the ground contributes only 1 per cent of our gross national product. Their replacement by nuclear power could hardly usher in a golden age of plenty.

We still hope and expect that atomic energy will some day cost less than the present conventional power.* However, the primary objective of nuclear technology is no longer inexpensive power but permanent sources of power: not to compete with coal and oil, but to replace them when they become scarce, as they will during the next century.

We were mistaken enough in expecting a postwar prosperity based on cheap nuclear power; but to expect atomic weaponry to do away with international conflict was our greatest, and least excusable, failure of insight. Far from promoting world security, atomic weapons have led to the current "balance of terror," and many of us today have come nearly full circle in believing that only the abolition of such weapons can avert war and that nuclear disarmament *will*, in fact, have this effect. Even those of us who do not subscribe to this view have come to realize that our original premise failed to stand the test of the times.

What was the blind spot in our vision? How could we have been so wrong? As scientists, and therefore eager to enshrine reason, we made the false assumption that, with the survival of humanity at stake, nations would set their goals accordingly; that the very existence of nuclear weapons would neutralize potential conflicts and insure world peace. Any other outcome seemed utterly irrational.

What we failed to take into account is the rather obvious fact that conflicts do not arise logically, but emotionally; that they are caused by incompatible ambitions and desires, whether between nations or within a single country. The role of reason is real enough, but it does not determine our goals; it merely teaches us how to attain these, and at what cost.

In other words, the existence of nuclear weapons may shape a nation's strategy without resolving incompatibilities in its ambitions and desires or fundamentally altering its goals vis-à-vis other nations. A lion is still a lion, no matter how high-powered the rifle that prevents it from attacking the lamb.

Considering Hitler's goals, the history of the world would have been tragically different had Nazi science realized in 1939 or 1940 (as the reports so ominously indicated) that a fission bomb was feasible. On the other hand, considering the traditional goals of the United States, the world might be a far more secure place to live in today if this country had gone all out to develop and control nuclear fission right after

---

* This expectation is in the process of being realized now, around 1966.

Einstein's letter to President Roosevelt in August, 1939, advising "quick action."

We could have had the bomb during the winter of 1943-44, when Stalin's armed forces were still bottled up inside Russia, instead of in mid-1945, when the Soviet Army had overrun much of Central Europe and the Communist movement inside China had gained momentum. Had we got the bomb ready a year and a half sooner, we might have had time to use it as a psychological weapon before—or rather instead of —using it as a military weapon. At any rate, many more lives would have been saved. Furthermore, a document much less favorable to Stalin would have come out of the Yalta conference, and China might never have become an international threat.

So much for what might have been. What actually happened was that German nuclear scientists dropped their uranium project after deciding that an atomic bomb was impossible to achieve soon enough, while we in America waited until the day before Pearl Harbor, then spent $2 billion trying to catch up with Hitler in a race he had already abandoned.

Germany's failure to develop the bomb saved humanity from the Nazi nightmare; America's delay prevented humanity from achieving its dream of security in the postwar world. The reality—the cold war we ended up with—is not nearly so good as the dream of perpetual peace, but even a "balance of terror" is more desirable than to have risked the unbalanced terror of a "Thousand-Year Reich," with Hitler controlling atomic power.

In view of all this, I do not find it difficult to answer the question which others often ask me, and which I have also asked myself: whether, given another chance, I would again help to establish the nuclear chain reaction; whether (to put it more bluntly) I have pangs of conscience about my part in Fermi's experiment.

In a way, I would like to say that I do have such pangs—if only to please some of my questioners. But the fact is, I do not. I do not have them either emotionally or intellectually. I do not, because the nuclear chain reaction was bound to be achieved in any case, and I shudder at the thought that it might have been discovered first by an aggressive nation rather than our own.

19

Recall the Ends—
While Pondering the Means

As a result of a variety of studies, conducted mainly in the United States, there is a substantial body of literature on arms control. The general impression one receives from a study of the available literature can be summarized in a short sentence: the problem is very difficult. This applies particularly to the physical methods of inspection, and one cannot escape the impression that a good deal of wishful thinking has entered the articles on this subject. The nonphysical inspection techniques discussed by Jay Orear appear more promising, but even these show, on closer inspection, very serious gaps. In order to obtain a fair estimate of the difficulties of physical inspection, one has only to read the papers of the proponents of nonphysical inspection; the difficulties of the latter method are aptly analyzed in the papers on physical inspection. Also, present efforts are directed solely toward the elimination of weapons which are now known—they will not prevent the discovery of new, possibly even more dangerous weapons. Every such discovery will necessitate a new effort—probably just as difficult as the present one—toward new measures of control.

The ways in which an unsympathetic but self-reliant population can thwart inspection are too many to recount. But the very idea of a nonphysical inspection presupposes some rapport between control organs and at least some of the population. It is most questionable that such rapport could be established by as superficial means as monetary rewards. As to "guaranteed sanctuaries," there were too many violations of such promises; no circumspect person would take them at face value. These points are too self-evident to have escaped anyone who has made a detailed study of the question of arms control *without mutual confidence*. More subtle are two other points, because they contain hidden assumptions. The first of these assumptions is that there is no real temptation to conceal armaments; because of the nuclear stalemate, armaments are useless and their use would entail such severe losses that even the victor would suffer more than his gains are worth. This last statement is true only in the present state, when both parties are heavily armed. The same measures of disarmament which would increase the safety of every nation also would tempt each to evade the measures of disarmament. In a disarmed world, armaments are of very great value. As a result, it is most doubtful that an agreement on disarmament can be devised which it would be in the interest of both parties to observe.[1]

The second hidden assumption is that a reasonable probability of detection would deter nations from violations of the disarmament agreements. In the present state of the world, there is no reason to believe this. The only "penalty" envisaged in the case of a violation is that the other side of the disarmament agreement would abrogate the treaty. This is no serious penalty since it would, at worst, restore the pre-treaty situation. It would do even less, because the abrogating nation would

---

[1] It is often claimed that the U.S. has no "interest" in attaining military ascendancy over Russia and conversely, the USSR has no "interest" in a military ascendancy over the U.S. This argument, if taken seriously, makes it necessary to analyze the concept of "interest." What we call our interest is the fulfillment of our ambitions. The argument therefore amounts to the assertion that the government of the USSR, for instance, has no desire to assume military superiority over the U.S. It would be irresponsible to base the future of the independence of one's country on as delicate a psychological judgment as the assertion implies. Furthermore, no matter how much we trust the present rulers of the Soviet Union, in particular Premier Khrushchev, the motives and desires of his successors are surely unpredictable. This point has been emphasized by Dr. Leo Szilard.

It is of some interest to note that the proponents of unilateral disarmament do not share the belief that the USSR has no "interest" in subjugating the U.S. "We know perfectly well that the consequences of such radical action—unilateral disarmament—include invasion, conquest and tyranny." This opinion is not quoted to oppose unilateral disarmament, but to show that at least some who consider themselves to be highly moral have a different evaluation of the "interests" of nations than those who subscribe to the thesis that the rulers of the different nations have no desire to extend their realm.

have to act on the basis of suspicions only—thus incurring the disapproval of the rest of the world—and because the violator may have gained military ascendancy by the time the abrogation took effect. It follows that the temptation to violate the disarmament agreement would remain great.

In no control of disarmament which has been proposed to date can the violation be proved absolutely: it must be inferred from a number of minor indications. In Dr. Orear's system, these indications include the microscopic shift of the flap of an envelope; the fact that someone happened to turn up around the corner when the control organ's agent mailed his letter. Even the fact of these indications can be flatly denied by the violator, and even those who will accept the reality of the shift in the flap of the envelope (or the spying on the control agent) may not consider that these circumstances constitute adequate reasons for abrogating a treaty on disarmament. The abrogator will become unpopular throughout the world. A democracy will find it difficult to convince a sufficient majority even of its own public opinion that abrogation was necessary. Abrogation undertaken on the basis of suspicion would divide the country. At any rate, from the point of view of the violating nation, the abrogation would not be a serious calamity. It would merely restore the pre-treaty condition with some added propaganda advantage. Even this may be a too pessimistic appraisal from the point of view of the violator. By the time of the abrogation of the treaty, and by the time the rearmament of the opponent becomes appreciable, the violator may have secured his military ascendancy.

Past Disarmaments

Past history indicates the difficulties implicit in disarmament attempts. The attempt to limit the armaments of Germany, as provided in the Versailles treaty, gives an example of these difficulties. Germany eluded the disarmament clauses of the Versailles treaty, originally by the formation of the *"schwarze Reichswehr"* and otherwise.[2] This was done in the early days of the Weimar Republic, that is, under a government which surely had peaceful intentions. It was possible for a defeated nation to create a secret army. And although the signatories of the Versailles treaty surely

---

[2] I am much indebted to Prof. H. J. Gordon of the State University of Massachusetts for a review of the literature on the "schwarze Reichswehr."

suspected the existence of this paramilitary organization, they could not formulate and prove their suspicions clearly enough to intercede.

Return to Fundamentals

It may be argued that the paramilitary organizations in Germany did not constitute a truly significant military power. Still, an organization of a similar size, equipped with modern weapons, would constitute a decisive force *in a disarmed world*. Thus, all that we suspected as likely to happen under an uncareful program of disarmament did happen, and happened, furthermore, in a defeated country which was, militarily, at the mercy of its opponents.

If arms control in an atmosphere of tension is so difficult as a first step, it behooves us to investigate its relation to our ultimate objectives. Our true objective is a peaceful world, as much as possible free of tensions, in which all mankind can prosper and progress. Clearly, disarmament may be at best a first step toward this objective; it is not the objective itself. It is not even clear whether it is the most effective step: if the tension remains and hostilities break out, it will be a meager comfort that atomic weapons will be used only after a few months, rather than at once. The art of the preparation of atomic weapons will stay with us and the temporary absence of these weapons may soothe our fears but is not a solution of our problems. Even the permanent abolition of atomic weapons would be no solution. As Premier Khrushchev reminded us, new and and more terrible weapons can be discovered in the future. The Thirty Years' War, for instance, bears witness that untold misery can be generated also with relatively primitive weapons.

All this indicates that we have perhaps formulated our objective in too narrow a fashion. The true objective is a world in which everyone can breathe freely, in which no nation is worried lest it be confronted with a surprise attack tomorrow, and in which human dignity is respected. Armaments are more nearly a consequence of the tensions which follow from our not having achieved these aims than their cause. They do aggravate the tensions in their turn, but if the tensions are not present to begin with, their effect remains small also. The fact that U.S. armaments arouse no fear in Italy, or USSR armaments in China, illustrates this. Nevertheless, as a means to reduce tensions, it is clearly imperative to reduce the almost hysterically excessive amount of present armaments.

But this is not itself our ultimate objective. As one of our means it may be realizable—as the *objective*, it is not.

More Than Disarmament

It is clear that the reduction of tensions, the establishment of confidence, are at least as important as is disarmament, and the rest of the present paper will be concerned with measures in this direction. Such measures should not endanger the safety of the nations which adopt them.

The first and most obvious measure is to desist from inciting hatred toward any other nation. This point has been mentioned before but it remains ineffective because it requires fine judgment to distinguish between moderate, justifiable criticism of another government and the fanning of hatred toward it. A measure for dealing with hatreds based on ignorance was proposed at the time of the incipient conflict with the Nazi government. It had no prospect of adoption then because the Nazi government was opposed to the soothing of passions. The situation is probably different now. The proposal is that each government allot to the potentially hostile government a certain amount of space in every one of its journals and a certain period of time on its radio. There is no danger that the guest writer or guest speaker would abuse this privilege by insulting the host government or by propagating gross distortions. Such a procedure would be self-defeating, because most of the journal or radio time would be available for rebuttal before an intrinsically sympathetic audience. On the contrary, the guest statements would have a chance for sympathetic hearing only if they were strictly objective and honest. They might educate not only the audience but also the speaker.

There are two great advantages to this plan. First, it can be introduced as gradually as anyone might wish. Second, the measure is almost self-monitoring and violations would be resented not only by the host government but also by the host population as an insult to its power of discrimination. It would also force every government to articulate its aspirations and objectives and to prove to a skeptic audience that they are in the interest of all. This might lead to a critical reappraisal of the objectives and elimination or modification of some of them in a most salutary direction.

Together with this measure might go the freedom of circulation of all foreign papers in every country. The circulation of these would probably remain limited; nevertheless, the possibility of reading other papers remains very reassuring.

The second measure is an extension and modification of the summit conferences. A friend of mine proposed that a direct telephone line be established between the White House and the Kremlin.[3] Perhaps one should go even a few steps further and arrange for a scheduled meeting between the heads of government every month, between some on the next-to-highest level every week. At present, the heads of government see only people with whom they share the intention to maintain the power of their own country. This would be at least diluted if heads of government would meet regularly. To the loyalty to their own organizations would be added loyalty to all of mankind. When undertaking a decision as heads of government, at the backs of their minds would be the thought that their actions might come up at the next multi-nation discussion. Surely, the heads of government have no more important purpose than to secure peace and understanding; they must have the time to attend the meetings which serve these objectives.

The third measure is to strive more vigorously toward the open world which Professor Niels Bohr advocated eloquently in his letter to the United Nations.[4] Surely, nothing has contributed to mutual suspicion as much as the ubiquitous presence of secrets and prohibitions. The knowledge that there are no secret installations or secret intentions will contribute conversely to mutual confidence. It is unreasonable and probably hopeless to demand of another nation that it disarm because "I am disarming myself, but surely you must not know what happens in my country; you are excluded from vast territories in it." A world in which one can travel freely, in which there are no secrets, in which one can communicate with one's fellow men everywhere, such a world is a better world toward which we can strive with true enthusiasm. A world merely disarmed, with controllers nosing about everywhere and being thwarted at every step, is not. As Niels Bohr said in his open letter to the United Nations: "The efforts of all supporters of international cooperation, individuals as well as nations, will be needed to create in all countries an

[3] A "hot-line" between the White House and the Kremlin was established on June 6, 1963. *Eds.*

[4] Niels Bohr, "For an Open World," *Bull. Atomic Scientists,* 6, 213 (1950).

opinion, to voice with ever increasing clarity and strength the demand for an open world."

As far as I know, the desirability of the preceding propositions is generally admitted. One often hears, however, the argument that the propositions are not sound because, in the early stages of the program, Russia would have to make greater concessions than would the United States. This surely does not apply to the first two proposals and the opposite applies to many propositions which we discuss seriously and which may even be adopted. However, this is not the crux of the matter. We are not seeking reciprocity but a better world. As long as the process of the establishment of the better world does not endanger the safety of any nation, reciprocity is not a relevant consideration.

SOVIET TERRITORIES CLOSED TO FOREIGNERS

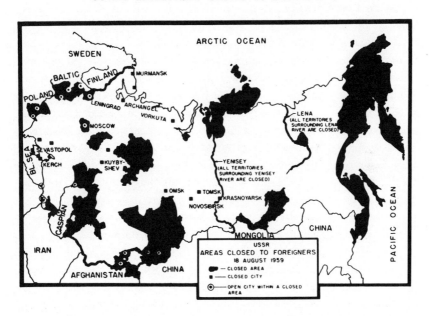

Territories of similar size, although not identical with those shown in this map, have been closed since 1941. In retaliation, in 1955 the United States government made similar territories in the U.S. inaccessible to citizens of the U.S.S.R. However, the United States government has repeatedly offered to abolish all travel restrictions to Soviet citizens on a mutual basis. The last note in this matter was presented August 19, 1958, but has been unanswered to date.

20

Enrico Fermi

Enrico Fermi was born on September 29, 1901, in Rome, Italy. He died on the twenty-eighth of November, 1954, in Chicago. He was one of the great physicists of the past quarter-century.

Fermi's ancestors were simple people. His father was an effective official of the Italian State Railway system, his mother a former school teacher. Enrico was the youngest of three children. The two boys, only a year apart in age, devoted to each other, shared an early interest in technical matters. Fermi's gift to improvise whatever material was at hand must already have been strong at an early age: among other things they built electric motors which actually ran. The sudden death of Giulio, at the age of fourteen, interrupted this companionship. However, the lonesome Enrico's interest turned even more to books and the study of mathematics and physics. This interest was further strengthened by his new friendship with Persico, then a budding mathematician.

At the end of his high school studies, Fermi won a scholarship at the Scuola Normale in Pisa. After four years of study, he apparently outgrew his teachers at that venerable institution and his doctoral dissertation, at twenty, seems to have shocked his learned audience by being a good margin above their heads. This was an experience which Fermi took to heart: never in later years did he overestimate his public and his addresses were so composed that the least advanced group in his audience could follow them.

Reprinted by permission from the *Yearbook of the American Philosophical Society*, 1955, pp. 435-39.

After a couple of fellowships, in Göttingen and Leyden, and teaching at Rome and Firenze, the young Fermi was called to Rome, as a result of O. M. Corbino's initiative, as a full professor of theoretical physics. He was twenty-five at that time. Fermi was soon joined, also at Corbino's initiative, by Rasetti and Amaldi, and a little later by Segré and Majorana. All of these early companions of Fermi in Rome are now highly respected physicists excepting the very ingenious Majorana, who died young under somewhat mystifying circumstances. The whole group acknowledged the leadership of Fermi, the "pope," and remained his life-long friends.

In 1929 Fermi married Laura Capon, a student at the University. She often helped him in his work, they wrote a book together, and she wrote his biography shortly before his death. It is a charming book about a great man as seen through the eyes of his affectionate wife.

In 1938 Fermi received the Nobel Prize for his work on neutron absorption. Italy was at that time already strongly under the influence of her northern neighbor and life there threatened to become intolerable, particularly for Laura Fermi, who was of Jewish ancestry. The family, therefore, decided not to return to Italy after the Nobel celebrations in Stockholm but to emigrate to America. Fermi had an invitation from Columbia University and he joined the faculty in 1939.

Hardly a few months in America had passed when Fermi began to assemble a group of collaborators, in place of those he left behind in Rome. Anderson, Marshall, Weil, Zinn were the most devoted members of his team. The work was, at first, a straight continuation of the general neutron research in Rome. However, when the discovery of the fission process became known, the group's attention turned to this subject. Some of the most important basic experiments necessary for establishing a neutron chain reaction were carried out at Columbia in collaboration with L. Szilard before the group joined Dr. A. H. Compton's laboratory in Chicago in 1942. The work was directed toward a technical goal: the establishment of a self-sustaining chain reaction and the production of the new element plutonium.

While the work at Columbia was carried on more or less on a shoestring, ample funds became available in Chicago. The self-sustaining chain reaction was established well within a year after the move, and within twenty-four hours after the receipt of a sufficient amount of metallic uranium. Fermi and his "gang" personally stacked up the graphite bricks—he always preferred to do a thing himself rather than prepare plans for others to follow. As a result, it took less time to build the first chain reactor than any of its successors. After having established the possibility of the chain reaction, Fermi's interest in reactors soon narrowed to their function as a research tool and neutron source. He was happy to leave the technical and administrative problems of the large scale chain reactors to others. However, he remained a trusted and respected adviser to all who participated in the solution of engineering problems and was always ready to help with word and deed. The writer remembers, for instance, that when the magnitude of the radioactivity induced by slow neutrons in oxygen became important, Fermi measured it within a day.

Fermi developed a great admiration and sincere affection for the leader of the project, A. H. Compton. It was on Compton's advice and invitation that he joined the faculty of the University of Chicago and remained in Chicago when the original uranium project disbanded at the end of the war. With him stayed most of the team he had assembled at Columbia. The interest of Fermi and of his immediate group soon shifted to high energy phenomena and Fermi was one of the foremost leaders in that field when he died. He left a deep gap in the hearts of his friends and collaborators and an equally deep gap in Chicago's Department of Physics and Institute of Nuclear Studies.

Fermi's most striking trait was his simplicity and realism, his willingness to accept facts and men as they were. He disliked complicated theories and avoided them as much as possible. Although he was one of the founders of quantum electrodynamics, he resisted using this theory as long as possible. His article on the Quantum Theory of Radiation in the *Reviews of Modern Physics* (1932) is a model of many of his addresses and lectures: nobody not fully familiar with the intricacies of the theory could have written it, nobody could have better avoided those intricacies. However, when he tackled a problem which could not be solved without the explicit use of the much disliked concepts of quantum field theories, he accepted this fact and one of his most brilliant papers is based on quantized fields.

The same simplicity and realism, which was manifest in Fermi's scientific work, manifested itself also in his human relations. Although he never engaged in subtle analyses of personalities, he knew what he could expect of his friends and colleagues and he seldom went wrong in his estimate. On a heroic scale was his acceptance of death. He faced it squarely and was able to joke about it with his most intimate colleagues a couple of weeks before his passing. The writer of these lines visited him ten days before he died. He was so completely composed that it appeared superhuman. "I hope it won't last long any more." It did not.

Fermi was a friend and mentor of almost every Italian physicist and of all who collaborated with him. His relations with his collaborators were always simple, friendly, and free of complications. "He was always completely fair with me, he never treated me either unkindly or with too much consideration," were the words of one of his most gifted students. This almost complete predictability, this simplicity and kind but unostentatious fairness doubtless were some of the cornerstones of Fermi's leadership and of his success in human relations.

Fermi's name is mentioned most often in connection with Fermi statistics, the Fermi-Thomas atomic model, his theory of β decay, the discovery of the effectiveness and nature of the slow neutrons, and the establishment of the first nuclear chain reaction. As is not uncommon, the first and best known of these accomplishments, the Fermi statistics, does not do justice to his genius. He has written scores of more imaginative papers, scores of papers that required deeper insight. His work on quantum electrodynamics, rarely mentioned, is a telling example. The theory of β decay, on the other hand, is a true picture of the scientist Fermi. This is the article which is based on the concepts of quantum field theories. However, the simplicity of the presentation puts at his ease even the reader who is unfamiliar with these theories. The paper is pervaded with an apparent naiveté which invites criticism and generalizations and a more learned presentation. In this writer's opinion this apparent naiveté is characteristic of Fermi's taste and did not represent his state of knowledge when he wrote the β decay article. He certainly could have added to it even at that time a good deal of abstract material which others would have considered highly significant.

The discovery of neutron-induced radioactivity, of the effectiveness and nature of slow neutrons, shows all the marks of a great experimental physicist. It was Fermi's first significant excursion into experimental physics and the choice of the subject and the timing of the excursion show deep intuition. The execution was speeded by his wonderful ability to make use of whatever equipment was handy in a laboratory not at all equipped for these investigations, and by the enthusiasm he inspired in his collaborators. Fermi received the Nobel Prize for these investigations in 1938. He was elected a member of the American Philosophical Society in 1939. In April, 1946, he was awarded the Lewis Prize of the Society for his part in the development and application of the concept of chain reactions.

Fermi's establishment of the first chain reaction is a lasting credit not only to his thoroughness and vision but also to his qualities of leadership. All his team followed his suggestions without question. He never hesitated either in outlining the next step or in retracing one if necessary.

Fermi was in full possession of his mental and physical powers until and throughout most of his last fatal disease. His institution and colleagues lost a great leader. Science lost one of the century's most productive physicists, and the world lost a simple and great man.

21

John von Neumann

The Canadian Mathematical Congress held its meeting last summer in Edmonton, Alberta. Professor Dixmier of Paris lectured on Algèbres de von Neumann. Dr. Zassenhaus' lectures on Group Theory started with von Neumann's definition of infinitesimal operators and their commutators. Dr. Tucker of Princeton lectured on the Theory of Games—another subject which was partially founded by Dr. von Neumann and greatly enriched by his ideas. Von Neumann made important contributions to all parts of mathematics, excepting number theory and topology, and he left his mark on theoretical physics and economics. His work during the war was vital for the success of several projects, and his contributions to the national welfare and national security did not cease, but rather intensified, with the termination of the war. He died as a member of the U. S. Atomic Energy Commission.

John von Neumann was born on December 28, 1903, the son of a well-to-do banker in Budapest, Hungary. He was a student of the Lutheran High School in his native city. This school was, at that time, perhaps the best high school of Hungary and probably also one of the best of the world. At least two teachers carried out independent research work, though on a modest scale; the majority of the teachers had an abiding interest in teaching and the guidance of the young men under their tutelage. Von Neumann's talents were soon recognized by the staff and the mathematics teacher, L. Ratz, to whom the present writer is also

Reprinted by permission from the *Yearbook of the American Philosophical Society,* 1957, pp. 149-153.

deeply indebted, took "Jancsi" (nickname for John) under his wing, gave private lessons to him, and introduced him at the University. The relations between University and at least some of the high schools were quite close, and von Neumann became well known in the flourishing circle of Budapest's mathematicians even before he was graduated from high school. The spiritual father of many Hungarian mathematicians, L. Fejer, coined the phrase "our country's greatest Jancsi" and this appellation stuck with von Neumann throughout his life.

In school and among his colleagues, Jancsi was somewhat retiring. He participated in the pranks of the class, but a bit half-heartedly, just enough to avoid unpopularity. He had a few close friends and was respected by all—intellectual strength was recognized and approved of by the student body, if not always envied. Jancsi loved to talk, and to talk about mathematics, even at that early age, and his friends often arrived late at home after a walk with him.

After his graduation from high school, von Neumann studied chemistry for two years at the University of Berlin and for two years in Zurich. The study of chemistry was a kind of insurance against the uncertainties of a career in mathematics. For a mathematician, only teaching positions appeared to be available and there were very few of these at the University. The salary at the high schools did not come up to the standards of his banker parents. Hence, a career in chemistry was decided upon as a compromise between Jancsi's scientific inclinations and the harsh realities as seen by his family and also by himself. However, much of the time of the chemistry student was spent in the company of the mathematicians of Berlin and of Zurich, and the attachment of the young student of chemistry to his subject of study was never very intimate. He finished his studies in chemistry, but took his Ph.D. in mathematics in Budapest during the same year in which his diploma in chemistry was granted in Zurich. Evidently, a Ph.D. thesis and examination did not constitute an appreciable effort.

After receiving his Ph.D., von Neumann continued his studies in Göttingen, Hamburg, and became Privatdozent in Berlin in 1927. Chemistry was quietly dropped and he turned increasingly toward mathematics and theoretical physics. He published some of his most lasting contributions during this period.

In 1929 von Neumann was invited to spend a term in Princeton. America proved to be a love at first sight to him and he took to the social and scientific atmosphere of Princeton as a duck takes to water. The invitation for a term was soon extended to a half-time appointment and, in 1931, to a full-time professorship. He and his wife, the former Marietta Kövesi, whom he married just before his first visit to Princeton, acquired many close friends in Princeton whose affection did not change for either husband or wife in the many years to come. Marietta's parties, and the gay atmosphere of their house, were proverbial in Princeton and a favored topic of conversation long after they separated in 1937. They had one daughter, Marina, who is now married and lives in Princeton.

In 1933, soon after the foundation of the Institute for Advanced Study, von Neumann was asked to join its faculty. The Institute was, at that time, a grandiose experiment in higher learning and research in this country, fathered by A. Flexner and O. Veblen and their forward-looking friends, who provided the funds for the venture. Von Neumann's invitation to the Institute—a thirty-year-old young man among some of the most distinguished and recognized mathematicians of the country—was not only a signal tribute to his abilities, but also manifested his complete integration into American life. He spent the rest of his scientific career at the Institute. It was still before the war that he married Klari Dan, whom he met in Hungary, and who survives him.

Von Neumann's activities during the war were manifold. The accomplishment which became most famous was his espousal of the implosion method for bringing nuclear fuel to explosion. He thought of this method independently of others, no doubt as a result of his intimate knowledge of shaped charges. Von Neumann did not sever his connections with the Services and with the work on nuclear energy at the cessation of the hostilities, but devoted much of his time, his energy, his ingenuity, and his judgment to an effort to strengthen the armed power of his adopted country. His last years were entirely devoted to work for the Government, and he died, after several years of service, as a member of the U. S. Atomic Energy Commission, on February 8, 1957.

It would be impossible to describe adequately von Neumann's contributions to the sciences—mathematics, physics, economics, technology—in less than a dozen pages. His work in mathematics—which was always closest to his heart and in which his brilliance could manifest itself most decisively—was strongly under the influence of Hilbert's axiomatic school. This applies not only to his work in mathematical logic, but also to his approach to other problems to which he contributed fundamentally: to the theory of Hilbert space and of unbounded operators, to quantum mechanics, to the theory of games. He characterized the objects with which his theory dealt by enumerating the properties which were to be used in the mathematical argument that followed, so that the results of the argument would apply to all objects which possess the properties enumerated. In addition to the subjects already mentioned, von Neumann contributed decisively to the theory of groups, and the algebra of operators. His work in theoretical physics culminated in the *Mathematische Grundlagen der Quantenmechanik,* published well before the war, but translated into English and republished only recently. His work in economics found its final expression in *The Theory of Games and Economic Behavior,* published in collaboration with O. Morgenstern, one of his closest friends in his later years. The principal result of his work on computers is, of course, the Princeton Computer and its many sisters. He has also published many articles dealing with the basic principles of computers and his work did much toward providing an axiomatic basis for their analysis.

Only an extraordinary mind could have made the unusual contributions to science which von Neumann made. The accuracy of his logic was, perhaps, the most decisive character of his mind. One had the impression of a perfect instrument whose gears were machined to mesh accurately to a thousandth of an inch. "If one listens to von Neumann, one understands how the human mind should work," was the verdict of one of our perceptive colleagues. Brilliance was the second, perhaps even more striking characteristic of von Neumann's mind. This property was clearly evident in the youth of fifteen. The third characteristic of his mind was its retentiveness. It was his exceptional memory which enabled him to pursue a host of hobbies, in addition to his scientific endeavors. He was an amateur historian as intimately familiar with long stretches of history as any professional. He spoke five languages well, was able to read Latin and Greek. He had read and remembered innumerable books, both fiction and popular summaries of other sciences. Of all the subjects this writer ever discussed with him, only the descriptive natural sciences did not arouse his interest. He was ever ready to help and he was genuinely interested in every problem that presented a challenge. I have learned more mathematics from him than from anyone else, and much more about the essence of creative thinking in mathematics than a lifetime's study without him could have taught me. "If he analyzed a problem, it was not necessary to discuss it any further. It was clear what had to be done," said the present chairman of the U. S. Atomic Energy Commission.

A deep sense of humor and an unusual ability for telling stories and jokes endeared Johnny even to casual acquaintances. He could be blunt when necessary, but was never pompous. A mind of von Neumann's inexorable logic had to understand and accept much that most of us do not want to accept and do not even wish to understand. This fact colored many of von Neumann's moral judgments. "It is just as foolish to complain that people are selfish and treacherous as it is to complain that the magnetic field does not increase unless the electric field has a curl. Both are laws of nature." Only scientific intellectual dishonesty and misappropriation of scientific results could rouse his indignation and ire—but these did—and did almost equally whether he himself, or someone else, was wronged.

When von Neumann realized that he was incurably ill, his logic forced him to realize also that he would cease to exist, and hence cease to have thoughts. Yet this is a conclusion the full content of which is incomprehensible to the human intellect and which, therefore, horrified him. It was heart-breaking to watch the frustration of his mind, when all hope was gone, in its struggle with the fate which appeared to him unavoidable but unacceptable.

Dr. von Neumann received much recognition for his scientific accomplishments. He was elected a member of our Society (1938) and of the National Academy of Sciences at an unusually early age. He was a corresponding member of the Royal Dutch Academy, of the Istituto Lombardo, of the Accademia dei Lincei, an associate member of the Peruvian Academy, a member of the American Academy of Arts and Sciences. He received the Medal for Merit, the Distinguished Civilian Service Award, and the Fermi Prize of the U. S. Atomic Energy Commission. His accomplishments were manifold, his was a great mind—perhaps one of the greatest of the first half of this century.

22

City Hall Speech—Stockholm, 1963

I wish to thank you first, in the names of Drs. Maria Goeppert-Mayer and Jensen, as well as in my own name, for the honor we received and for the beautiful celebration, for the truly heart-warming festivities, which we all enjoyed. We are all deeply grateful. However, new gratitude should never efface old ones and I wish to say at this occasion a few words on a subject about which we think little when young but which we appreciate increasingly when we reflect on our intellectual development. I mean our indebtedness to our teachers.

Man's knowledge has become man's knowledge rather than individual knowledge because he has developed codes in which sound signals correspond to objects and actions and he can learn one of these codes early in life in some mysterious way. Hence, people can communicate their knowledge and teach each other. Much of what we know, and most of the science which we know, was taught to us in this way. This process may be called manifest teaching-learning. Much can be said about this, in fact much has been said about it, but this is not my concern this evening.

What I wish to draw attention to is how much of our interest in science, and how much of our attitude toward science, we owe to our teachers. My own history begins in the high-school in Hungary where my mathematics teacher, Ratz, gave me books to read and evoked in me a sense for the beauty of his subject. I cannot mention all to whom I am indebted but I do wish to mention the inspiration received from Polanyi. He taught me, among other things, that science begins when a body of phenomena is available which shows some coherence and regularities, that science consists in assimilating these regularities and in creating concepts which permit expressing these regularities in a natural way. He also taught me that it is this method of science rather than the concepts themselves (such as energy) which should be applied to other fields of learning.

We have not only teachers who are older than we, we learn also from contemporaries and younger colleagues. The contemporary from whom I learned most—in fact immensely much—was von Neumann, but that was mostly mathematics. In leadership a young man at that time, Ray Herb, was my tutor. My scientific attitudes were greatly influenced also by students—some of whom had a more mature outlook than I. Perhaps I better not mention names lest they ask for a return of the tuition fee. To all of them I am deeply grateful, as we are to you for all that we have experienced today.

23

Convocation Address, University of Alberta

It is always a pleasure to speak to younger people and this pleasure, unlike other pleasures, comes more often as one grows older. It is more than a pleasure to speak to you today, it is a great honor and privilege.

We live in an anxious world and one in which all that is dear to us hangs in the balance. It is true enough that we are ourselves the principal causes of our troubles but this helps us in no way and we must face them. We indeed hear much advice and even commands on how we should behave but our problems are so great that our preoccupation with them may be too small rather than too deep. Now I expect to be recognized as a lawyer and hence a counsellor only for the rest of this day and only by the grace of my hosts. Nevertheless, I wish to seize the opportunity presented to me to add my own voice to those of others and tell you of some of the principles which I hope we may follow.

"Future is uncertain," says the optimist. You may have heard this joke; it is very old. Yet it was never more true than today. The destruction which threatens us today is a destruction of a completeness and extent hitherto unimagined. Furthermore, it is a threat common to most of the world, known to a large percentage of mankind, and yet man-made and man-controllable.

Nevertheless, it does not seem to me that the predicament in which we find ourselves is more novel than the joke which I quoted. Men have

Address presented when receiving honorary doctorate of law. Reprinted by permission from the *Proceedings of the Fourth Canadian Mathematics Congress* (Toronto: University of Toronto Press, 1959).

always feared for their own future as well as for the future of their world, feared for all that was dear to them. The world of the prehistoric man was his family, and it was only his family about which he was concerned. Even a few hundred years ago, his tribe or his village was the world of a man, containing all that was precious to him. Hence, his anxiety for the future of his family or tribe appeared as vital and important to him as ours appears overwhelming to us. The progress of technique and of communications has brought the whole earth to our doorstep and our heart has grown big enough to take in all humanity, to be worried about all mankind. Our anxiety, however, would not be smaller if we were concerned only about our own family, if only our immediate surroundings were dear to us and if only these would be threatened. New weapons, in particular, were always supposed to spell the doom of all. As early as 1139, the Lateran Council forbade the use of a new weapon, the crossbow, at least against Christians.

Neither is it a new phenomenon that the danger which we fear is man-made. It is a measure of the success of man as a biological unit that the enmity of other animals and the adversity of nature's forces have constituted, ever since historical times, a smaller threat to him than his own brothers. Our history books are filled with the story of the struggle of man with his neighbours, not with the story of his struggle with nature or with other animals.

Lastly, I am afraid, our situation is similar to that of our forefathers inasmuch as the conflicts which threaten us do not appear to be amenable to a solution by solely rational means. No amount of persuasion on the part of the Greeks would have moved the Persians to stay at home and cultivate their fields in peace; no amount of persuasion on the part of the American patriots would have succeeded in making the British abandon the rule of their country and no amount of persuasion on the part of the British would have encouraged the patriots to pay their taxes peacefully. Our intellect is our servant, our desires are the masters of our actions. Man will always satisfy his desires if they seem easy to satisfy.

What I have been trying to say so far is that our predicament, the present predicament of mankind, horrible and menacing as it is, is, as the mathematician would say, "not new in principle." Our situation is essentially the same as that of our forefathers. If we are hypnotized by the danger in which we are, so were often our forefathers—so is the mouse at the sight of the snake. We must fight our fear just as we wish the mouse would fight its own terror.

If our situation is similar to that in which our forefathers found themselves, we should act in the way we wish our forefathers had acted, in the way they did act in the majority of cases. We must think and act in the way those people thought and acted whom we admire most in their victories and whom we continue to admire in spite of their defeats. There were many groups which we can thus admire and one of their characteristics, perhaps the most important one, was a love of peace, patience, endurance, and even the desire to make sacrifices to avoid a conflict. The groups which we admire, however, had also courage. They had the courage which is ready to face today what must inevitably be faced tomorrow. They did not run away from a conflict if they knew that by running away they only postponed the conflict and would have to face it tomorrow under more adverse conditions.

Loyalty and the knowledge of the value of friendship is another characteristic of those whom we like to remember most. They knew that one stands and falls with one's friends, that one cannot forsake one's friend and ally without sacrificing one's spirit. They were able to establish a community with their friends in which the stronger one never spoke the words, "I am the stronger one" to his friend, and the weaker one did not hope to purchase the indulgence of the common foe by withholding his help from his friend, by standing aside when his friend was in peril. Standing here before you today as a friend but also as a stranger, I am doubly conscious of these follies. May we be saved from them.

But may we be saved also from the folly of not being willing to face today what we shall have to face tomorrow. Among these things is death. Our culture is committing a sin by covering our eyes against the realization that none of us will be here always. As a result, we do not prepare for the inevitable last hour, we do not realize that having lived in peace, the way we die—whether fighting evil or, having abandoned our friends and been abandoned by them in turn, delivered to our enemies—is a decisive element when we consider the success of the whole life.

An unusual honor came to me today and I could not thank you for it more truly than by saying what I feel most deeply. May I, may we all, be able to live up to the principles which we profess when strong and not in immediate danger.

24

The Growth of Science—
Its Promise and Its Dangers

The Success of Science

The statistics of the growth of science in the U. S. during the postwar years read like a success story. The total expenditures for research and development were 3.5 billion dollars in 1947; they were over 20 billion in 1963. It is true that the gross national product also greatly increased during that period: it grew from about 200 billion dollars to almost 600. Nevertheless, even the percentage of the gross national product devoted to research and development more than doubled by 1963 its value of 1¾ per cent in 1947. This means that more than three people in a hundred now work directly or indirectly for increasing our store of knowledge, or for developing new methods of production of commodities now available, or on the design and production of new commodities. The increase of the annual federal expenditure on science and development was even more spectacular: it grew from one billion in 1947 to its present value of 15 billion dollars. None of these figures includes the compensation of the science teachers in our high schools and colleges—those on whom we depend to produce the scientists of tomorrow.[1]

J. F. Carlson lecture, presented April 13, 1964, at Iowa State College.
[1] The best source for statistical information is, of course, government publications, such as the Statistical Yearbooks of the U.S. and the publications of the National Science Foundation on Federal Funds for Science. A quick survey can be obtained from Spencer Klaw's article in *Fortune*, 158 (Sept., 1964).

Some of the increase in the attention which science now receives was caused, unquestionably, by the increasing need for the protection of our nation, by the requirements of the so-called cold war. Yet this point can be easily exaggerated. Thus, research on biology and medicine, having little to do with defense, was responsible for about 20 per cent of the federal expenditures for research and development, and the government also supports other nondefense sciences generously. Privately financed research—which was on the average over the last fifteen years about half of the total effort—is not directly connected with defense needs. There is every indication that science would grow almost equally rapidly if the defense needs were less urgent.

Furthermore, this growth took place not only in the expenditure of money and in the number of people participating in the scientific and technological endeavor, but also in the interest and attention of the average citizen. Twenty or so years ago, scientific discoveries were briefly mentioned on the back pages of newspapers and the reporting on them often lacked competence. Today, prominent newspapers have a competent science writer on their staff, and it is not unusual to find the report on a discovery started on the front page and a careful description of it continued through several columns further back. There is also an increased emphasis on science in our schools and colleges—and this in the face of an acute shortage of science teachers. As a result of the increasing interest of our fellow citizens in science, scientific theories and the thinking of scientists greatly influence the outlook on life of most of us.[2] The confidence in divine justice on Earth, in a happy afterlife in Heaven, had all been shattered by the turn of the century. Even the recognition of the human will as a primitive reality was shaken under the influence of the success of deterministic physics, only to be restored when—and perhaps because—deterministic physics proved to be inadequate. Genetics taught us that we are all captives of our inheritance, and biophysics that the human spirit, once considered to be supremely independent, can be deeply affected by drugs. The effect of science on our most fundamental convictions, on our image of the human spirit, may well be even more significant than its effect on our everyday life. As I said, the story of science reads like a success story.

Evidently, the fraction of gross national product devoted to science

[2] Cf. in this connection P. W. Bridgeman's essay in *The Nature of Physical Knowledge* [Bloomington: Indiana University Press (1960)].

and development cannot double many more times. However, there is every indication that it will continue to grow for some time and our way of life will be increasingly affected directly by scientific developments and indirectly by the scientist's mode of thinking. It seems to me, therefore, that the scientist has an obligation to try to understand the effects of science on our way of life and to try to act in such a way that the influence of science be for the better.[3] Because it could be for the worse. Most, if not all, that I have to say on this subject may not be very original or striking. However, there has been until recently very little discussion on the subject and I would feel more than satisfied if this writing contributed a small amount of stimulation to an imaginative discussion of the effect which the growth of science will have on science itself and on society.

Past Contributions of Science to Human Welfare

The effect of science and civilization on human happiness, although certainly present, cannot be measured. Its direction and magnitude have been, nevertheless, the subject of much discussion and debate. Freud, in particular, wrote with feeling and deep insight about *Civilization and Its Discontents*.[4] It is undeniable that our increased knowledge enables us to provide food and shelter for several times more people than could live on the Earth only a few centuries ago, and that these have a much longer average life span than did the man of earlier days. People who complain about inequities and suffering caused by our progress remind me a little of the hard-working teacher, whose class showed splendid progress but who complained that half of the class was still below average. It seems evident that even the least developed nation suffers less from want today than any nation did before. It is true that some of the romance of old days has been destroyed by modern methods of production, but much more of the misery has been abolished. People who knew primitive tribes in their primitive days of pre-civilization, such as Peter Freuchen, who knew Eskimos and Indians intimately, are eloquent in their praise of the blessings which contact with more advanced civilizations brought to these people.[5]

[3] The Interim Committee on the Social Aspects of Science of the American Association for the Advancement of Science states this case very compellingly.

[4] S. Freud, *Civilization and Its Discontents*, translated by Joan Reviere [Garden City, N.Y.: Doubleday (1958)].

[5] P. Freuchen, *Book of the Eskimos* [Cleveland: World Publishing Co. (1961)], p. 417.

The preceding discussion refers, of course, only to those effects of our culture which have brought freedom from want and alleviation of suffering. Furthermore, it refers perhaps more to the effects of civilization and primitive science than to science as we now like to understand it. It is, indeed, difficult to go beyond this because, as has been mentioned before, happiness cannot be measured and we know the conditions therefore only from experience and introspection. At the present stage of our understanding of human emotions, we cannot say with certainty whether an educated man or a more simple child of nature would be happier "on the average," given the freedom from want now prevailing in our nation. There is at least one exception to the preceding statement: the scientists themselves. The smaller number of work hours required by the community to supply its daily needs in reasonable abundance has meant the release of a large number of the community for the arts and sciences. It has been said that the only occupations which bring true joy and satisfaction are those of poets, artists, and scientists, and, of these, the scientists are apparently the happiest. Scientists derive an immense amount of pleasure from the study and understanding of science, and even more from discovering or rediscovering relations between phenomena, and from the discussion and communication of these to students and to each other.[6]

If the joy of learning, understanding, and discovering could be extended over large groups of people, the positive contribution of science to human satisfaction could vie with the negative one, which is the alleviation of suffering and want. Since the fraction of people in scientific endeavor constantly increases, can we not hope for such an extension of the positive contribution?

What we have to be concerned about is whether the growth of science will not change its character, whether it will still be the same science, bringing the same satisfactions to its disciples, if a much larger fraction of mankind would try to partake in its cultivation. Such a situation would cause, first, great changes in the mode of operation and the character of the scientific world. Second, it would bring a much more rapid spread of the scientific effort into new areas than would be the case otherwise. The rest of the thoughts which will be presented here will be concerned with problems raised by these changes.

[6] M. Polanyi, *Personal Knowledge: Toward a Post-Critical Philosophy* [Chicago: University of Chicago Press (1958)], speaks of an "intellectual passion."

It is natural to ask whether it is desirable for us scientists to discuss these questions. I believe so. First, if we do not bring them up, others will, and their discussion, which may not be always kind, should not find us unprepared. More importantly, as was said above, we have a moral duty to try to visualize the effects of our endeavor. There is at least one example in man's history when a most noble conception became, for a while, a parody of that conception.* We should do our best that history should not repeat itself in this regard.

The Subject of Science—Now and Tomorrow

When a physicist speaks about science, he thinks about the so-called natural sciences, by which he means the sciences dealing with inanimate nature. He believes, and I share this belief, that only concerning the behavior of these have we succeeded in developing a coherent set of regularities which are, in some well-defined sense, complete.

No similarly well-rounded body of knowledge is available concerning the functioning of the mind, even though ministers, psychologists, philosophers, and many others know more about it than we physicists realize. This knowledge, such as it is, is separated from our knowledge of the inanimate world and the points of contact are few.[7] However, the desire to build a bridge between the two areas—nay, the need to eliminate the chasm between them—is natural not only for the generalist. Its need has become apparent to the physicist as a result of the understanding of the structure of quantum theory,[8] and I am sure similar tendencies exist also on the other side. The simple fact is that it becomes increasingly evident that the primitive idea of separating body and soul is not a valid one, that "inanimate" is a limiting case which could be understood more deeply if it were recognized as such.[9] Simi-

---

* Some of my friends, when reading this passage, thought that I had communism in mind. Actually, and very unfortunately, Christianity is an equally good example.

[7] This point has been popularized, perhaps even exaggerated, in the well-known writings of C. P. Snow. See *The Two Cultures* and *The Scientific Revolution* [Cambridge: Cambridge University Press (1959)]. Cf., on the other side, the Preface of R. E. Peierls' *The Laws of Nature*, which emphasizes the more encyclopedic interests of the scientist than *The Two Cultures* would lead one to believe.

[8] See, for instance, F. London and E. Bauer, *La Théorie de l'observation en mécanique quantique* [Paris: Hermann and Co. (1939)], or this writer's article in *Am. J. Phys.*, 31, 6 (1963).

[9] See the present writer's "Remarks on the Mind-Body Question" in *The Scientist Speculates*, I. J. Good, editor [New York: Basic Books (1962)], reprinted in this volume.

larly, the dependence of the character and soul on the chemical constitution of the body is becoming increasingly, and even frighteningly, evident.

The extension of our understanding from the inanimate world to the whole of nature is indeed a noble task. It may even, eventually, lead to the determination whether and under what circumstances a greater satisfaction from life could be derived on the average. For reasons on which I wish to enlarge a little, it will be greatly stimulated by the increase in the number of those who devote their attention to science. If this attention were confined to those parts of science which are now under intense cultivation, there would be an overcrowding of these fields and the same new realizations would be made independently by many. There are already signs for this in the physical sciences.[10] Such new realizations would not give the individuals the kind of satisfaction which comes from having had an influence on the development of science, and they would not clearly contribute to the growth of our knowledge. As such situations develop, and, as I said, they may be developing right now, people will drift into new fields of endeavor—and what field would be more attractive than where the most obvious gap in our understanding is? The drift toward new areas of science will not be easy because it requires less effort to add to a building, the foundations of which are already firmly laid, than to start new foundations on ground which appears to be soft. As a result, if the number of scientists did not increase, the drift toward new areas would be slow. However, the interest of many other active minds in a field will be unquestionably a strong stimulation to seek satisfaction in another branch of science, and the proliferation of scientists will surely stimulate the cultivation of new areas, the shift of the second kind, as I called it when thinking about the subject some years ago.[11]

Evidently, the development which I just described will be a wholesome and desirable one. Does it hide any dangers? Not if it takes place slowly enough so that we can remain adjusted to it. However, our penetration into new fields of knowledge will unquestionably give us new powers, powers which affect the mind more directly than the

[10] One of the most important discoveries in physics, that of parity-violation, was made practically simultaneously by three groups; the "correct" interaction for beta decay was also proposed thereupon, independently, by three groups.

[11] "The Limits of Science," *Proc. Am. Phil. Soc.*, 94, 4221 (1950), reprinted in this volume.

physical conditions which we now can alter. Although the power of nuclear weapons has been much exaggerated, it is true that they enable us to alter the inanimate nature around us to an unprecedented extent. However, the governments have acquired a monopoly of them, and only those whom we have entrusted with such a responsibility can cause their employment on a scale that would be globally significant. It is also helpful that there are many people who understand the nature of nuclear weapons—the only global weapons for the present. On the other hand, if there were many means which could alter the conditions of life on our planet, and if there were no one person who would understand all of them and their interrelations, the balance would be much more precarious. Already, we have more trouble in controlling the spread of dangerous and of habit-forming drugs than of nuclear weapons, and they have caused more unhappiness than the latter. Their more dangerous nature is due to two circumstances: their manufacture needs much less of a concerted effort and their use does not advertise itself with a big bang.

What one may fear even more is something more subtle. If the purpose of life is individual happiness, why not acquire it by any means available, by detachment from reality, if this is the easiest way? Surely, this must be possible. Few can avoid thinking about this possibility when learning about the effects of modern drugs and the frequent consequences of modern psychiatric treatment. The deeply disturbing fact is that no logical argument can be brought against detachment from reality if it abolishes our pains and sorrows, as no logical argument can be brought against drug-addiction. Fortunately, most of us have a deep revulsion against both. Is this based only on tradition, or will mankind be saved by the fact that what we truly strive for is influence on the real world, exercised through ourselves and our children, rather than abstract happiness? Will the world be populated by the progeny of those in whom the desire for influence is particularly strong? These are frightening questions, largely tabu in our circles. Unless we can come to an equilibrium with them before our power to change the world of the mind becomes overwhelming, our increased knowledge and understanding of wider areas may bring more suffering than joy, it may bring a deterioration of our genetic heritage rather than the advent of a nobler man.

There is another point that should be mentioned. The progress of science will give increasing power to the individual scientist, and to small groups of scientists. This has not yet come to the fore in the course of the progress of the physical sciences, such as the development of nuclear weapons. No such weapon can be produced by the individual scientist; a much larger group effort, involving not only scientists but also industrial enterprises, is needed. However, the situation may be, and probably will be, different with respect to the power which the study of the life sciences and psychology will yield. At present, we are used to trusting the individual scientist and cannot imagine his harboring diabolical schemes for increasing his power. We believe that his desire for influence is not excessive. The same may not be true of groups of scientists, and may not be true of the management of such groups. In these, the desire for influence on the real world, which we recognized as an important factor for the preservation of humanity, may be excessive. They may want to use the power yielded by their research or that of their group to extend their influence in ways as ruthless as those of a dictator. Will it be necessary to establish strict controls in scientific institutions similar to those which we now have in the mints and weapons factories? Again, one is repelled by the mere idea. I feel reassured that the directors of the scientific institutions and the management of the laboratories with which I am familiar show no particular desire to accumulate power and influence. They are all meditative, kind, and almost self-effacing people. It is true, however, that in order to manage an enterprise which depends on the cooperation of many individuals, the manager must be able, and occasionally willing, to wield power. This may form a bad habit and corrupt some of the scientific leaders, just as political leaders are often corrupted by similar circumstances and opportunities. Nevertheless, when I think of those who are now the directors of our national laboratories, it is impossible for me to take quite seriously the danger that their colleagues and successors may be beset by lust for power.

The role of large laboratories, and their management, naturally bring us back to the second question which I wanted to discuss: the changed mode of the cultivation of science as a consequence of its great expansion. However, before turning to this question, let me try to summarize what I tried to say about the effects of the increasing area of the subject matter of science. The increase in question will be surely stimulated by the increasing number of scientists because the pleasure which each scientist can derive from his work can be maintained at a high level only if the scientists scatter their interests over a wide field and do not tread, figuratively, on each other's toes. A rapid expansion of the area of scientific endeavor does give cause to some apprehension. Success in any field will bring not only increased insights, it will bring also new capabilities and powers. The great number and variety of capabilities and powers scattered widely all over the world threatens to have elements of instability. There is particular reason to fear the knowledge which the understanding of the mind will yield because this touches on the reasons and purpose of our life and existence. Mankind, on the whole, prospered under the traditional, not searching, attitude toward these questions. Will the more inquiring attitude, which is sure to come, give equal vitality?

The Mode of Science: Two Extreme Pictures

Evidently, the whole character and mode of operation of science will change if it becomes a significant endeavor of the community and if it claims a large fraction of the total effort of mankind.[12] Gone will be the days when the leaders of science could pursue their work playfully and with levity. The responsibility of scientific leaders will be quite similar to the present responsibility of leading members of the Administration or of the directors of large companies. An error in judgment may mean the frustration of thousands of hours work of others—it may mean, for the leader, embarrassment before a large and possibly unsympathetic audience. A leading position in science will entail responsibilities from which present-day scientists would and do shy away; its acquisition may be accompanied with as much intrigue and politicking as a political election or the election of the president of a large company. It is doubtful that scientists who will occupy such positions can derive the joy from their work which present-day scientists cherish. It is possible that many of these positions will not be occupied by scientists, but by a new breed of administrator. We have conjured up here the picture of big scientific institutions, of "big science," as Alvin Weinberg has called it.[13] It exists already today, though not in the extreme form here evisaged.

[12] This point has been well articulated, and perhaps a bit exaggerated, in a perceptive article by N. W. Storer [*Science*, 142, 464 (1963)].
[13] A. M. Weinberg, *Science*, 134, 161 (1961).

At the opposite end of the spectrum, science can be pursued by a large fraction of all people, not as a national effort, but playfully, each for his own amusement. This picture cannot, of course, be realized as long as national survival depends on a vigorous and well directed scientific effort, and indeed we are not now progressing in the direction of making science a source of pleasure and a means for recreation. However, if the leaders of all nations could somehow reconcile their desire for influence and domination with the true welfare of their subjects, science could become its own purpose by bringing satisfaction to many disciples. It would then play a role in human affairs somewhat similar to that of sports but much more powerful and intense. Arts and poetry, and perhaps some other avocations, can perhaps also play a similar role, and it would be desirable to devote more thought to them as sources of general human satisfaction. However, we are concerned with the role of science at present.

The first picture, that of big science, is the more grim one. It is possible under all circumstances. The second picture, that of little science, is possible only in a peaceful world. Assuming a peaceful world, therefore, two extreme possibilities of the role of science can be imagined. The first of these is science as a concerted effort of mankind, to augment the store of knowledge and to build, so to say, a superpyramid not of stone but of our understanding of nature. The second picture is individual science, pursued by those who want to pursue it, everyone for his own satisfaction and pleasure. At present, we are moving in the direction of the realization of the first picture, with the difference that it is not a pyramid but a shield that we are building. Otherwise, the picture has much reality; it was not necessary to invent it. The second picture is not new either: it could have been taken from the last act of George Bernard Shaw's *Back to Methuselah*.[14]

Both pictures are extremes and both have attractive as well as repulsive features. As to the first, it would provide humanity with a purpose and objective which seems worthy. It would call for collaboration toward a common goal, rather than competition—collaboration toward a goal which, considering the limitations of human intellect, could well utilize the best efforts of many people.

The trouble with this concept is that, if the goal of maximum scien-

[14] G. B. Shaw, *Back to Methuselah* [Oxford: Oxford University Press (1947) (World Classics)].

tific production is taken seriously—and only in this case could it command the loyalty of its members—its pursuit would require a strict organization of the scientific endeavor. This would be necessary because, even today, no single mind can understand all parts of our knowledge in depth. This will be even less possible as the content of scientific information continues to grow. Each scientist can now speak to a thousand others, but no scientist can listen to and understand more than a few others. Hence, in order to maintain the consistency of the whole scientific edifice, a constant review would be necessary. Since no single individual could undertake such a review, an organization would have to be created for the purpose.

As a member of Alvin Weinberg's Committee on Science and Information, I designed such an organization in outline.[15] It consisted of several layers of scientists, each layer being more highly specialized than the layer above it. Three or four teams of each layer would communicate their findings to a team of the layer above theirs, and this team would harmonize the findings of the reporting teams and evaluate them. The teams of the bottom layer would be the true scientists who "get their hands dirty," the teams of the top layer would consist of philosophers.

This concrete design is, of course, only one possibility, and quite possibly not the most effective one for the organization of science. In spite of this, it would be effective—if its members were in their hearts united toward the common goal. This requirement is, then, its *conditio sine qua non*, and it shares this, probably, with other designs which envisage science as a concerted, purposefully organized effort. Unfortunately, it is hard to see how such a science could remain the enjoyable study which it is now. One may well fear that it would become a heavy-handed enterprise and the participants therein might not be much better off than the builders of the Egyptian pyramids. They would no more retain the impression that they build their own science than the communist worker retains the impression that he builds his own factory. One does not have the satisfaction which creative work, as we know it today, provides, if one's activities are too closely directed by others. For one, the desire for influence remains frustrated. Even if there were enthusiasm in the first, and perhaps second, generation, this would wane in the third and later ones unless the human mind and human emotions

[15] *Science, Government, and Information* [Washington: Government Printing Office (1962)].

were deeply changed for the purpose. Even if this could be done, it appears doubtful whether really penetrating ideas would be conceived in a system the spirit of which is so contrary to the spirit of spontaneity of our best scientific atmosphere.

Let us now look at the opposite extreme: science for individual satisfaction. Shaw's picture, in which everyone goes off to the woods at the age of four to think in solitude about number theory, is unnecessarily grim or, put differently, presupposes an unnecessarily large change of human emotions and conditions of satisfaction. In order to avoid the regimented extreme of a hierarchical organization of science, it is not necessary to have cognition as one's only desire, or to try to satisfy this desire in complete solitude. Science could become the avocation of many. Even a somewhat dilettantish pursuit could give a similar but deeper and more elevating satisfaction than sports give nowadays.

The trouble which I see with this picture—and I admit that as a scientist I may be biased—is that, the more it deviates from Shaw's grim picture, the more does it treat science as a pastime and not as something that gives coherence to human society and fires it to a purpose. It does seem to me that society needs such a purpose and I can see nothing on the horizon that could constitute an equally strong purpose. The common purpose should, at the same time, leave enough freedom to the individual so that his desire for influence and uniqueness—a desire of which both the absence and the excess are so pernicious—should find reasonable satisfaction.

Both Alternatives: The Golden Middle Way?

The extremes which were discussed so far may be so unsatisfactory exactly because they are extremes. It seems to me that there is a need for both big science and for little science and the choice between the two, and their natural competition, would lend charm, significance, and vitality to both. Furthermore, both may find specific areas in which they may be more effective than the other. As to big science, let us not forget that, at least for the time being, there are specific capabilities which we would like to have—it is not only deeper insight that we wish to acquire. Very generally speaking, the capabilities which we wish to develop would render the Earth habitable by a larger number of people. For this, sources of more food and fresh water, and greater skill in combating disease, are necessary. Capabilities to acquire these can be effectively developed only by large enterprises and indeed, our large laboratories, our big science, were created to provide us with technological capabilities, for better living, and for better defense. On the other side, little science, the individual scientist, is also needed. Deep insights, radical departures from the consensus, rarely originate in closely knit groups, working in well organized laboratories. Such new insights—only Planck's conception of the elementary quantum needs to be mentioned—have had a decisive influence on science in the past and a similar influence can be expected in the future. It is hard to imagine how they can be developed other than in comparative solitude. As research will increasingly turn away from technology to search for insights, the role of little science should increase.

What is more difficult to visualize than either big or little science is the relation between them. I thought, some time ago, that they should be separated by working in different fields—big science where elaborate and costly equipment is necessary, little science where fundamental paradoxes have appeared. However, the two types of science need each other, both intellectually and emotionally. If separated, they would both show the weaknesses of the extremes which were discussed before.

At present, the trend is very strongly toward big science, and those who are convinced of the fertility of little science are often considered to be unable to understand the voice of the future and of progress. This, it seems to me, is unjustified. It is true that many of the young men are attracted by the big machines of big science and that it is difficult to resist the easy success which these machines promise. There are others, however, both among our young colleagues and our students, who prefer to work for themselves and to search devotedly and patiently for the deeper truth. It was said, with some malice, that some of the great physicists of the former group were appointed as great physicists more nearly by the government which gave them big accelerators than appointed by Providence by giving them a devoted interest in knowledge, an appreciation of the true problems and mysteries, and the humility necessary to search for the solution of these patiently.

Nevertheless, the present trend is toward big science. Furthermore, big science creates its organization spontaneously, whereas the individual scientist of little science is inclined to shun organization. I do wish, however, that little science be recognized for what it is: a necessary element for the vitality of science, a moral force which can act as the conscience of all science, and as public opinion when groups of big scientists disagree. The fact that it does not seek the easy glory but is willing to search under the less glamorous conditions of an earlier period should win for it respect and authority. Perhaps the middle road, that of supporting big science vigorously but extending encouragement and high esteem to little science also, even if it may not be a golden road, is at least the best.

Our theme has been the promise and the dangers inherent in the growth of science. We have seen that there is much of both. The promise of future science is to furnish a unifying goal to mankind rather than merely the means to an easy life, to provide some of what the human soul needs in addition to bread alone. If it can fulfill this function, it will play one of the great roles in the drama of mankind.

The danger with which the growth and increased significance of science may confront society stems from the increase in power and capabilities which results from increased knowledge and which necessitates new restraints. The growth of science will cause a dilemma also for science itself. The *Weltbild* it will generate when it is extended to more and more areas may outgrow the capacity of any single mind. This may result in the fragmentation of science or in a superstructure of organization. The organization of science could destroy the detachment and sublime satisfaction which is the reward of the scientist of our period and which keeps him from coveting power and undue influence. It will be easier to avoid the dangers posed by the growth of science if we do not try to forget them; its promise is more likely to be fulfilled if we keep it in mind.